MW01026536

Let The Radiant Yang Shine Forth:
Lectures on Virtue
by Liu Yousheng

LET THE RADIANT YANG SHINE FORTH:
LECTURES ON VIRTUE
by Liu Yousheng

讓陽光自然播洒:
劉有生演講錄

TRANSLATED BY
LIU ZUOZHI & SABINE WILMS

HAPPY GOAT PRODUCTIONS
CORBETT, OR ❧ USA

PUBLISHED IN THE UNITED STATES OF AMERICA

ISBN-978-0-9913429-1-4

All artwork by Sunjae Lee
www.fermatawellness.com/portfolio

Published by Happy Goat Productions
Corbett, Oregon ▪ USA

For more information and to purchase
other works by Sabine Wilms, visit our website:
www.HappyGoatProductions.com

Dedicated to the work of Wang Fengyi

Contents

Introduction

"The difference of being in command and losing command over the emotions is the root of life and death, and the starting point of living and dying." Thus the 2,200 year old Confucian classic The Annals of Master Lü sums up the essence of being human, a timeless voice from the past reminding us that mastery of one's emotions is an absolute prerequisite for maintaining health and longevity. Unfortunately, most systems of natural healing have failed to integrate this vitally important piece of experiential wisdom into their therapeutic approach. While Traditional Chinese Medicine (TCM) acknowledges the pathogenic influence of the "seven emotions" (*Qi Qing* 七情), there are no concrete treatment methods that have made it into the mainstream of TCM practice. This fact is all the more unfortunate when considering that the original tenets of all holistic medicines are based on the premise that body, mind and spirit are intricately connected, and that the mental-emotional part of our being assumes the leading role.

Typically, religious sources from various tradition call for an outright "elimination" and "rejection" of the emotions. Confucian teachings generally prescribe a more moderate approach, advocating the balancing of strong feelings by channeling them in appropriate ways. The Chinese term used in this context is *jie* (to harmonize, to moderate, to create rhythm). Many of the relevant texts, however, define moderation as a distinct quality of the sages, who alone are said to be capable of using emotions appropriately, achieving a state of deep spiritual connection without being led astray by selfish feelings and eventually succumbing to illness. For the average person, it was the institution of social rituals that was used to moderate the agitated spirit. The 1st century historian Ban Gu explains:

> The human being contains both: the Yang influence of Heaven, and the Yin influence of Earth. Consequently, all of us manifest the emotions of

partiality, hate, excitement, anger, sorrow, and pleasure; hence the divisive nature of humanity that is so hard to navigate. The sages alone are capable of moderating this aspect of the human condition. Guided by the example of Heaven and Earth, they created the institutions of ritual and music, using them to stay connected to the all-governing light of spirit. Furthermore, they established the laws of human behavior, rectifying the relationship between true human nature and the emotions, and seeking to achieve moderation in the myriad affairs of life. For the feelings between a man and a woman and the sensation of jealousy they created the ritual of marriage; for the bonding of older and younger members of the community they created the ritual of celebratory banquets; for the feelings of grieving the dead and missing loved ones they created the ritual of sacrificial mourning; for the desire to venerate one's leaders they created the ritual of public audience. A mourning ritual features ritual wailing and stomping; music has a set format for dances and songs—sufficient to warm the sentiments of the straight, and to prevent missteps by those who are crooked. If the ritual of marriage gets abandoned, then the Tao of husband and wife will become lacking, and consequently the sins of sexual decadence or radical abstinence will increase; if the ritual of celebratory banquets gets abandoned, the proper order between the older and younger generations will be lost, and the crimes of quarreling and flattery will blossom; if the ritual of mourning and burial gets abandoned, then the gratitude we owe our own flesh and blood becomes weak, and many of the dead will forget about the living; if the ritual of audience gets abandoned, then the proper position of ruler and servant becomes confused, and war and turmoil will gradually arise.

As a scholar of Chinese medicine, it was an illuminating experience to discover the intimate connection between ritual and emotional regulation in the Confucian classics. More importantly, I was positively surprised when in 2004 my colleague Dr. Liu Lihong introduced me to a group of Northern Chinese peasant healers who still utilize the Confucian teachings of virtue, ritual, and social relationship as their primary treatment tool. Their approach to healing is radical, especially when considering the fact that they are practicing in the territory of the People's Republic of China. Their work is ostensibly devoid of pharmaceuticals, herbs, or needles, but exclusively uses methods of storytelling, ritual confessions, and chanted affirmations to heal the sick. Echoing the principles first introduced in ancient sources from more than 2000 years ago, these practitioners believe that most diseases originate from an overshadowing of the bright aspects of human nature by the veil of unmitigated emotions.

The origins of this healing modality—still practiced in the Northern Chinese provinces of Liaoning, Jilin, and Heilongjiang—are rooted in the teachings of Wang Fengyi (1864–1937), a Confucian educator and charismatic emotional healer who was extremely influential in this part of China during the early part of the 20th century. Wang's biography relates that he grew up as a poor and illiterate peasant, and became enlightened to the nature of human emotions and their disease-causing consequences while listening to traditional storytellers who made rounds through the impoverished villages of the Manchurian tundra. These insights germinated and caused a spiritual awakening during his strict observation of the traditional three-year watch over his father's grave. In a fortnight, he realized that all emotions arise from social interactions, especially within the most intimate nucleus of community relationship, one's immediate family. Following this insight, an abdominal abscess he had suffered from for 12 years healed spontaneously overnight. Driven by an urgent sense of mission to help save his community from the curse of disease amidst the misery of poverty and eventually civil war, he began traveling from village to village, spreading a neo-Confucian version of everyday-life spirituality that focused on proper family relationships. His oral presentations, some of them preserved in the form of reprinted lecture excerpts, were legendary at the time, drawing large rural audiences. Many participants were reported to be crying, fainting, or vomiting when triggered into a state of recognition and ruefulness by the transmission of the peasant saint.

During his later years, Wang Fengyi packaged his educational philosophy into a comprehensive system of healing that incorporated the five element teachings of Chinese medicine. In this process, he greatly contributed to the revolutionary movement of bringing education to Chinese women. He was instrumental in establishing and maintaining 700 schools for girls, since he considered it to be a shortcoming of traditional Confucian doctrine that women were not entitled to an education. In contrast, Wang viewed the roles of women (mothers, wives, daughters-in-law) as the central element for the health of every family, and by extension, the health of every family member as well as the country at large.

He felt, moreover, that women were best able to exemplify the core essence of his social philosophy, namely the virtue of granting compassion to others while reserving judgment and criticism for oneself.

As an often forgotten historical figure, Wang Fengyi thus needs to be recognized as the most important modern transmitter of the original Confucian teachings by Kongzi (551–479 BCE), Dong Zhongshu (179–104 BCE), and Zhu Xi (1130–1200). Many of his teachings, as well as those of his still practicing students, sound remarkably like the following passage written by Dong Zhongshu more than 2000 years ago:

> What the Annals are teaching us to regulate is how to deal with the self and how to deal with others. How to deal with the self and how to deal with others is exemplified by the virtues of compassion and selflessness. With compassion we make others feel good, while with selflessness we set the self straight; that is why compassion is associated with others, and selflessness with self. …Compassion is manifested by loving others, not by loving self; selflessness is manifested by straightening out the self, not by straightening out others.

From the perspective of Chinese medicine, it is the elaborate system of five element associations that is the most significant part of Wang's legacy. This system contains the familiar relations of the five phase elements with the five organs, the five colors, the five smells, etc., but synthesizes them with the ancient teachings on human virtue as well as Wang's own remarkable insights and experiences as a therapist. Now as then, patients are generally asked to relate their stories and then are diagnosed with a specific breach of virtue caused by one of the five emotional poisons, specifically anger (wood), hate (fire), blame (earth), judgment (metal), or disdain (water). Wang himself was known to be an exceptionally clairvoyant healer and some of his students maintain this gift. At the same time, he left behind a system of detailed descriptions that outlines how affliction in different body parts may be related to specific emotions and specific family members.

The curative process of Wang's system often involves the therapist's weaving a narrative, ranging from very few words to night-long marathons of story-telling that are able to "turn the heart of the patient." The material for stories is often taken from the treasure trove of Chinese moral history, but most typically involve the daily environment of the patient: stories of Master Wang curing someone just like them, or vivid tales of the cure or demise of someone in the next village, or, ideally, someone present in the room or the village square who offers heart-wrenching and tearful testimony of their own healing process. This method is referred to as xingli jiangbing, literally "talking the disease away by appealing to one's higher nature." The curative effect is considered to begin when the patient is moved to acknowledge his own emotional involvement in the disease forming process, and commits to transform his/her blame toward others into a thorough reformation of self. At this point, which skillful storytellers are sometimes able to trigger in minutes while others may need days or even weeks, the patient typically begins to vomit into ready made buckets, or exhibits other sign of physical cleansing such as crying, sweating, or diarrhea.

Table 1 - Wang's Five Element Associations

5 Phase Element	Wood	Fire	Earth	Metal	Water
5 *Zang* Organs	Liver	Heart	Spleen	Lung	Kidney
5 Sources	Original Nature *yuanxing* 元性	Original Spirit *yuanshen* 元神	Original Vitality *yuanQi* 元氣	Original Affectivity *yuanQing* 元情	Original Essence *yuanjing* 元精
5 Virtues	Compassion *ren* 仁	Propriety *li* 禮	Integrity *xin* 信	Selflessness *yi* 義	Wisdom *zhi* 智
5 Positive Qualities	Sense of Direction and Strategy *zhuyi* 主意	Understanding Sacred Connection *mingli* 明理	Trust and Reliability *xinshi* 信實	Radiance of Sound and Light *xiangliang* 響亮	Soft and Harmonious *rouhe* 柔和
5 Powers	Containment *rong* 容	Respect *jing* 敬	Commitment *zhi* 執	Discernment *bie* 別	Awareness *lin* 臨
5 Emotional Poisons	Anger *nu* 怒	Hate *hen* 恨	Blame *yuan* 怨	Judgment *nao* 惱	Disdain *fan* 煩
5 Taboos	Kill	Inappropriate Sexual Behavior	Lie	Steal	Drink

5 Phase Element	Wood	Fire	Earth	Metal	Water
5 Family Roles	Oldest Child	Father	Ancestors	Young Children	Mother
5 Social Roles	Workers	Leaders	Farmers	Scholars	Businessmen
5 Religions	Christianity	Confucianism	Daoism	Islam	Buddhism
5 Facial Features	Long	Pointed	Square	Round	Plum
5 Speech Instruments	Teeth	Tongue	Nose	Lips	Throat
5 Vocal Expressions	Abrupt	High	Level	Drawn Out	Low

When I first visited Liu Yousheng, the author of this book, I was surprised to hear him remark matter-of-factly that "liver cirrhosis can be disgorged in one week, while in the case of some cancers it can take three weeks or longer until no more tar-like materials are vomited up."

Transcripts of these healing sessions may often appear flat to the eyes of the modern Western observer, but both healers and patients insist that it is the transmission of the storyteller herself—achieved by a non-compromised life-style of virtuous conduct—that is needed to trigger a powerful response. These healing sessions may look similar to the phenomenon of the Qigong baogao (Qigong transmission lectures), which were so common in China before the government crackdown on Falun Gong and other Qigong practices during the year 2000. By virtue of their humble demeanor and their radically selfless conduct, however, the virtue practitioners of the Manchurian plains tend to cut a different figure than the entrepreneurial Qigong masters of the 1990s.

To me, the author of this book represents the most remarkable example of a living practitioner in the Confucian tradition of virtue healing. Like Wang Fengyi himself, Liu Yousheng travels much to conduct group healings, but primarily practices in his home near the Russian border. When I first visited him in his home village in 2006, his simple house had been converted into a make-shift hospice where deathly ill patients traveled to from far away and stayed for free, were fed for free, and received treatment for free—day after day for the last 25 years, sometimes adding up to 20 – 40 people per day. Prior to receiving permission from his mentor to start the practice of therapeutic storytelling, moreover, he had spent 20 years preparing for this work through the radical pursuit of clearing his own emotional issues. His patients, therefore, lovingly call him Liu Shanren—Liu the Good Man, a name generally only attributed to Wang Fengyi himself.

Since then, I had the privilege of spending many weeks with Liu Shanren and other practitioners of the traditional healing method synthesized by Wang Fengyi. I was able to directly witness and participate myself in the intense process of storytelling, ritual confession and ensuing physical cleansing. While it is premature for me to say that I can verify all of the miraculous outcomes that this method of treatment is said to have achieved during the last century, including the complete cure of diabetes, aplastic anemia, congenital heart disease, and many types of cancer, it is my distinct impression as a medical professional that I have the privilege of touching something very profound. Most important for the readers of this book, I can say that this method affects the "true nature" of humanity and thus works on all people, regardless of their cultural background. I have, for instance, witnessed one example where an American patient suffering from an aggressive type of stage IV cancer was healed completely after applying herself to the principles and practices introduced during a 2-week retreat fashioned after the original teaching sessions in Wang Fengyi's schools for female cultivation.

It is important to note that Liu Shanren's book represents the pure and unadulterated narration of his own life story. It is an uncensored account, presented through a cultural lens that is unique to the traditional villages of Northern China. Some of the case stories included in the book may appear disturbing to a Western reader who has carefully cultivated a sense of modern identity. The story of the woman, for instance, who was advised to offer a broom to her choleric and abusive husband, asking him not to injure his hand in the process of beating her. When looking beyond the trappings of Confucian household rules that appear to be limited to the social confines of Chinese village life, however, the essence of timeless wisdom begins to reach the heart of the reader. Liu Shanren's life, conducted in the midst of a rapidly industrializing and increasingly materialistic China, represents a most inspiring example of the radical teachings of surrender, self-responsibility and compassion transmitted by most of humanity's sages and saints. Therefore, I recommend that you open your heart and your mind as wide as possible when reading this book.

In conclusion, I feel that the Confucian healing system presented by Liu Yousheng offers a profound example of the relevance of ancient medical theories. Confucius himself once emphasized, "He who by reanimating the Old can gain knowledge of the New is fit to be a teacher." Wang Fengyi and his students have demonstrated that no matter how antiquated or out-dated an ancient concept may look, truly classical knowledge is timeless and has the capacity of being fiercely relevant for the present.

Many people have cooperated in making the English version of this book possible. Many thanks to Dr. Liu Lihong, who has tirelessly worked for the last decade to recognize and preserve this forgotten style of ancient Chinese psychotherapy. Dr. Liu's father Liu Zuozhi produced a first version of the translation, which was edited by Dr. Tamara Staudt, Gloria Joslove and Dr. Cindy Reuter. The indefatigable Anne Goldberg kept the process motivated. Special gratitude is due to Dr. Sabine Wilms, who graciously took on the time consuming project of integrating (and frequently retranslating) all efforts into a coherent and academically accurate whole. The artistic talents of Sunjae Lee were shared in the form of radiant orange ginkgos on the cover.

Heiner Fruehauf, PhD, LAc
Founding Professor, School of Classical Chinese Medicine
National College of Natural Medicine,
Portland, Oregon

LECTURE ONE

Establishing A Commitment and
Following Through in Actions

I. Establishing an Ironclad Commitment

I am a peasant. I do not have any special education or skills. When I talk about the standards and principles of being a good person, this all comes directly from my life experience. Someone once asked me, "What is this Dao that you are talking about?" I answered, "Talking about the Dao, talking about the Dao, I am specifically talking about the Dao of being a good person." The person then asked: "In that case, what is this Daode[1]?" "What is Daode? Turn the Dao around and it becomes De." Daode, right action, virtue. What do I mean by "Turn the Dao around"? I mean that you point the Dao directly towards yourself, become true to yourself in your actions, become true to yourself in your words…this is the true Dao. "When forging iron, do not leave the anvil. When speaking of the Dao, do not leave yourself." When we speak of the Dao, this means to speak of our own experiences, our own ability to act as good human beings or not, and our own standards for being a good person. In the

---

1   Daode 道德: Two crucial characters in Chinese culture and philosophy. Literally, Dao means "the way," while De is most often translated as "virtue." In a much deeper sense, though, Dao is the Way of Heaven, the Way in which the universe functions that we humans have to align ourselves with instead of going against. And related to this, De is the outward manifestation of this alignment with the Dao, the inner power that stems from being in accord with the Dao.

past I got it wrong. I didn't understand the Dao of how to be and act as a true human being. As a consequence, I suffered from disease for twelve years.

I.1 CONTRACTING ILLNESS AND RECOVERING

I come from a small village in Keshan County in Heilongjiang Province. Growing up, there were nine people in my family: my father and mother, an older brother, five younger sisters, and myself. Ever since I remember, my family was very poor. So poor that we didn't have enough food to eat or clothes to wear. While all the other children went to school, I had to herd pigs instead, which is what I did from the time I was eight years old until age thirteen.

At age thirteen, I started going to school and it was then that I started to get sick. Why did I get sick? Because from early childhood on, I had a bad temper. Beating on people, yelling at people, I had no control over myself. When I started attending school, I brought this bad temper with me. On the very first day of school, I had a fist fight with a schoolmate. He struck me with his hand, so I took off my shoe and beat him up with that. I didn't listen to the teachers either. I even dared to threaten to get in a fight with the teachers. Everyone at school was afraid of me. Even the teachers had to let me have my way. At that time, I thought Heaven was number one and I was number two, and therefore I would listen to nobody.

When I had been herding pigs, I had also had this type of poor temperament. So why hadn't I gotten sick earlier? Because ever since early childhood, my health had been fragile so my family had doted on me. No one had dared to make me angry. It had been impossible for my family to control me. My elder brother and younger sisters had not only been too afraid to tell me what to do, on the contrary, they listened to my orders. Otherwise, I would show my temper and throw tantrums. In fact, they had spoiled me rotten, and thereby dispatched me to hell. What is this thing we call "hell"? Suffering from disease is what I mean by hell. Anybody with free time can go to a hospital and look for themselves to see situations such as patient's eyes or tongues being cut out or chests and stomachs cut open. Aren't these people living in hell? If you get sick, you have to get surgery. Not only that, but you have to pay for it and even smile about it while the doctors operate. Otherwise they won't even be willing to operate on you.

When I brought this violent temper to school with me, this just didn't work out. Because school was not like my situation at home, the minute I started attending school, I began to get ill. First I contracted pulmonary tuberculosis. No matter what the season, whether winter or summer, I coughed and spit up phlegm. As the disease worsened, I started coughing up blood. Later, I suffered from cirrhosis of the liver, nephritis, heart disease, and high blood pressure. By the time I was 24, I was in critical condition and couldn't even get out of bed any more. The circumstances then were not like today and if you had a disease that you could not afford treatment for, the only option was to await death. At exactly that point in time, an old woman in our village gave me a book: *The Record of Sincere Doings* by Wang Fengyi.

After I finished that book, I contrasted my own actions to those of Wang Shanren[2] and realized how profound my own shortcomings, how grossly inadequate my actions had been. Wang Shanren had always taken care of his brothers, looking after them no matter what. My own actions had been just the opposite. Being right in the middle between my seven siblings, I had only respected myself. I had done whatever I wanted and said whatever I wanted. Not only had I failed to take care of my siblings, but I had burdened them and ordered them around. I had acted controlling not only toward my younger sisters but even toward my elder brother.

And my parents? I had not listened to them either. As a result, I was suffering from severe headaches, my head hurting as if constricted by a tight band. Why headaches? Because I had been defying those above me. Parents and the older generations are above us, as are our teachers and leaders. I had not been listening to the elders, my teachers, and ultimately the political leaders. Because of some historic social issues in my family and our bad economic status, I had always felt that our leaders had been oppressing me. In reality, though, this is not the case. Our leaders are merely carrying out the policies and laws of our

---

2   Wang Shanren 王善人 ("Virtuous Person Wang") is the reverential title by which Wang Fengyi is generally referred to in Chinese. Related to this, Wang Fengyi's system of emotional healing is called *Shanrendao* 善人道 ("The Dao of the Virtuous Person").

country, thereby implementing Heaven's destiny. So if you defy the law, this means that you are defying the will of Heaven. If a leader implements a law incorrectly, then this is that leader's individual problem, but the laws of the country are not wrong, the policies of the country are not wrong. Hence we must submit to them. When I understood this principle, I silently began to confess my wrongs to Heaven (?). As Wang Shanren said, "Heavenly principle is reciprocal." If you have trust in Heaven, Heaven can also have trust in you. If you don't have trust in Heaven, then how can Heaven have trust in you!

How did I recover from my many diseases? By recognizing my own mistakes and then silently confessing deep remorse for all my past transgressions. I recalled any incidences in the past where I had wronged my parents, where I had wronged my brothers and sisters. Above all, when I thought about my parents, I experienced deep anguish in my heart and wept endlessly. Wang Shanren always said that sincerity results in clarity. When I repented with true sincerity, I instantly felt my good conscience return. At that point, I felt a churning in my stomach as if the rivers were flowing upstream and the oceans turning upside down. Gushing upward with great urgency, this force caused me to spit and vomit spontaneously. The phlegm I vomited out was bitter, pungent, sour, sweet, and salty, all five flavors present together. Every night after supper, as soon as I lay down on my bed by the stove, I would begin throwing up like this until around midnight. I continued vomiting like this for seven and a half nights, releasing all the diseases of the past twelve years by vomiting them out.

Of course, just because I had begun to recover physically, this did not mean that I had completely gotten rid of my bad temper. As the old saying goes: "It is easier to move rivers and mountains than to change one's emotional patterns." I still frequently got angry and had temper outbursts, and every time this happened, my health deteriorated. Now, however, I was aware why this was occurring and therefore immediately repented and would soon recover my health. Over time, through a long period of tenacious resolve, not only were my diseases completely cured, but my character also experienced a major transformation.

1.2 ESTABLISHING MY COMMITMENT AND FOLLOWING THROUGH IN ACTIONS

Looking at this situation, I saw how wonderful this method was. No need to take medicine, receive acupuncture, or spend money, but still able to cure disease! As I had personally benefited from this method, I now wished that everybody else could benefit likewise. At that time, I made a secret vow inside my heart: For as long as I lived, I would teach this principle and method to subsequent generations and ensure that it would not get lost! I established this ironclad commitment, which shall not move even if I were struck by lighting, shall not change even if tested a thousand times, and from which I shall not budge even if ground down a myriad times. And on the day I die, I shall have no regrets.

Why did I want to establish such a commitment for myself? Because I wanted to enable all those people who had contracted diseases that could not be treated to recover from their diseases, and I wanted to enable those people who had no money for the treatment of diseases to not fall ill in the first place. Disease cannot be treated completely with medicine and there are diseases that medicine cannot treat. What is the reason for this? Many diseases arise as the result of our unhealthy disposition and even magical pills and ingenious cures cannot easily cure diseases of our disposition. When the body has a disease, you must understand it from the heart. And for disease of the heart, you can use medicine of the heart. That was exactly what I had done, to use medicine of the heart to cure the diseases of my own body.

We have all heard the saying, "Where there is a will, there is a way." Nevertheless, will or commitment alone is not enough. I also had to put this commitment into practice. How did I put it into practice? I had to actively change the perspective in my heart on how I looked at my life. This was not a matter of talking about it, but of quietly putting it into practice. And in the process of doing it, following the transformation inside my heart and the progressive deepening of my actions, I slowly realized how my own life went through a transformation.

Because there had been so many areas in my life where I had violated the Dao but the most serious violation had been against the Dao of *xiao*[3] and of caring for my siblings, I set about to get my act together in these two aspects of my behavior. I began with *xiao*, to enact *xiao* to its fullest extent towards the elders around me. To carry out *xiao* to its fullest extent is not an easy task. You must be willing to give a lot and do whatever is necessary to nurture the body of your elders. You must go along with their heart and respect their character. Also, perhaps even more importantly, you must protect them from worrying. What does that mean? The body of the child is the heart of the parents. If the children are in poor health, won't that worry the parents? My failure in my duty to my brothers and sisters was also serious. I had an elder brother above me and five younger sisters below me. In the past, I had forced them all to listen to me, with no exceptions. We hadn't gotten along well and that had worried our elders greatly, often to the point of tears. After reading Wang Shanren's book, I felt deep regret for my serious shortcomings and frequently wept in secret, feeling sorry for how I had treated my siblings, and even more sorry for how I had treated my parents.

Previously I had actually enjoyed offending my parents to make them angry and because of that I had contracted disease in my head. So I began by cleaning up the aspects of my behavior associated with my head. After I cleaned up all the anger that I felt towards my parents, I continued to do the same work in regard to my community and social connections. Rural China was then organized in production teams of The People's Commune. At that time I was dissatisfied with some of the leaders in the commune, to the point of resenting them. After I cleaned up this wrongful behavior of mine in the social sphere, I began examining my relationships with all the other elders in my community to look for any areas of disrespect and defiance. Every little detail had to be cleaned up. If there is even a single area left that is not cleaned up, you will not recover completely from your disease. As Chairman Mao said, "If you fail to reach it with the broom, the dirt will not just disappear on its own." So I had to sweep out all the hidden corners.

---

3   *Xiao* 孝: One of the core virtues of Chinese culture, this term is impossible to express adequately with a single English word. Most often translated as "filial piety," or more recently as "family reverence," it refers to the deep love, devotion, respect, and gratitude towards our parents and family elders, in our heart as well as our actions.

At that time, people only knew that I had recovered from my illnesses, but no one knew how this had happened or what medicine I had taken to heal myself. All of this happened right during the Cultural Revolution and you had to be careful with what you said. If you said the wrong thing, you would be labeled as a "demon" (the word the government used to imprison people). So, I did not say a word about my recovery. I just silently carried on with my actions. Didn't Wang Shanren say, "Carry out those actions that nobody else is willing to do, pick up what others do not want, bear what others cannot bear, and endure what other cannot endure"? So I began to act in accordance with these four principles.

Wang Shanren spoke only of giving, not of receiving rewards. I followed his example. When it came to jobs, I purposely chose the hardest work. Even though I hadn't fully recovered, I still chose the hardest work. Whenever others were not willing to do something, I went and did it. The bullying that others could not take, I took for them. I just took it, again and again. What is the big deal, after all, with tolerating a few sentences? In the final analysis, all that matters is our own wrongdoings.

Eventually, my body got stronger and I was able to do even more work. I did more work than others in the production brigade and earned less money for it. I did not argue about the conditions or about the pay but simply did whatever the leaders assigned to me. Whatever jobs others considered too dirty or tiring, I took the initiative and carried out myself. I did this because I remember the following passage from *The Record of Sincere Doings*: The foreman earned 140 strings of cash in one year and Wang Shanren received only 70 strings. When the foreman said that Wang Shanren was being treated unfairly, Wang replied that he was not being treated unfairly, because he knew with certainty that the law of Heaven was reciprocal and fair. Remembering this story, I worked hard, enduring exhaustion and complaints, without any concern about whether or not I was earning work-points or money.

During that time, we earned several Mao in pay for a whole day of hard work. But if you went out on assignments to other places, you could earn one Yuan and two Mao. Sometimes a leader assigned me a task and made clear that I had all day to complete it. But I would make the best use of my time and complete it in a morning. If I came back in the morning, I refused to accept the additional pay for having gone out on an outside assignment and furthermore continued working in the afternoon. In the evening, I would register for only one day of work points. The production brigade leader said, "You finished a whole day's assignment in half a day and in the afternoon you worked as usual. I will register you for a day and a half of work points. " I replied, "It wouldn't be right. You must register me for only one day of work points." He said, "Isn't that unfair to you?" I answered, "Not at all." Why did I act in this way? It was because Wang Shanren had said that to do more work and earn less money was to cultivate virtue. If I had not performed the job that they were paying me for and still earned the pay for it, wouldn't I incur a certain type of debt? I simply followed in my actions how Wang Shanren had acted.

As time went on like this, the leaders and the community all developed a positive impression of me, and I enjoyed a good reputation with everybody. Nevertheless, I didn't acknowledge my status because there is precariousness in high positions while the Dao is always in the lower place. The high place is always a terrible place to be, and I didn't dare to go there. Whatever the leaders of the production team ordered me to do, I did for them. And yet I refused to accept a promotion in the production team. What truly mattered to me was that in the eyes of the community I was as bright and clean as fresh snow. The community is, after all, the same as Heaven. Even though Heaven is so high that nobody can see it and nobody can touch it, when the community says you are a good human being this means that Heaven approves of you.

II. Making My Relationships Complete

II.1 FULFILLING THE DAO IN MY DUTIES TOWARD MY SIBLINGS: CARING FOR MY SISTER-IN-LAW'S FAMILY

Once I understood the principles of proper conduct in alignment with the Dao, I evaluated myself critically in my every-day behavior. My elder brother loved me very much and always agreed with me, regardless of whether or not I was in the right. My five younger sisters were also always willing to be of service to me and followed my orders. When I recognized that I had failed to fulfill my duty to my siblings, I began to work hard on compensating for these wrongdoings. But how was I to do this? I had to retreat and step down, little by little, which was extremely hard to do in the beginning. One's acquired personality is very difficult to change. And yet, I gradually persevered in my transformation. Later, my brother and sisters all remarked, "How is it that you have changed like this?" Thinking to myself that perhaps I truly had changed if they all said that I had, I raised my commitment to become even greater. As an old proverb says, "As virtue rises by one foot, vice rises by ten. As virtue rises by ten feet, vice soars overhead." If you don't establish a commitment, it seems that nothing will happen, but as soon as you establish a commitment, vice really escalates. The greater the commitment you set for yourself, the more tribulations there will be.

Just as I was making progress on the Dao with single-minded heart and intention, the ordeals really intensified. At the age of 38, my elder brother contracted cirrhosis of the liver and, after a long period of spitting blood and excreting blood in the stool, he ultimately passed away. I was only 36 at that time. Because of the fact that there had been only two sons in our family, namely my brother and myself, his death was particularly devastating to me. All of a sudden, I was at a loss over what to do and thought about him every day, missing him to the point of foregoing sleep or food. My brother and I had been as intimate as if we were one body, so whenever I thought of him, the grief was unbearable. Compounding this was the fact that I had not fulfilled my duty to my brother, otherwise I would not have been thinking about him so much and feeling such deep remorse.

At this point, I asked myself, "Where are the Heavenly laws?" If Heavenly laws existed, my brother should not have died! With me acting with such a degree of sincerity, how was it possible that he had died anyway? In my heart, I was truly unable to accept what had happened and thus began to falter in my commitment. I was no longer willing to fulfill my vow that I had committed to in the past. And just at that moment when I began to retreat from it in my heart, my illness returned with a vengeance, and my physical condition was quite critical. My entire body swelled up until I resembled a round clay figure, and I also experienced excruciating pain in the heart.

At that time, the teacher who had introduced me to the Dao was still alive, and I could see no other alternative than to immediately go to visit her. When I arrived at her home, she asked me only one question: "What have you been thinking about that your illness has worsened to such a degree and what are you going to do?" I was at a complete loss and simply answered, "My parents had only two male children, my elder brother and me. Now that my older brother has passed away, if I should also die, who would my parents have to depend on? I would have no complaints if I died tomorrow, as long as I could provide my parents with the proper funeral rites." Hearing these words, my teacher said nothing else but allowed me to stay at her house.

My teacher did not speak to me again until three days later, when she said: "The fact that at this critical juncture, when your life hung in the balance, your first thought was for the welfare of your parents rather than for your wife and children shows that you still have a heart of *xiao* and that your primary Qi is still sufficient. Therefore Heaven has again granted you life, to allow you to help others." Just like that, my health quickly returned, I survived, and furthermore regained my original trust.

This experience provided me with a deep revelation as well as with a valuable tool for my subsequent activity in teaching about illness. At a time when our life is in grave danger, if your first thought is for your elders, this demonstrates that your *tianming*, your Heavenly destiny, is still present. What you consider at that moment is your *tianming*, and not your Yin *ming*, your Yin destiny. Considering your wife and children is your Yin *ming*, considering your family elders is your *tianming*. The fact that you are considering your *tianming* means that there is hope for survival, that you can meet your lucky stars that will help you.

I stayed at my teacher's house for a total of 41 days. By the time I returned home, I had almost completely recovered my health. Still, I knew that I had not yet fully fulfilled my duty to my brother. What could I do about this? My brother had left behind five children, so I now wanted to fulfill the Dao of mercy by taking responsibility for the care of my nephews and nieces. Also compensating for my failure to fulfill my duty to my brother and relieving my parents' concern for their grandchildren, this allowed me to make the Dao come full circle in three areas, namely in *xiao*, in my duty towards my brother, and in the realm of mercy. So I resolved that as long as I lived I would take responsibility for my brother's five children until they reached adulthood. Care of my brother's children would take priority even over the welfare of my own children.

In those days, my health was still not too strong, so I discussed this situation with my wife: "What do you think we should do? Our sister-in-law is caring for her five children. If she doesn't remarry, we must take care of them all the way." My wife replied, "We certainly can take care of the children but your health is still fragile." I said, "Regardless of my weak health, I still must take care of the children." My wife responded, "Alright. You needn't be concerned with the needs of our family. We only have two children, and I will take care of them myself, I can support them on my own. If you try and take care of two families, I am afraid that you work yourself to death. It is enough if you look after our sister-in-law's entire family." Hearing my wife's reply, I couldn't help crying. I had not anticipated the extent of her magnanimity and felt such deep gratitude and emotion towards her that she was willing to support me like this.

My wife did as she had said, handling all the household tasks while I shouldered the responsibility of supporting a total of nine people: my parents, my sister-in-law, her five children, and one elderly sister of mine. I provided for all their food, drink, clothes, fuel, and other household expenses. Supporting my family left me exhausted, forcing me to walk endless distances just to haul water. But even though my body was exhausted, my heart was not. Complying with the Dao, I felt no resentment but shouldered the hard work without complaint.

In this way, I looked after my sister-in-law's entire family for nearly two years. Finally, my sister-in-law, fearing that we could not continue on like this, said to me, "My eldest daughter is disabled and cannot earn a living. My second daughter being 13 and my sons being 10, 7, and 4 years old, all are too young to earn a living. How will you be able to raise them to adulthood? If this situation continues, won't you work yourself to death? And if that is the case, both of our families will collapse. I had better remarry." Hearing this, I had one thought in my head: I was committed wholeheartedly to doing my very best in carrying out the Dao. If my sister-in-law wanted to get remarried, I did not want to let her rationalize her decision by saying that the children's uncle had given up on taking care of them. So I answered, "If you want to leave, I cannot force you to stay because it is indeed true that our family is going through hard times. But if you stay, I will continue to provide for you even if I need to become a beggar." Breaking down in tears, she said, "You have relinquished affairs in your own family and placed your priority on caring for us, all out of obligation to your brother. You surely are worthy of your brother." Subsequently, when she was leaving to get remarried, she told me: "It was not that you, second uncle, have failed us. Sadly, the circumstances of our lives do not permit it and have forced me to leave." Even though my sister-in-law ended up getting married in the end, my actions in following the Dao fulfilled a debt to my older brother but at the same time also relieved my parents' concern for the welfare of their grandchildren.

My sister-in-law remarried and moved to a village called Hailun, which was more than a hundred and thirty miles from our home. But not long after she had moved her family to Hailun, the children began to feel like they could not stay there any longer, so one day her second daughter and eldest son returned to our home. As soon as they entered the door, they said, "Uncle, we are not leaving." How was I to deal with this problem? As their uncle, I couldn't just tell them to stay. So I just said, "Come in, your grandmother has been missing you." Yet I felt greatly unsettled. I knew I had to discuss this situation with my wife.

After the children went inside, I asked my wife, "Two of the children have come back and don't want to leave again. What do you think we should do about this?" My wife answered, "Their mother only left our family in order to support them all. We couldn't let them stay with us." I said, "Is it really not possible for them to stay? The children have come back and we cannot possibly drive them away." My wife replied, "I still think it is better for them to leave." At that time, I still had some difficulties controlling my temper. Upon hearing my wife's words, I immediately answered in rage, "If you will not let them stay, then you go back to your parents! I will take those two children and our two children to live with my parents. You can go find yourself a better home!" As soon as my wife heard my words, she began to cry and said, "Let's do this. We'll let these two children stay with us but if any of the other children come back, we won't allow them to stay. We have two sons of our own and might have wanted to have a third one. But we have to work so hard already so that we can afford for the two boys to get married when they grow up. If our own children would not be able to get married because we are too poor, would this not make us criminals?" Hearing these words, I felt joy in the bottom of my heart. More than two months later, on a bitter cold winter day, my wife braved heavy snow to go to Hailun and returned after having changed over their household registration.

Nevertheless, it was not many months before my brother's eldest daughter and second son returned to our home as well. As soon as he entered our yard, my second nephew grabbed my legs and pleaded, "Second Uncle, we will not leave again!" As soon as I heard these words, an instant thought came to me: "If you also refuse to leave, how can I afford to support you all! If I had been able to support you all in the past, why would I have let you go in the first place?" My eyes welled up with tears but I refused to cry. At the same time, I couldn't express my thoughts out loud.

There was no alternative: I had to brace myself and discuss this situation with my wife again. This time, she proposed a brilliant idea. She said, "I will go to Hailun to find our sister-in-law and ask her to leave." I asked, "What would be the purpose of asking her that?" My wife answered, "I will let them move back here. Anyhow, her husband is just one person." I asked again, "Do you think she will be able to come back here?" "I do think it should be possible. After they move back here, we will just give them back all of their original belongings. In addition, we'll have your parents live with us but without letting your sister-in-law's family shoulder any of the burden. This way your parents can see their grandchildren often and will not be concerned about them. Isn't that a plan that would be satisfying to everyone?" As soon as I heard my wife's suggestion, I found it sound. If our sister-in-law was able to come back, it would allow the whole family to reunite, which would certainly be in harmony with the Dao.

In November of that year, my wife again braved the bitter cold to go once more to Hailun. Upon her return, she told me, "When I arrived, our sister-in-law and I wept in each other's arms. Finally, our sister-in-law agreed to return, because otherwise the children would be going back and forth, which would make our elderly parents worry a lot and moreover confuse the children about where their home was." In accordance with this decision, in the first month of the lunar year, I borrowed two horse-drawn carriages from the production brigade. It took me five days to travel the hundred and thirty miles and bring them back.

II.2 FULFILLING THE DAO OF MERCY: HELPING MY NEPHEWS ESTABLISH THEIR FAMILIES

After my sister-in-law and her family had returned, we still needed to find a way to take care of everyone's life. My sister-in-law's new husband was a man with a good character, a devout Buddhist who became close to me like a brother. Even though we were originally not related, the affection between us surpassed that of blood relations. He had never hit or yelled at my elder brother's five children, so when my mother met him, she also had nothing to complain about. Nevertheless, because he was too polite to bring up a certain issue, my mother asked me, "Is he going to be able to help all three of his wife's sons get married? It appears that it will be difficult for each of my grandsons to take a wife." I consoled her: "Mother, you needn't worry about this matter. It will be fine as long as he can provide support for them now." My mother asked, "How about the marriages of these three sons?" I answered, "Mother! Set your mind at ease. If my sons will be able to take a wife, I surely will also provide for my nephews to take a wife." My mother was angry with me. "You are talking nonsense. How could you be able to do such a thing?" I said, "Mother, I am determined to do so. Please just go on with your life and I will show you."

With my kind of determination and commitment, I just had to figure out a way and then implement it. Just when the five boys were ready to find wives, I had the good fortune of meeting somebody who asked me to join him in running a noodle factory, so I became his business partner. I figured that if I worked at this shop for forty full days each fall, I could earn enough money to pay for the expenses of one boy's marriage. With this number in mind, I said to my mother, "In addition to my farming, I plan to run a noodle factory. In that way I can earn enough money each fall to cover the expenses of one of my sons' or nephews' marriage. I'll work at the shop for five falls and thereby earn enough money to enable all five boys to take a wife. Now do you still doubt

•

that I can achieve this goal?" My mother's reply was, "Don't boast!" I said, "With due respect, esteemed mother, I am not boasting. Please just wait and see." To enable each of these children to take a wife, I thus worked the land and ran the noodle shop on top of that, experiencing innumerable hardships and often working night and day. I toiled like this for eight full years until finally I had enabled every one of the five boys to take a wife.

After my eldest son was betrothed, I searched far and wide for the right match-maker for my eldest nephew. In the end, I found two possible matches but both were inappropriate. While they approved of my nephew, I did not approve of them. Why did I not approve? The reason was that my thinking was very conservative and I could not stand looking at girls who wore lipstick and short skirts. Nevertheless, my nephew obeyed me without objection, saying simply: "If my uncle approves of a girl, I shall have no objection."

Because I was too selective, no one wanted to introduce a girl to us. Since nobody else would find a girl, I went to look myself. Finally I found the girl that ended up becoming my eldest nephew's wife. She was my brother's mother-in-law's granddaughter. Her mother had originally stopped by to visit me because she was suffering from a particularly severe liver condition, couldn't live without drinking sugar water, and had such poor eye sight that she could hardly see. When she had told me that she was quickly losing her eyesight, I had immediately asked her, "You are losing your eye sight. Among the more than thirty members of your family, who do you look down upon the most?" She had answered, "I look down most upon my mother-in-law." So I had replied, "If you look down upon your mother-in-law, some day your daughter-in-law will surely look down upon you." After I had said this, she had realized that she had found the root of her disease, and she was able to see again. This had caused her great happiness. When I later visited her to request her services as a matchmaker, she told me, "I know who it is you are trying to arrange a match for." I asked, "For whom?" and she replied, "For your nephew." I told her that she was right and said: "If you approve, let's come to an agreement. If you don't approve, then forget it. This is not something that should be forced." She replied that she approved of the match, and in this way, my eldest nephew's marriage was decided.

Thus, twelve days after my oldest son's wedding, I had managed to arrange my eldest nephew's marriage. And when my oldest nephew's bride arrived, my mother was truly pleased. So I asked her, "Mother, did you see what happened? Did you see how I have solved all your worries?" My mother answered, "Yes, I saw what you have done. I would have never thought that you could do this." So I told her: "Mother, please stop worrying and you shall see what else I will do in the future. After my second son is married, I will prepare for my second nephew's marriage. And once these two are married, arranging for the youngest nephew's marriage will be even easier." My mother then responded, "I won't be concerned any longer. Since I saw your first son get married, I have stopped worrying."

Speaking of the elderly, as soon as their heart's desires are settled, they are ready to pass on to the other world. Just a little more than a month after the weddings of the two first boys, at six o'clock in the morning on the eighth day of the last month of the year, I was engaged in a conversation with my mother, when she suddenly started coughing. My mother was not sick at all, so my wife asked her why she was coughing. Mother answered, "I just coughed." I interjected that she appeared perfectly fine, and she responded, "Yes, I am just fine. I am not sick at all." But as soon as those words had left her mouth, she continued, "Actually, I am not well. It is time for me to go," to which I responded, "Just now you said that you were perfectly fine. How come you feel like it is time for you to go?" Saying, "The earth and the sky seem to be spinning," my mother passed on.

For us as sons and daughters to truly carry out *xiao* to its fullest, we must simply solve the worries they harbor in their heart. After my mother's passing, I continued to carry out my vow. After my youngest son's engagement, I got busy arranging my second nephew's engagement. A month after my youngest son's wedding, my second nephew also got married. And not long after that, we celebrated the wedding of my youngest nephew who I was moreover able to build a house for. After we finished building that house, we then built a house for my eldest nephew. My second nephew was the only one who didn't have his own house, and he thus lived with us for the following six years.

As a result, my sons, daughters-in-law, nephew, and his wife all lived together in our home for a long time. When strangers came to visit, they couldn't tell who were my daughters-in-law and who was my nephew's wife. One time, somebody saw my nephew's wife and asked me whether this was my own daughter. I told her that this was not my daughter but my nephew's wife. She responded, "Ah, that your nephew's wife would treat you with such concern! Not even daughters always go to such lengths in their actions." This is the way things happen in the world: If you don't give, nothing will be reciprocated. If you don't treat others well, how can you possibly expect them to treat you well?

In our family, my nephew's wives and my daughters-in-law get along very well, with no distinction between what is mine and what is yours. The five sisters-in-law are never on bad terms because of differences of opinion. They all yield to each other but are eager to do the dirtiest or heaviest work. My three nephews all live near us now. If they happen to stop by my house around mealtime, they eat with us. If they happen to stop by while I am working on something, we all work together. If they happen to know that I am working away from the home somewhere, no matter how far it is, they rush over there to do the work for me. Our relationship is better than that between many fathers and sons.

The order of nature today is reflected in the way in which the Dao is expressed in the family. Home is nothing but an opportunity to practice the Dao, the place of concrete evidence for genuine cultivation. Are we able to make our families perfect, to completely walk this aspect of the Dao? Nowadays, so many people disregard the Dao of the family, believing that they can only practice the Dao when they leave the family. In fact, though, the family is the true practice of the Dao. Leaving your family is just like leaving the root to pursue the branches, or in other words, attending to mundane matters while neglecting the essentials. Aren't you then going in the opposite direction, away from the Dao?

II.3 DISREGARDING FAME AND PROFIT, ESTABLISHING MYSELF AND PRACTICING THE DAO

Wang Shanren once said: "If it is your money, you cannot run away from it. If it is not your money, no matter how forcibly you pursue it, you will bungle it and lose it sooner or later." After I understood this truth at age 25, I became indifferent to money.

I had an uncle who lived in Harbin in Heilongjiang Province. At the very beginning of the economic reform period in 1978, my uncle asked me to join him because he wanted me to run a tofu factory for him. He claimed that within a few years I would be a millionaire. Considering this situation, I was, however, very clear about my objective. What I was seeking was not money but to follow the Dao. How could I possibly give up my life's objective for the sake of financial wealth? For many years after that, my uncle was unaware of my affairs, until he visited me at my home 3 years ago and gained a general impression. Incredulously, he exclaimed: "Ah! You are really a fool. You gave up an opportunity to earn money but instead chose this life?" How was I to answer him? I could not do anything but smile.

My wife had spoken similar words to me before: "We both are so busy from morning until evening, yet we have not earned any money. Why on earth are we living like this?" I replied, "How can you say that we have not earned any money?" She said, "Where is all the money we've earned?" I replied, "Is that really difficult to figure out?" She said, "I don't see even a penny. You are bluffing." I explained, "Don't you know? How many patients have managed to escape from the pain and suffering of disease? All this has happened without spending any money. Under ordinary circumstances, how much money would have been needed to treat them? Are you now able to settle our accounts?" Hearing this answer gave my long-standing companion great happiness.

My wife and I farmed 16 *mu* of land for our livelihood. It was not until I turned 67 years old that I stopped farming and no longer concerned myself with this. Why had I continued to farm until then? The reason was that I was determined to lead an ordinary life for half of the time and the life of a sage the other half. Specifically, I wanted to spend half of my time teaching the Dao and the other half doing farm work. Though I taught the Dao for the benefit of others, I still could not allow them to support me. I wanted to put forth new life by my own efforts, as much as I possibly could. Harvesting 16 *mu* of land could provide food not only for my wife and myself, but even for many others as well.

In the process of practicing the Dao, I followed the example of the famous scholar-official Yuan Liaofan (1533-1606) and put aside a red bean whenever I did a good deed, and a black bean whenever I did a bad deed. By avoiding any evil actions and practicing a great number of good deeds, I progressed step by step. When water reaches the right level, the ditch appears. In this way, I slowly developed my morality through perseverance. These days, I grow healthier and healthier with each passing day. Even though I am 70 years old now, I feel stronger than when I was 50. How can this be? The reason is that I have dedicated this body to service to the world. The commitment that I had set for myself in the past was: To make the whole world my home and roam far and wide, to teach about Dao and De. To exhaust every ounce of energy I had in me to teach people how to become virtuous and upright and to leave the world a better place. This is the single desire of my life in my heart.

III. My Wife's Help in My Practice of The Dao

The Dao of the family! The Dao of the family! The Dao simply is in the family! It is only after we put in order and perfect the Dao of relationships in our own family that we are able to go out and teach others about the Dao. And the first challenge in the Dao of relationships is precisely the relationship between husband and wife. Husband and wife are Yin and Yang, and Yin and Yang are one unit. Didn't Wang Shanren say: "Looking at the woman's intention, we know the man's behavior. Looking at the man's heart, we know the woman's behavior." To know whether a man will succeed or not, simply look at his wife. To know whether a woman will succeed or not, simply look at her husband. If husband and wife do not support one another and are unable to live peacefully with each other, isn't this a great failure to practice the Dao? And even if they were able to practice the Dao, this could not possibly be the true Dao. Truthfully, my ability to lecture about disease to patients who are linked to me by karma and to teach everybody about the Dao is inseparable from my wife's support of me. So I will explain this matter here in a little more detail.

III.I HELPING ME TO ARRANGE THINGS IN MY FAMILY

My wife's name is Li Fengzhen. She is five years younger than me and was married to me when she was 18. At that time, my family's social status was not high and we were the poorest family in my village. In addition, I was not in good health, and yet she never uttered a word of complaint.

After we were married, she was extremely diligent and willing to do any kind of work, inside or outside the home. At that time, my father's temper was extremely explosive and he cursed or beat anybody whenever he had the slightest reason for dissatisfaction. Even though my wife had been at the receiving end of his cursing and beating, she continued to serve him with utmost devotion. This behavior of hers caused me to feel greatly at ease.

At the time my wife got married to me and joined my family, my five younger sisters were not married yet and were still all living with us. My wife took care of all their needs and always accommodated them, to the point where none of my sisters had anything negative to say about her. Later, after they all married and formed their own families, they continued to seek my wife's advice whenever they had any kind of problem. And my wife was always able to be of real help to them.

Thirty years ago, my second sister gave birth to two girls in succession but was unable to bear a son. Her husband was the only successor in his family line and the family therefore was greatly concerned about a male heir. But ten years passed without her getting pregnant again. So my wife told her: "I know how worried you are deep inside because you want to bear a son. I have decided to get pregnant again. If it is a son, I will give him to you; if it is a girl, I will keep her." As soon as my wife spoke those words, my sister started crying. And so my wife became pregnant for a third time. But to the great surprise of everyone, my sister also conceived very soon thereafter. So my wife had no choice but to secretly induce an abortion. When my younger sister found out about this, she embraced my wife and cried sorrowfully: "Sister-in-law! For my sake you wanted to have a child, and now you again for my sake have had to abort it. How will I ever be able to repay the debt of my gratitude? Not even a blood-related sister would do what you have done for me!" Even after several decades, there has never been as much as a cross word between them, and they are even closer than if they were blood sisters.

My wife's generosity toward my elder brother was even greater. When he fell ill and needed blood transfusions, I wanted to donate my own blood, but my wife loved me dearly and insisted that her blood be used instead. She said, "You are not in good health. If you donated blood, what would happen to our family afterwards?" While my brother was in the hospital, my wife and I cared for him day and night for a month without her ever uttering a single word of complaint. And this is how it should be between husband and wife. Both should treat each other with the respect due a guest. If they encounter good fortune, they should enjoy it together; if they happen upon difficult times, they should bear them together; if they have committed a sin, they should face it together. This is what a true full husband-wife relationship looks like. You cannot only enjoy the good times and then not suffer through hard times together. These days, many people only chase after the wealth and power of a family, to enjoy their good fortune. And when that family has lost its money, they simply divorce and look for another one. This is wrong.

Because my wife is such a warm-hearted and capable person, she gets along exceptionally well with all the people in our village, and there is not a single person who does not look up to her. Whenever somebody has a problem that weighs on them, they come to her for help. Regardless of the occasion, whether good or bad, joyful or mournful, they always seek her out, and she always embraces the opportunity to help them.

III.2 HELPING ME TO LECTURE ABOUT ILLNESS

When I first began my teaching activity of lecturing about illness, my wife was not supportive initially but later on changed her attitude completely. One day, she said to me: "The situation with sick people is truly lamentable indeed! A single person falls ill, and the entire family suffers along with them. Especially when it is children who contract a disease, their paternal grandparents, their maternal grandparents, their parents, uncles and aunts, and all the other relatives worry a great deal and stand by with anxiety. From this moment on, I also commit myself with all my heart and soul to abandoning any concerns about myself. The happiness of a million people depends on a single person's suffering." And ever since then, she has always served my patients as if they were part of our own family, with no distinction between self and other.

For more than thirty years now, our home has welcomed a constant stream of sick people every year, with anywhere from more than ten to more than thirty or forty people a day, to the point where it always looks like a small hospital. I myself do not concern myself with the affairs of the household at all. I just sit there and talk to everybody, explaining and advising without thinking of anything else, while my wife handles all the household affairs that come up in our family. In addition to planting the 16 *mu* of land, there is the vegetable garden that needs tending, the care of the chickens and ducks, and last but not least the work of attending to all the patients. Eating and drinking, going to the bathroom, sleeping, every detail is handled by my wife. From morning until night, there is no time for her to rest her feet, with a thousand chores needing to get done.

Let us first talk about her cooking. The people who come to our home have travelled from all over the place and arrive at any time of day or night. As soon as a new patient arrives at our home, the first question she asks them is invariably whether they have eaten. And if they haven't eaten, she immediately drops all her other chores and makes them something to eat. As soon as somebody comes, she makes them something to eat and they eat. If another person happens to arrive when the first person has just finished eating, she cooks something for that person. At our busiest times, she might cook as many as seven meals in a single day, and she has been doing this for thirty years now. Why else would I jokingly say that cooking is her destiny!

These sick people not only eat in our home, they also live in our home. When there are a lot of people staying with us, she has the patients sleep on the Kang while she herself sleeps on an improvised bed on the floor. And if there truly are too many people and we cannot accommodate them all, she takes the members of our family to sleep at our relatives' home. Our grandchildren have already gotten used to this situation so when they come home from school and see that there are a lot of people at our home, they take the initiative on their own to go stay with relatives. My wife not only cooks meals every day, she also has to wash sheets and quilts. Every time a person leaves, she has to wash their bedding. Hygiene is something that we must not ignore, so there is no way around that. In earlier times, how could we have had a washing machine, so it all had to be done by hand! The climate in China's Northeast is cold. Because sometimes there were a lot of people and a lot of chores, she was unable to keep up with the laundry and became exasperated. She'd holler at me and at those times, I also had to help her with the chores.

A great many of the patients who come to our home suffer from infectious diseases. Hepatitis A, hepatitis B, tuberculosis, we have seen it all. These patients are afraid that they might infect us and therefore bring their own dishes with them. My wife, however, often takes their dishes and puts them away so that they have to eat together with us. She does this in order to dispel the worry in their heart. In more than thirty years, not a single person in my entire family has ever contracted an infectious disease.

Previously, we also often had patients with mental disorders come to our home, and my wife was beaten up by such patients numerous times. Around 1990, one particular psychiatric patient all of a sudden suffered a relapse and slapped my wife in the face several times, causing her face to swell up quite badly. She simply smiled and bore it with grace. Later, that same patient had another relapse, this time at night, and started yelling and shouting and wildly smashing things. Completely unreceptive to being calmed down, she broke all the glass in the house. All of us took turns trying to restrain her by holding her arms or legs until we finally brought her under control. That evening, the Northeastern wind was particularly fierce, blowing straight into the house, and all of us froze and trembled from the cold so that nobody was able to sleep. After that night, my wife slept with this mentally ill patient every single night, holding her arms tightly because she feared that the patient would have another relapse and might run outside and freeze to death. Eventually, the patient completely turned around and revealed a great good-heartedness, vomited for seven days, and then recovered. Another time thereafter, my oldest son was cut with an axe five times by another mentally disordered patient, and we decided to stop allowing mentally ill patients to come to our home.

In 1998, a widow who was originally from our village came to our home to see me, walking 15 miles on foot to get there. When she was just leaving, my wife took out 5 Kuai of money and pressed it into her hand. The old widow started to cry and said: "After you have shared your food and drink with me, not only do you not want money, but now you even give me money!" My wife answered, "Your family is in dire straits and on top of that your son has a mental illness. Please just accept this money!" This is just the way she is, with an open hand and heart and with no concern at all for money or material things. Whenever patients bring money or gifts for us, she just gives them back. Seeing that she will not accept anything under any circumstances, some patients leave things behind in such a way that she cannot return them. In such cases, she just takes these things and passes them on to patients who are in need.

As my wife often says, "When patients arrive, their expressions are full of worry and suffering. By the time they leave, I must make them very happy." So, whenever patients are leaving, my wife always sees them off with great care and admonishes them several times to conduct themselves according to the highest moral standards. Not just a few patients tell her as they are leaving: "Aunt! Please rest assured. If I act in any way less than virtuous after I get home, I will feel like I have let you down."

At present, my wife is already advanced in years, and I myself have passed 70 years of age, so sometimes we certainly do get tired and feel like we can't carry on. Nevertheless, the door to goodness is hard to open, but the door to goodness is also hard to close! When there are sick people coming from far and wide, we still cannot help but receive them with an open heart. Whoever should eat here, eats; whoever should stay here, stays; and whoever should leave, leaves. Ultimately, I must say this: Working by my side, my wife has surely suffered innumerable hardships, borne innumerable burdens, and faced innumerable wrongdoings. Without my wife's quiet support, I could hardly have walked the path I have chosen in this lifetime. I feel the deepest gratitude towards her!

LECTURE TWO

Lecturing About Illness

I. Internal Illnesses of the Five Elements in the Body

In the human body, the five elements are associated with the five *zang* organs and the six *fu* organs. The five *zang* organs (heart, liver, spleen, lungs, and kidneys) are solid, which is a characteristic associated with Yin. The six *fu* organs (gallbladder, stomach, urinary bladder, large and small intestines, and "triple burner") are hollow, which is an attribute associated with Yang. What is Yin? What is Yang? Women are associated with Yin, while old people are associated with Yang, and men are also associated with Yang. For this reason, diseases in the five *zang* organs in most cases originate because women get angry, as a result of which internal fire rises in the body. Diseases in the six *fu* organs in most cases originate because men or old people get angry, as a result of which internal fire rises in the body. In this lecture, we discuss mainly the diseases in the five *zang* organs.

I.I ILLNESS OF THE LIVER

If the liver and gallbladder suffer from illness, where does that come from? It comes from anger! The Qi of anger damages the liver, which can cause muddle-headedness, dizziness, deafness, toothache, deviated mouth or eyes, heavy arms, numbness in the limbs, pain in the anterior chest or rib-sides, and disease in the mammary glands. In more serious cases, the result can be apoplexy with aphasia or hemiplegia, or even liver cancer. Just look at how the Qi of anger can cause so many symptoms! The poisons from this Qi can persist inside the vessels throughout the entire body, and when they are discharged to the outside, their taste is sour.

When I was young, I never saw anybody suffering from hemiplegia. Nowadays, however, it is a disease that we encounter quite frequently. Why is that? I frequently ponder this question. In China's past, the family system was autocratic, and the words of the elders were law, which the younger generations had to obey without question. At present, the opposite is true. Not only do the younger generations refuse to obey their elders, but the elders even have to obey them! Consequently, the elderly easily develop a tendency to brood in silence, and if this happens frequently, they become prone to developing cerebral embolism or hemiplegia. In such people, the ability to think is impaired, and if you therefore ask them to recall the past they are unable to. And because they cannot remember the past, it is very difficult to generate a heart full of remorse in them. But if this kind of disease, which is caused by anger, is not countered by developing remorse and the poisonous Qi instead lodges in the tendons instead of being discharged to the outside, it is very difficult to cure indeed.

In the course of my teaching about disease, I once encountered exactly this kind of patient, a cadre from Heilongjiang Province who was suffering from liver carcinoma. At the point when I met him, his condition was quite desperate and he was close to death. He had sent somebody to ask me to go and see him. I refused to go, and when his messenger wanted to know my reason I answered, "Since this person certainly has family members, why did he send an outsider to ask me to go see him? That is proof that he lacks sincerity and does not have full trust in me." The next day, the patient's daughter-in-law came and I thus followed her to his home.

When I arrived, I saw that he was completely unable to lie down but was forced to sit up all night long. I began by chatting with him about his family life, because before you can explain to a patient about disease, you must first talk about their family life. In this way, once you understand the situation in somebody's family, you can then find out about the cause of disease. I stayed at this man's home for two nights and left only when the patient was once again able to lie down. That was our first meeting.

The next time I met with him was at a clinic we had established in Beian. I asked, "Seeing that your disease has progressed to such a critical stage, have you thought at all about the future? What kind of plans have you made?" He answered that he had indeed made plans, and when I asked him what they were, he replied: "The only concern in my mind has been what to do about my mother. I have worried about nothing else. When I am no longer of this world, what will my mother do?" At hearing these words, I was no longer so concerned about the seriousness of his disease but thought that regardless of how bad it was, I might still be able to save him. He added, "I also have a large number of children, none of whom have had any success in life yet." I replied, "Alright! You may stay here for a few days before you go back home."

When it was time to leave, he asked: "What do I need to do when I get home?" I told him: "You are the leader of a production team. Look deep within yourself and recall over and over who you may have gotten angry at in the past. Write all their names down on a piece of paper. Afterwards, recall carefully in each case the specific reason why you had gotten angry. Previously, you must have been convinced that they had done you wrong. As I have explained to you Wang Shanren's method of treating disease through one's disposition and emotions, I would like you to now think carefully about who it was who ultimately wronged who. Even if the other person might have made a gigantic mistake, if you became angry, the fault is with you, since you should not have gotten angry. Anger can never resolve problems but is only a fierce flame that everyone else has to hide from." After hearing my words, he went home and then filled four large sheets of paper with name after name of all the people who he had gotten angry at in the past. With sincerity, he carefully analyzed and deliberated each of these incidents and, recollecting each event one by one, expressed his remorse to that person. In so doing, his illness gradually began to retreat. And when he realized that he was recovering, he became evermore cheerful and energetic, coming to visit us consistently every few days. Within about a year, his disease was almost completely cured.

On a previous physical examination, the ultrasound had revealed a shadow on his liver that was 9.75 x 8.4 cm large. When he now went for another examination, the tumor had clearly shrunk to only 5.4 x 4.0 cm, and continued to shrink from then on. He was no longer worried about his physical health and was able to ride his motorcycle anywhere he wanted. As he told me, his disease was practically cured. Bimonthly follow-up examinations continued to show that the tumor became smaller each time, with only a faint shadow left behind a year later.

Some time thereafter, the production team had to re-elect officers. Previously, he had served as team leader but this time around he wanted to serve as secretary. As he told me, "I still want to be in a leadership position." I replied: "Do you want to continue living or not? If you want to continue living, you must not serve in such a leading role because you cannot afford to get angry. Your liver has already been damaged and is now in the process of recovering. What you must fear more than anything is anger. If you get angry again, the poisonous Qi will directly attack the part of your liver that has been damaged. If you want to continue on with your life, let go of that goal. If you do not care about your life, do as you wish." He answered: "Not to worry! I can control myself." Hearing his reply, I understood that he was truly somebody preoccupied with seeking high office and being a leader! He further added: "I have three sons and want to save fifty thousand Yuan for each of them, as well as needing to earn another fifty thousand Yuan for myself. Only then can I give up my position." Just see how far he was reaching with his hands! So I said: "Since you are so determined, there is nothing else I can do."

In order to be elected to the office of secretary, he had to plead with and cozy up to people but ultimately was indeed elected as secretary. On the very night of his election victory, his opponent hired somebody to stab him with a knife. Even after being stabbed with a knife, was he still courageous enough to accept the position? He acted as if nothing had happened. An attack with a knife didn't cause him to lose a single hair. He was really a dauntless person! Afterwards, he had another follow-up examination, which showed no shadow at all on his liver. Cutting wheat, threshing, carrying heavy loads on his back, he was able to do anything. He thought his troubles were behind him.

His opponent, on the other hand, after finding out that the stabbing had not disturbed my patient the slightest bit, went to my patient's office in the production brigade, slamming his fist on the table and yelling at him. But my patient simply observed that somebody had come to yell at him, quietly stood up, and left, unmoved by the whole affair. Witnesses said, "He is extraordinary indeed. Even when he got yelled at, he still did not get angry!" It was truly as in the saying, "Respond to yelling as if listening to opera, respond to being beaten like a knock on the door."

Ultimately, though, he was unable to control himself after all. For the next three years, he worked day and night with his wife, cultivating dozens of *mu* of land. In the fall of the third year, after he was done with the threshing, he was driving a tractor to his land to transport maize stalks when he happened to come across the man who had yelled at him previously. And sure enough, the man yelled at him again. This time, though, my patient lost his temper and responded: "I am simply driving a tractor along, minding my own business, and I am not in your way. Why are you still yelling at me?" In that instant, my patient could not take it any more. He stopped his tractor and took down the winch that was used to start the tractor. Walking up to the man, he roared: "What are you yelling at me for?" The other man said calmly: "I didn't yell at you. My daughter-in-law who is sitting on my tractor next to me is who I was yelling at." If nobody has yelled at you, who are you going to hit? So, my patient ended up filled with pent-up anger and nowhere to vent. He drove the tractor back to his land, carrying the maize stalks. After he got home, he immediately didn't feel quite right. That night, as he was lying in bed, he pondered deeply: "That man has bullied me again and again even though I have never argued with him. If he continues to bully me, I am going to have to find a way to settle with him." After engaging in this kind of thinking all night long, he failed to get up the next morning. His belly had swelled up to look like a small mound. He lay like this in his home for nine days, unable to get out of bed.

In the end, his daughter-in-law said to him: "This will not do! Go immediately and visit Liu Shanren!" And so the patient returned to my place yet again. As soon as he saw me, he said, "My disease has struck me once again!" When I asked why his disease had returned, he answered, "I lost my temper with someone." I thought to myself that I had advised him not to serve as leader but he had insisted on doing it anyway. This time around, the relapse of his disease might mean the end of his life. But the patient had come and I had to provide some consolation. Therefore I said to him, "Haven't I told you before that if you got angry, your disease would return? For now, stay here for a few days.'"

So he stayed with us for seven days. His stomach became noticeably smaller and softer and he was able to walk two to three miles without getting tired. As soon as he saw his condition improve like this, he wanted to go home. My wife pleaded with him to recuperate for another two days, because that is just the kind of generous person she is. Any time a patient with a serious disease gets a little better and wants to leave, she insists and asks them to stay a little longer: "Don't be in such a hurry to go home! Don't worry about your family! If you end up dying, will your family still be there? You had better stay here a little longer." But the patient said: "I will go home just to see what is happening there, and I'll be back tonight." Nevertheless, after he went home, he didn't come back to us. Within a matter of days, he went off to Shenyang, the capitol of Liaoning Province, where he received some injections and, after being confined to bed for less than a month, passed away. Truly, it is easy to cure a disease but difficult to contain it!

In 1993, I encountered a similar kind of patient, a woman by the name of Geng Xiuping who lived more than thirty miles from our home in the city of Beian, in Heilongjiang Province. At the time she arrived at my home, I was right in the middle of weaving a basket. When I first saw her, I was deeply shocked at how extraordinarily thin she was, indeed nothing but skin and bones, so that she was barely able to stand. I simply said, "So you have come?" to which she answered, "I have come." I next asked her what her disease was and she replied: "I am suffering from too many diseases to tell: stones in the right lobe of the liver and bile duct, cholecystitis, a feeling as if the heart stops beating, stomach disease, headaches, and lumbar pain." I told her to come in and sit down, so she came in.

Her arrival coincided right with the busy season for farming, so I was farming all day and lecturing about illness at night. As I was explaining to my patients about resentment, hatred, irritation, anger, and annoyance, Geng Xiuping spoke up: "Liu Shanren! You have never even met me before. How is it that you understand me so clearly and address my issues so precisely?" I answered: "It is not that I am addressing your issues so precisely, but rather that you are earnestly applying what I have said to your own life." Then I continued: "The reason why you suffer from disease in the liver and gallbladder is your hot temper. Who is it that you are so angry at?" She was a straightforward person who immediately responded with honesty that she was angry at her husband. So I asked her why she was so angry at him. She said: "He does not help at all around the house. Regardless of what I ask him to do, he doesn't do it. So we yell at each other and sometimes even exchange blows." I told her: "Taking care of the household is the wife's responsibility. You should simply concern yourself with carrying out your own job, and that is enough. Why do you try to manage your husband? Wang Shanren once said, 'Blaming others is to live in an ocean of suffering. To try to manage others is to live in hell.' You do nothing but blame him and get angry at him. In this way, you have made your body completely sick. Is this not an ocean of suffering? You do nothing but try and manage him. You do not submit to his will, and he does not submit to yours, resulting in constant yelling and arguing, fighting and blow-ups. If this is not hell on earth, then what is it?" She argued: "He refuses to work for a living. All he does is get drunk." So I asked her: "Before you two got married, did he drink?" To this she answered that he did not. I said: "Look at that! Isn't it your husband's drinking that has forced you out? He got angry with you but didn't have anybody to talk to about it, so he was forced to drown his sorrow in liquor. It is you who has forced your husband into drinking, and now you add further injury to this by blaming him!"

Hearing my words, she suddenly began to weep bitterly and said: "After hearing you speak like this, I finally understand. Now I see how I have indeed greatly wronged my husband. I have always deliberately found fault with him and intentionally yelled at him. My words have been so fast that he has been unable to out-argue me so he has raised his hand and beaten me. We have fought with each other constantly, causing me to now suffer from all these diseases. He also has been very upset and is therefore suffering from liver disease. Thus we are both living a miserable and unbearable life." I explained that in the Dao of husband and wife, as soon as one spouse's Dao is injured, the other spouse's Dao is injured as a consequence as well. When there is no harmony between husband and wife, moreover, the elders on both sides of the family worry. Is this what you consider being a good daughter? When there is no harmony between husband and wife, and there is fighting and arguing all day long, it is the same as giving your children poison. Is this what you consider being a good mother?" Geng Xiuping responded: "I have indeed greatly wronged my mother-in-law. I have intentionally expressed anger toward my husband in her presence, scaring her to the point of trembling in fear." So I said: "While you have suffered many wrongs, you also must repent. So go now and cry it all out!" And indeed, she went and wept for a long time, crying her heart out and tossing and turning all over her bed.

She cried so hard and long that she began to hiccup, expelling Qi endlessly, without being able to stop. After a while, her stomach also swelled up as if it were holding a small basin inside. I noticed that she became a little nervous about what was happening to her, so I told her: "This is a good thing. The Qi that you have generated with all your anger has been too much, and this is precisely the poison that you are now expelling." A little later, she next began to retch and vomit, spitting up white foam and water. After she stopped vomiting, she said that she felt completely comfortable all over her body. This is what occurred during her first visit to our home.

After she stayed with us for a few days, Geng Xiuping went back to her family. As soon as she opened the door to her home, she prostrated herself before her mother-in-law, knocking her head on the ground, and said in tears: "Mother, in the past I have failed to be a proper daughter-in-law, constantly fighting with your son and threatening you all with divorce. This has caused you a great deal of worry and broken your heart. I beg for your forgiveness. This daughter-in-law knows that I have wronged you." Her crying and pleading touched her mother-in-law who now also started to cry. She said: "It is not you who has not been a good daughter-in-law, it is me who has not been a good mother-in-law!" Both women embraced each other and had a good cry together, thereby releasing all the grief and hang-ups between them. And ever since, this mother-in-law and daughter-in-law got along extremely well, closer to each other than mother and daughter. And eventually, when the time came and her in-laws passed away, Geng Xiuping prepared all the funeral arrangements for them, thus making the Dao of *xiao* come full circle.

Now concerning her illness, how did Geng Xiuping ultimately recover? When she returned to her family after her first visit with us, she realized that her health had greatly improved and this greatly strengthened her confidence and trust. She came to see me consistently once a month until, after a total of thirteen visits, she had completely recovered. What does this tell us? This tells us that illness is the result of our own doing. If your disposition is not good, you invite illness. Illness in the heart requires medicine and a doctor for the heart. Depending on how you transform your character, your illness will recover to that same degree. Didn't Ms. Geng's husband also suffer from liver disease? Afterward, he also allowed me to cure him by explaining his illness to him. At present, husband and wife interact with mutual respect, understanding, and support for each other, and the atmosphere in their family is truly harmonious.

By studying Wang Shanren's ideas about Daode, Geng Xiuping not only recovered completely from her illness without spending a single cent, but she also made her family complete again. As a result, she formed a commitment to dedicate herself wholeheartedly to serving the community, to serving society at large. For the past ten years, she and her entire family have privately practiced the Dao by helping many patients at no charge and serving as an excellent model to others. In my thirty years of teaching about illness, I have come across a great number of people like Geng Xiuping. What do we call such a thing? We call it a great transformation in people's lives. Those who were bad people before have now transformed into kind people, and those that were evil people before have now transformed into good people.

One of the principles I expound in my teachings about illness is this: Even for ten thousand tael of gold, do not sell the Dao! If you offered me ten thousand tael of gold, I still would not sell the Dao to you. All that you need is a sincere and upright heart and a true desire to transform yourself, and I am only too happy to give you the Dao as a gift. I take the Dao and teach it to the world, without wanting anything in return. I only want everybody to go home and act in accordance with and in service to these teachings, to deeply transform your lives and create harmony and peace in your family. That alone is what leaves me deeply content and satisfied.

I.2 ILLNESS OF THE HEART

Where does illness of the heart come from? It simply comes from an over-abundance of fire Qi, from the existence of hatred in the heart. Hating others injures the heart, which manifests in symptoms like feeling hurried or flustered, heart palpitations, heat in the heart, insomnia, strange dreams, cough, vomiting blood, insanity and inability to speak, etc. In severe cases, this leads to mental illness.

Mental illness forms as the result of hatred that has grown too big. When hatred is generated, if it is not Qi that confounds the heart, it is the blood that confounds the heart. And when Qi and blood confound the heart, the circumference of the organ may be filled with white foam or static blood, which is precisely what is known in Chinese medicine as phlegm stasis obstructing the orifices of the heart. A person suffering from such a condition is unable to sit or stand with stability. When fire Qi is overly abundant, fire and hatred go hand in hand, and this can easily lead to mental disorders or derangement.

And once somebody has contracted a mental illness, this is very difficult to treat. The reason is that no matter what you explain to such a person, they are unable to truly hear you, so you can only use medication to control the condition. When I began to explain to people about illness, I had the courage to address any illness that I encountered and was not afraid to lecture even on mental illness. It was only after we experienced injuries from patients with mental illness that I stopped addressing such cases. What happened? One time, a patient with a mental illness came to my home to listen to my teachings about illness. As it turned out, his illness suddenly erupted and he grabbed a hatchet and whacked my son on the head with it five times until his skull collapsed. My son had previously been run over by a car, which had caused such severe injury to his head that even after surgery there was a part of his skull that could not be repaired. And now these five whacks with the hatchet on top of that, wasn't this really too much? Even now, when I think back at that situation, I am still afraid. This mental illness had been too dangerous. When the patient said there would be a relapse, the relapse invariably occurred; when the patient said he would injure others, he invariably did just that. So what can we do in cases like this? Just make them direct their intention deep into the lower abdomen at a time when they are calm and quiet, keep their thoughts stable, and make them carefully recall the past to reflect on who might have engendered such hatred in them, who they might feel such hatred towards. If the patient is able to look back in self-inspection, there is still hope.

In addition, coronary heart disease, cardiac arrest, myocarditis, pericardial effusion, disorders of the mitral or tricuspid valve, myocardial infarction, and congenital heart disease also all originate in hatred. In the five-element system of emotional healing, these kinds of conditions are the most dangerous ones. Hatred persists in the blood, and the heart, as the organ that governs the blood vessels, is most closely linked to the blood. Hatred that persists in the blood is therefore most likely to affect the organ of the heart and lead to disorders in the heart. If patients who suffer from heart disease recognize their own problems, become aware of which people they feel hatred towards, and truly and sincerely repent, it is possible to expel the illness along a specific path. And if their method of expulsion includes vomiting it out, the flavor of the vomit is bitter.

Among the great number of patients for whom I have explained their illnesses of the heart, the first person was a patient with the last name Liu, from a village called Rixin in Keshan County in Heilongjiang Province. He was suffering from coronary heart disease that was so severe at times that he would go into a coma up to nine times in a single day and was on the verge of death. When his relatives brought him to my home, I happened to be extremely busy, running in and out of house. In the midst of doing my work, I asked him why he had come. He answered that he was sick. When I asked him what disease he was suffering from, he replied that he had coronary heart disease. I said: "Do you know how you have contracted this type of disease?" He said that he didn't know. So I explained: "Heart disease is created from hatred. If people do not generate hatred, there is no poison of hatred in their blood, and they cannot possibly contract illness in the heart. Please think carefully and reflect on which people you feel hatred towards. Are you able to know that?" After thinking for half a day, he told me that he knew. I said, "If you know, you are able to recover. Who do you hate? Can you tell me?" He answered: "Who do I hate? I hate two people. Why is it that I want to hate these two people? There was a time when I badly needed help with a difficult matter and I went to these two people for help, giving them a large sum of money. In the end, though, they spent all my money but never took care of this task, so I have hated them ever since." I explained to him: "This is your own fault! You wasted all that money and now you feel like you have wasted it because the task did not get taken care of. Nevertheless, it was you who took the initiative to look for somebody else to take care of this task, rather than others coming to look for you. Again, in regards to the money, it was you who went to them and pressed it in their hand, not them who looked for you and asked for it. Who in the world can guarantee that every single thing can be taken care of with certainty?" He responded: "So with regard to this affair, am I at fault for hating them?" I told him to think it over and contemplate whether he was at fault or not. He mulled this over for half a day and then told me: "Yes, yes! It was indeed wrong to hate them." After a while longer, he began hiccupping. As soon as I saw that, I knew that he would be able to recover from his disease because the Qi of his hatred was being expelled along with the hiccups. In a moment, he pulled five boxes of Suxiao Jiuxinwan, a Chinese medicine formula for urgent treatment of heart disease, from his pocket and tossed them in the garbage. I asked him what he was doing, and he explained: "These are useless. No matter how I take them, they don't work anyway. With these few sentences that you have said to me, on the other hand, my heart has stopped trembling and become steady." From that point on, he was cured, one of my fastest-cured patients I ever had. This was the first case of heart disease that I ever explained.

There was another exemplary case, an older man of more than fifty years of age named Yin from Heilongjiang Province, who was suffering from necrosis in the heart (myocardial infarction). According to the diagnosis he had received in the hospital, one third of his heart had necrotized and the hospital saw no means of rescuing him. After he heard about my work from another person, he went to see me. He stayed at our home for five days, and then, seeing that his condition had not improved, stated: "You don't treat illness here! You do nothing but deceive people! I must go home." Somebody else encouraged him: "Don't leave quite yet but stay and listen more closely and look more closely at where your illness has ultimately come from." As a result, he stayed for another two days.

It was not until the seventh day that he finally understood my teachings and knew the place where he had gone wrong. All of a sudden, a wave of deep regret swept over him, and then he fainted. After about half an hour, when he awoke, the first sentence out of his mouth was: "How come I am cured? My heart no longer hurts!" What is the reason that we could see results so quickly? Because he had found the root to his own illness, and as soon as he had found the root of his illness, he was able to expel the hatred right away. What was the reason for his illness? He hated his son because he had disappointed him greatly, falling short of his expectations. According to my observation over the past few years, when older people contract heart disease, it is very often related to their children, to worrying about them and resenting their lack of success. The body of the children, the heart of the parents. Holding a grudge like this all day long, how could they not fall ill?

The patient mentioned above is now already more than seventy years old and is still able to escort goods in transport all the way to Guangzhou. I asked him:"You dare to escort vehicles and go to such distant places still?" He answered affirmatively and gave the following as his reason: "Ever since I recovered from my illness, I have understood the reason and no longer get angry at people. If things do not work out well, it is because we ourselves have not done something right. We cannot blame others for that."

Lastly, I have also encountered not a few cases of congenital heart disease. In 1997, an older woman from Shenyang came to see me, bringing a child of seven or eight years. Whether he moved or not, that child immediately said: "Grandma, I can't do it. I am too tired." I asked the child's grandmother what illness he was suffering from and she informed me that it was cardiac arrest. When I asked who she was, she responded that she was his grandmother. I told her that it was no good that she as the grandmother had come and that I needed the child's mother to come. She answered that the mother had died. So I said: "This means that this illness will not be easy to cure, because it was contracted from the mother. That is the root of it." The grandmother told me: "His mother died from heart disease herself, and now this child is also suffering from heart disease. His heart is always stopping. My old self and my husband, we have spent a great deal of money on the treatment of this child's condition, and yet, even with all this money, nobody has been able to treat his disease." I told her: "Not only is our treatment here a real struggle, but this condition is difficult to cure. Because his mother is no longer present, the root is no longer present, and all that is left over is this tip. I am afraid that we may not be able to stitch things together." She said, "Then I will still stay here for two days," and I told her to do so.

The sick child was very clever and quick-witted, and his grandmother was likewise very capable of teaching him, so he gradually came to comprehend quite a lot. But when it was evening, all of a sudden, seemingly out of nowhere, he started yelling at people. Who did he yell at? We had five helpers on hand right then and these five were precisely who he was yelling at. He did not yell at anybody else. You would give him food and he would yell at you. You would speak to him and he would yell at you. His grandmother said to him: "You don't act like this at home, child! How come you are yelling at people today like this?" But the child ignored even his grandmother and just went on yelling. After a while, the grandmother couldn't bear it any longer and led him to another room, where she clutched him tightly to the point where he started to cry. He cried and cried, with nobody able to console him. Passing by them, my wife said: "Grandma, don't try and make him stop! The child is releasing Yin Qi (the hatred passed down to him from his mother), and when he has finished releasing, everything will be good." His grandmother was doubtful, so my wife told her: "How could this not be true? You just let him cry, and when he has cried enough, he will be cured. Under normal circumstances, if you didn't dare to let him cry like this, who would? His crying is such that it is exerting all his strength." And sure enough, this child cried for a very long time, without ever letting up, until all of a sudden he stopped. No longer crying, he told his grandmother: "Grandma! My heart is no longer exhausted. My heart is cured!" And from this point on, the child's congenital heart disease was truly cured.

Later on, this old lady came one more time, again bringing the child with her. She said: "When my grandson's disease was cured, I was so overjoyed and just took him home, so I forgot that I was suffering from an illness myself. This time, I have come to cure my own illness." She again stayed with us for seven days, during which time her own illness was cured as well. After this, there were many more young children who came to us suffering from congenital heart disease, including some with pericardial effusion, and all of them were cured in the same way. How did they get cured? All of them were cured by crying. As a result of their crying, all the internal organs were stimulated and moved, and the pre-existing blockage in the heart vessels was opened up. To cure the disease, all that was needed was for the hatred and foolish fire that these children had contracted to be expelled.

1.3 ILLNESS OF THE LUNG

Seeing that illnesses of the heart originate in hatred, now what about illnesses of the lung? Illnesses of the lung arise mostly because of being irritated. Being irritated with somebody is the same as being jealous of them. This irritation damages the lung and can lead to panting, coughing, vomiting blood, lung deficiency, pneumonia, pulmonary tuberculosis, skin disorders, etc. These are all related to the notion from Chinese medicine that "The lung is associated with metal and its flavor is acrid." This type of irritation persists in the channels and network vessels of the lung and in the skin all over the body. When it is expelled to the outside, its flavor is spicy hot.

Besides the damage from being irritated, failure of sons and daughters to practice *xiao* towards both parents is also most likely to damage the lung. And in the opposite direction, having elders worry about their children also tends to damage the lung. Or in other words, failure to practice *xiao* and be in agreement with our elders but instead to get angry at them is most damaging to lung metal. In our current times, children all too frequently get angry at their parents so they suffer colds or coughs without the slightest reason. Common cold and coughs are by nature externally contracted conditions, but if you are able to stop yourself from getting angry, these externally contracted diseases will not affect you. As the common saying goes, "Without a thief inside the house, you do not encounter demons outside," meaning that even though these are externally contracted conditions, they must also have internal causes.

When I was once lecturing on the Dao (the Dao and De of relationships), there was a man who not only would not listen but even stirred up trouble for no reason, saying: "Aren't you talking rubbish here? I don't believe a word of what you are saying. Give me money, and I will believe you. Don't give me money, and I won't believe you!" I told him: "Where would I go to find the money to give to you? All the lecturing I do is for free, and I don't make any money with it. Do you still want money from me?"Later, this man contracted lung cancer and got so sick that he was forced to lie in bed, unable to move. Only at that point did he order his wife and daughter to look me up. He told his daughter: "You must make Liu Shanren come. If he comes, I will be able to get better. If he is unwilling to come, you must get down on your knees in front of him and beg him." Later, his young daughter came to me pleading: "My father has contracted lung cancer. Liu Shanren, please go to visit him! This time he truly believes in you." I told her: "It's too late! You build the dyke before the water comes and you repair the bridge by the river's edge. Reigning in the horse when you have reached the cliff is too late; fixing a leak when the boat is in the middle of the river is difficult. It is already too late!" She said: "Even though it is late, please go anyway. You simply must go." Finishing that sentence, she dropped on her knees in front of me and refused to get up. I truly had no choice here, so I followed her home.

When I entered the house, I saw the man lying on the Kang, unable to lie down or sit up without assistance from others. I asked him: "Do you believe me this time around?" He sighed and said: "Yes. This time, I am able to believe you." I said: "Since you believe me, will I be able to cure you by explaining your illness to you? You do have lung cancer after all!" He said, "Yes indeed, I do have lung cancer. I know that." When I then told him that I would be unable to cure his cancer, he simply replied that I surely would be able to cure him. So I said: "I am going to ask you a question, and if you are able to give me an answer, I will be able to cure you." He told me to go ahead and start asking. So I said: "From childhood on, you have been a grandson to your grandfather and a son to your parents, and you are also a father to your children and now even a grandfather. I ask you, how have you acted in these four roles, as grandson, son, father, and grandfather? If you are able to give me a sincere answer, I can assure you that I will be able to save your life. If you are unable to answer, I will just get up and leave." Then I sat there by his side for two full hours, without him speaking a single sentence. So I finally got up and told him that I was leaving. He answered: "Then just leave! If you want to leave, I just won't be cured." I told him that there was nothing else I could do.

His wife and daughter followed me outside the house and I told them that he could not be cured. His wife then asked me why he had contracted this disease. I told her: "The reason why he has contracted lung cancer is that he has been deficient in his practice of *xiao*. Do either of you happen to know where he has been deficient in his practice of *xiao*?" All the people standing around us responded that they knew the answer. Originally, this man's father had passed away when still very young, leaving behind his wife with a large number of children, of which my patient was the oldest one. When his mother had found herself truly unable to raise and feed all these children on her own, she had decided to remarry. My patient had gotten angry at his mother, blaming her for marrying another man, and when she had remarried, he had not followed her to her new husband's home. Later, when his mother had come to visit him, he had refused to see her. Eventually, when she had fallen ill and had been on her deathbed, she had really wanted to see him, asking even to have a letter delivered to him or receive a letter from him, but he had still refused to say a word or go to see her. So eventually his mother had died, without ever setting eyes on her son again. This time around, the tables were turned and my patient was the one who was ill. He had a son who was living not far from his house, so he called him up on the telephone, telling him that he was thinking of him and asking him to come to his home. But what about the son? He refused to visit even when he was passing by on the street right in front of the house. In the end, he lost his life without the son ever coming home to see him again.

So you see, in our role as fathers or mothers, if we have not acted fully in accordance with the principle of *xiao* towards our own elders, then the eventual results are truly unimaginable! There is a saying in Northeastern China that goes like this: "An old cat sleeps on the ridge of the house as his pillow. Everything gets passed on from one generation to the next." If you act in *xiao* towards your elders, your children will act in *xiao* towards you. If you want to go against the wishes of your elders, your children will in turn go against your own wishes. In accordance with the law of retribution, what goes around comes around.

I have also met some people who have been deficient in their practice of *xiao* towards their elders, constantly getting angry at them, and while they do not suffer from illness themselves, their children do, with conditions like skin disorders, rhinitis, pneumonia, encephalitis, hydrocephalus, paralysis, or brain tumors. I have encountered all of these. And where is the reason for these diseases in the children? It is always found in the mother! Especially during the mother's pregnancy, if her disposition was not good and she constantly got angry at her elders, this can most easily lead to these types of illness. For this reason, we can say that if children suffer from bad health before the age of twelve, it is always related to the mother or father. I have seen too many examples of this situation.

When sons and daughters fail to practice *xiao* towards either of their parents, this damages the lung most, and when elders worry and fret over their sons and daughters, this damages the Qi most, because the lung is in charge of the Qi. Sometimes I see elders just sitting there, and when you look at them, they do not suffer from any illness at all but as soon as they move a bit, they run out of breath, which is precisely the condition that originates in worrying and fretting over one's children. Somebody once asked me how I know this. I know this because this is precisely the way my mother was. My older brother passed away when he was thirty-eight years old and I was thirty-six. Before his death, my mother's health had been just fine, but not even half a year after his passing, my mother started suffering from shortness of breath. The slightest movement caused her to run out of breath. I explained to her: "Your condition is the result of you worrying and fretting about my older brother. Stop thinking about him with such concern, and let it go. He is dead and you cannot bring him back to life." But this old woman was unable to accept it for a long time, until her condition eventually improved dramatically, after my constant guidance.

People are always like this, saying "Ah, I can't get over it." But if you can just let something go, put it to rest, you'll get over it just like that. If you always think about something, on the other hand, you will not be able to let it go. We all know that when you boil water, as long as it makes a roiling sound it is certainly not boiling yet, but when it becomes still, it is boiled. Aren't we humans also like this? Regardless of what it is, don't think about it too much but simply respond when it comes and put it to rest when it is gone. If you can be like that, how could you contract disease?

1.4 ILLNESS OF THE SPLEEN AND STOMACH

How do people contract illnesses of the spleen and stomach? These come from the Qi of blame. So many people respond to things that happen to them not by reflecting back on their own involvement but always by blaming the outside, always by blaming other people. Blaming others damages the spleen and can lead to diseases like swelling and distention, hiccup and regurgitation, vomiting above and diarrhea below, deficiency in the stomach, gastritis, gastric ulcers, shedding of the gastric mucosa, or duodenal ulcers, etc., in severe cases even to stomach cancer. This Qi of blame persists in the muscles of the human body, and when it is expelled, its flavor is sweet.

Somebody asked me once: "How is it that I am sore all over my entire body? My bones, my muscles, all are sore, there is not a single place in my body that is not sore." This is precisely the sign that the Qi of blame in the body has grown too big. The Qi of blame infiltrates the entire body, lodging in the muscles all throughout the body, and as a result we see generalized soreness, lack of muscle strength, and in serious cases even atrophied muscles. When we encounter something that we do not like, do not direct blame towards the outside, because all things invariably must have a reason. Any of the people that we come into contact with, any of the things that happen in our environment, all of these have a specific cause. As Wang Shanren taught us, the injunction "do not blame", in only three words, is utterly wonderful indeed, and is the root of the great Dao of becoming a Buddha. If you want to become a Buddha, there simply is no other method, to exist as a living corpse in this world. If you look at the way the Buddha lived, isn't it just like a corpse? A corpse doesn't care about anything, doesn't care about being hit, doesn't care about being yelled at. If it is hit, it doesn't raise a hand. If yelled at, it doesn't open its mouth. Being hit is just like running into a doorpost, being yelled at is just like hearing somebody sing a song. What is it that I am describing here? It is nothing but a living Buddha.

When I first started lecturing people about illness, I encountered a man who was suffering from stomach cancer, a patient from Heilongjiang Province with the last name Wang. This man's condition was very serious and even the large army hospital in Shenyang was unwilling to operate on him. When he came to see me, I asked him whether he knew why he had contracted this disease.

He answered that he didn't know. So I said: "You are suffering from a disease that is contracted because of blame. Your Qi of blame has gotten too big. Do you know who it is that you are blaming?" He answered that he was blaming his father. When I asked him why he was blaming his father, he told me: "I do not like my wife. I have disliked her for her stupidity from the first time when my father stubbornly insisted that I marry her. And thus, whenever I lay eyes on my wife, I simply blame my father." And so he had contracted stomach cancer because he was annoyed with his wife and blamed his father for that.

I told this Mr. Wang: "For blaming and hating your father, you will have to acknowledge your fault. And for all your wrongful actions, you will also have to acknowledge your fault. If you truly are able to acknowledge your fault, there will be a way out for you. Will you be able to do that?" And in order to save his life, he sincerely kowtowed and acknowledged his faults, announcing clearly all his wrongdoings to everybody. Finally, he vomited out something that looked like shredded meat, and the substance he defecated also looked like shredded meat. In this way both vomiting and defecating, he expelled his illness, and was then able to once again eat and drink, walk and run. As he was leaving, I warned him: "At this point, you are not completely cured yet. Regardless of who says anything to you, you must not allow them to disturb your heart. As soon as your heart is stirred, I am afraid that you will suffer a relapse." He replied, "I will not allow that to happen. This time, I have definitely bettered myself!"

Little did he know that after more than a month a younger brother of his would visit his home, a brother who Mr. Wang had not seen in twenty years. As soon as this brother entered the courtyard of his home, he pulled on Mr. Wang and started crying: "Oh older brother! Your disease is not cured! You are bound to die! This is exactly how our father died." As soon as those words escaped the brother's mouth, my patient sat down right then and there, without any movement and died within a matter of a few hours. Why is that? Because as soon as his heart was stirred, his spiritual support collapsed.

An old doctor once told me that today 40 percent of cancer cases are due to being frightened to death. And indeed some patients, upon hearing the diagnosis of cancer, get so frightened that they die within a number of days. But if you had not told them about their cancer diagnosis, they might have been able to live for many years more. One time, a patient with cancer came to see me and I told him: "You must not take your illness lightly. You have cancer! The King of Hell has condemned you to death!" He answered: "Whenever it is my time to die, so be it! Please go ahead and explain to me, though, how it is that I have contracted this disease." So I told him, "This I am able to explain to you. Explaining this illness is in my hands, but curing it lies in yours. I am the key, and you are the lock. If you allow me, as the key, to open your lock, you shall still be able to cure this illness." Then I explained his illness to him so that he understood why he had contracted his condition. As a result, his happiness increased with every passing day that he survived, and as his happiness increased day by day, he continued to survive until he truly outlived his disease. This story shows how contracting illness as well as curing illness is all in our own hands alone. If you have contracted an illness, do not be afraid and do not succumb to the mental pressure. Even though you have generated this illness, you are still its master. You are the master of this illness and therefore you can stand up to it yourself. As soon as you become afraid and shrink back from it, you just make it very difficult to cure it.

There was an old man in the city of Nehe in Heilongjiang Province who was unable to eat pickled vegetables for three years, and ultimately could not even eat plain rice any more. He survived only by drinking powdered milk. In November of 1998, he came to our home, and because he couldn't eat anything else any more, he brought his own powdered milk with him.

At the moment he arrived, I happened to be giving a lecture to everybody on the topic of "blame" among the five evils of hatred, blame, irritation, anger, and annoyance. After he heard my lecture, he told me the following: "I have not come here to ponder over whether my illness is curable. I have come here to see the Liu Shanren, and when I die, my heart will be at peace." But little did he know, he stayed with us for three days, looking for the roots of his illness himself, and then said: "I have cleared out my bad habit of blaming others. Whether it's a good or a bad thing, I do not tell myself anything, I have simply cleared out this habit of blaming other people." After three days, he was once again able to eat things. What did he eat? Dumplings stuffed with pickled vegetables. Not long afterwards, he was able to eat cooked white rice and husked sorghum, and even steamed buns, and his illness simply disappeared. Where did it go? The disappearance of his illness was in fact identical with the elimination of his blame. The disease that this old man had contracted was the loss of his gastric mucosa. How did the eroded gastric mucosa recover? The poison of blame belongs to Yin, just like the others of the five poisons all belong to Yin. When Yin Qi is expelled, Yang Qi is able to naturally enter and repair the damage. As Yang Qi is able to transform and engender all the myriad aspects of nature, it is just naturally able to solve the problem of eroded mucosa. This is to say that when we have found our own faults and sincerely recognized our own transgressions, Yin Qi can be expelled and Yang Qi can enter to repair the damage. As soon as Yang Qi has entered the inside of the body, repairing the body is extremely quick.

For many patients who have contracted illness of the spleen and stomach, the liver then easily contract manifests problems as well. This aspect is due to the fact that spleen-stomach earth is closely linked to liver-wood (in the cycle of the five elements) and can therefore easily affect it. From another perspective, as soon as there is blame, this is very often accompanied by anger and if this Qi of anger is not expressed, it becomes depressed and damages the liver. Results are liver cirrhosis, water in the liver and abdomen, and in severe cases breakage and bleeding in the curvature of the gastric veins, manifesting in abdominal inflation and distention. For this reason, patients with liver cirrhosis in the majority of cases suffer from illness in both the liver and the spleen, which is directly related to the Qi of blame.

In my many years of explaining illness to people, I have encountered many cases of this type of illness. Similar to the production brigade leader from Yi'an County I mentioned above, I encountered another cadre from the same county who was the original production brigade leader of a newly established commune. He was suffering from illness of the spleen and stomach that had already progressed to the point where he was vomiting and excreting blood. I told him: "Come back home with me to Bei'an and stay for seven days, and things will work out. I will explain the reasoning behind your illness to you and you will reflect deeply and sincerely on your past actions until you have expelled the Yin toxin from your body. After you have expelled it all, though, for the results to turn out right, you must then go and get surgery." The patient's father who had accompanied him spoke up: "Regardless of what you say, we cannot have him undergo surgery! A relative of ours just recently had surgery in Tianjin and died within two days of returning home from surgery." I replied, "Esteemed elder! If you want your son to survive, please trust my words. If you don't want your son to survive, go right ahead. He may not survive though." This old man continued on forcefully: "He shall go with you but he cannot have surgery." So the two of them followed me back to Bei'an.

After the patient had stayed with me for seven days in Bei'an, I told him to go home right away and get surgery. He responded that his father would not allow the surgery. So I asked him to quickly call his father on the phone and ask him to come over. When the father came, I told him: "Immediately allow your son to have surgery! He is still young and it is only with surgery that he will be able to survive. If you, however, go against this advice, he will not survive." After the patient's father arrived at our place and took a look at our way of treating illness through disposition and emotions, he said: "This way truly does have benefits. I do in fact trust you." Afterwards, he agreed to allow his son to have surgery and as a result, the patient had his entire spleen removed.

When this patient left the hospital after his surgery, he did not go home but instead came straight to see me. Since his spleen had been removed in its entirety, his digestion should have been impaired quite a bit and he should not have been able to eat much, but he was able to eat quite well. He was able to eat two steamed buns the size of a rice bowl at one meal. So I told him that he was cured, which he wholeheartedly agreed with, stating that after a short recovery time after his surgery he felt of excellent health now. But I warned him: "Nevertheless, I must inform you that your illness is averse to you getting angry." He responded: "I will not get angry again in the future. Everybody argued in the past over my selection as the production brigade leader and yet I didn't get involved. This was because I was afraid that I might not be able to control myself. Losing control of myself and getting angry, wouldn't that be a complete waste now? I agreed with him. Because he was able to understand this key point, he was able to survive his illness and hold on to his life. To this day, his health is so strong that he does not care how heavy the burden is that he is carrying.

1.5 ILLNESS OF THE KIDNEY

Where does illness of the kidney come from? It is caused by being annoyed. Being annoyed by others damages the kidney and can lead to soreness in the lower back and legs, abdominal pain, a listless spirit, edema, kidney deficiency, nephritis, peritonitis, lumbar spondylitis, spinal disk herniation, and necrosis of the femur. Diabetes, gynecological conditions, uterine fibroids, cervicitis, ovarian cysts, etc. etc. also all come from being annoyed. The kind of disease a person contracts depends on the kind of person that they get annoyed with. The Qi of annoyance persists in people's bone marrow and when it is expelled, its taste is salty.

Once I was giving a lecture at the Confucian temple in Changchun. At the conclusion of my lecture, the main person in charge of the temple thought to herself: "Why did all these people surrounding Liu Shanren constantly ask about illness? What was the point of always asking about illness? How come they didn't want to talk more about the Dao of Confucius and his disciple Mencius?" And lo and behold, a few days later she fell ill. This time, she knew herself that this disease of her own wouldn't get better by taking medication but that she needed to wait for me to come back and give another lecture.

Three or four months later, I returned to Changchun and immediately noticed her unhappiness, so I asked her what the reason was. She answered: "It is not worth mentioning but I am ill." When I asked her what her illness was, she told me that she was suffering from stomachache. I replied: "How come you are suffering from stomachache? Who is it that you are annoyed with? Are you annoyed with your husband?" She denied that, and when I asked her again who it was, she in turn asked me to tell her how she had contracted the illness. I told her: "If you are not annoyed with your husband, you must be annoyed with somebody who is lacking decency." She replied: "This is truly what is going on. I have two friends, one a man and the other a woman, both of whom I get along with quite well. But these two began to fool around with each other until eventually they were having an affair. But both of them have their own families! This situation truly made me very upset so I went and gave them a good scolding. After scolding them, I went home, and that is just when my stomachache started. Right after that, my menstrual period started and it hasn't stopped since then."

So here we have a situation where somebody else has acted improperly and done something bad, but if you get angry about it, the body will respond by producing illness. You see, the body is like an implement that doesn't care about reason; all it cares about is the Dao. So even with all the reason in the world, if you get angry, that is a transgression against the Dao, and it will therefore produce illness. And if you get angry at people who are acting improperly (such as indecent affairs between men and women), the most likely manifestation that you will contract is a gynecological condition. If your general health is not great and you are already going downhill, you may even contract cervical cancer, uterine cancer, or vaginal cancer. Some women continuously doubt their husbands and worry about them having an affair. Lacking a feeling of security and under great mental pressure, if they add disturbance and worrying on top of that, and then annoyance, irritation, blame, and hatred, they can easily contract uterine fibroids, vaginitis, and even uterine cancer.

Another elderly person asked me why he was suffering from such pain encircling his waist. I told him: "You are annoyed at everybody around you. There is not a single person who does not annoy you; there is not a single action that does not annoy you." He replied: "That surely is the truth. I am indeed annoyed at everything around me." If everybody in front of you and behind you annoys you, how can you not fall ill! Looking for other people's faults is to collect dirt. Looking for their good points, on the other hand, is to gather inspiration. And if you always collect dirt to store inside of you, this bucket of dirt (because always looking for other people's wrongdoings turns such a person's body into nothing but a bucket full of dirt) of yours will simply become filled. For this reason, we want to learn how to look at people's strong points instead of at their shortcomings. If we are able to always focus on other people's strong points, at any time and under any circumstances, I guarantee that everybody here will enjoy good health.

In our modern age, we have a particularly large number of patients suffering from diabetes. After contracting diabetes, they do not dare to eat this or that, because it is assumed that diabetes is caused by what the person eats. I look at this disease in a different way: Where does it come from? One cause is fire, and the other is being annoyed, these are the two factors that cause diabetes. This fire here is a kind of pent-up grievance, the fire of desire that became bottled up in the heart when certain desires were left unfulfilled and could not be expressed to other people. For example, when people have failed to achieve success in their career goals or are dissatisfied with the way their children have turned out or are unfulfilled emotionally. This fire enters the pancreas and can there wreak havoc on pancreatic function. Because this fire does not have an outlet to be discharged from, it can then generate annoyance and agitation, to the point where people moan and groan all day long, and this in turn damages the kidney. Diabetes is closely related to the kidney, and some doctors of Chinese medicine hence treat diabetes by starting with the kidney.

In the paragraphs above, I have discussed the internal illnesses of the five elements in the body. Regardless of the cause of the illness, though, I want to emphasize one point here: When the demon of disease has arrived, do not be afraid! Do not be intimidated by it! Instead you must fight to overcome it. What method can we use to overcome it? Pure joy and happiness! Even if you have contracted cancer, do not allow it to act as a cancer. If you are eating, eat. If you are drinking, drink. If you are playing, play. If you are joyful, be joyful. There is only one thing you must pay attention to: Under no circumstances must you allow yourself to get angry and allow fire to flame up. If you can stop yourself from getting angry and allowing fire to flame up, everything will be all right. Over time, you will starve your disease to death. Because your illness depends on eating Qi for its survival, and wounds depend on eating fire for their survival. If you do not get angry, you do not give it water to drink. If you do not allow fire to flame up, you do not give it food to eat. And without food and drink, how could the disease not simply starve to death? I have personally experienced this process in my own body and all the various diseases I previously had been suffering from have been cured in this way. For the past 45 years now, I have not eaten a single pill or received a single treatment of acupuncture. And yet here I am, a seventy-year-old man from the countryside, still in great health!

II. External Illnesses of the Five Elements in the Body

In the paragraphs above, we have discussed the internal illnesses of the five elements, including the five *zang* organs and the six *fu* organs. In the following paragraphs, I am going to talk about the external illnesses of the five elements. What do I mean by the external illnesses of the five elements? This refers to a five-element differentiation of the body's outer parts. We start by dividing the human body in the middle, with the left half associated with male, and the right half associated with female. When the left side of the body has an illness, it is caused by getting angry at a man; when the right side of the body has an illness, it is caused by getting angry at a woman. In addition, we divide the body into an upper and a lower half. If an illness manifests in a person's head, this means that they have offended somebody in a superior position, or in other words, they have gotten angry with a parent, older relative, teacher, or boss. Illness anywhere below the knees means that they have injured somebody in an inferior position, or in other words, they have gotten angry at somebody from a younger generation. If illness manifests in the middle section and trunk of the body, this is caused by getting angry at somebody from the same generation and social status as oneself. The four limbs are one's siblings: Illness in the upper limbs is due to getting angry at one's older brother, older brother's wife, older sister, or older sister's husband; illness in the legs is due to getting angry at one's younger brother and younger sister. Illness in the left upper limbs is caused by getting angry at a man of your generation who is older than you, while illness in the right upper limbs is contracted from getting angry at a woman of your generation who is older than you. This same rule applies to the other cases in the same way.

I invite all of you to carefully reflect upon and observe with whom you have gotten angry, and any illness will surely have been planted at the corresponding location. This rule never fails. One time, when I was diagnosing a man's illness in Changchun, he stood up and exclaimed: "Ah! You truly have divine insight! How could you know my circumstances with such clarity?" I responded: "I do not have divine insight. I have simply diagnosed you in accordance with the five elements. The five elements exist in Heaven, on earth, and in the human body. The five elements in the human body coordinate with the five elements in Heaven and on earth. These five elements all correspond to each other, they all match each other, without even the slightest divergence.

II.I ILLNESSES IN THE HEAD

A great many people suffer from illnesses in the head. Where do these illnesses come from? From offenses against those above us! The parameters for offenses against those above us are very broad, ranging from failure to satisfy one's older relatives, teachers, or bosses and supervisors, to blaming Heaven and earth or berating the wind and rain, to actions by oneself or one's parents that go against the principles of Heaven, any of these can cause illness to grow in the head. In addition, great fire Qi can also rise up into the head.

Diseases in the head can manifest predominantly on the left, on the right, in the front, in the back, or right in the middle in the vertex, each of which can tell us something about the condition. If they are prevalent on the left, they are caused by getting angry with a male person from an older generation; if prevalent on the right, they are caused by getting angry with a female person from an older generation. If they are prevalent in the front, they mean disharmony or interference with a boss; if prevalent in the back, they mean failure to satisfy the requests of one's elders or superiors behind their back and secret efforts to go behind their back. In that case, why are there also diseases that manifest right in the top of the head? The top of the head is where our *tianxing* ("Heavenly nature") resides, the so-called "gate to Heaven." In the vast majority of cases, such conditions are caused by actions that go against the principles of Heaven, what the common people refer to as "lacking virtue (De)." Those of us who constantly blame Heaven, constantly blame the earth, constantly blame others, but never blame themselves, those kinds of people tend to easily contract such diseases.

I have come across quite a few people suffering from frontal sinusitis, and I once asked a lady with this condition: "How come that you always butt heads with your elders?" She replied with a single sentence: "Is it that I butt heads with my elders, or that they butt heads with me?" So I asked her what it was that they were arguing about and she replied that they had always been unable to agree on anything. And so I explained, "This is why you have gotten frontal sinusitis!"

Yet another cause for frontal sinusitis is a person's failure to yield to one's superiors but to lock horns with them instead. Just like our parents, older relatives, and teachers, our superiors are the Heaven above our head. Why is it that I say that our superiors are our Heaven? Because they carry out Heaven's mandate. If you do not respect rules and abide by the laws and do not follow their orders, this is just the same as going against Heaven. Leaders must act with righteousness, and followers must act with loyalty. Don't you concern yourself with what kind of a person your leaders are! Isn't your job to just do your work under somebody else's leadership? Simply focus on completing your own job to the very best of your ability. Life! Just carry on with your job in life and that's all there is to it! If you have done your job well, that is what is called doing your job well. And after you have gone elsewhere, if your superiors or bosses always remember you fondly and praise you, this is what is truly the meaning of "doing your job well."

In another context, students who disregard their teachers are most likely to suffer from dizziness. I have met a large number of this kind of students. One time, a High School student who was about to take his university entrance examination, came and asked me: "Why is it that my brain is not working properly? Whenever I am in class, I feel like sleeping." I explained to him: "When you are at school, is it true that you have a teacher there who you get annoyed with, who you dislike for not explaining things clearly and for not teaching well, to the point where you feel dissatisfied even when this teacher explains something to you? Is this happening to you?" He replied: "Yes. There is in fact a teacher who is not good at teaching. He speaks with such a heavy accent that is difficult to understand him, so I do get annoyed with him." I told this student: "Do not concern yourself with whether your teacher speaks in a way that sounds good to you or not. You are there to learn knowledge and culture, and your knowledge comes entirely from your teachers. So how can you look down on him? The relationship between teachers and students is just like that between a parent and a child. Without strict teachers, there will be no high-achieving students, just like without a stern parent, there will be no child with *xiao*." Without strict and dignified parents, children will not exhibit *xiao*. Without a strict mother-in-law, how can the daughter-in-law exhibit a heart full of *xiao*? But in our modern times, if you act with strictness towards somebody, they just think that you are being unkind. If the other person could understand the principles of Dao, though, they would know that you are truly helping them, that you are pushing them towards Heaven. When there is somebody who is challenging you, this is truly nothing but guiding you towards Heaven. When somebody is able to express your shortcomings and imperfections straight to your face, this is a true benefactor on your path to Heaven. If somebody always tells you what you want to hear, on the other hand, this is not necessarily a truly kind person.

And lastly, there are an exceptionally large number of people nowadays who are suffering from diseases of the cervical spine. What is the cause of these diseases of the cervical spine? Such conditions come from being dissatisfied with others behind their back. If not dissatisfied with the older generation, then they are dissatisfied with their superiors, such people most easily contract diseases of the cervical spine.

In 2003, I was lecturing at the Guangxi TCM College when a student came up to me with a question: "I am a graduate student of Chinese medicine and yet I am unable to cure my own illness." I asked him: "What is the disease you are suffering from? And why are you unable to cure it? Please give me some explanations." He responded: "I am suffering from pain in the cervical spine. Taking medication has had no effect, acupuncture has had no effect, and cupping has not helped either." When I asked how long he had had this condition, he responded that it had been three months. So I told him that his condition would be easy to cure since this was such a short time. When I asked him next how long he had been coming to this college, he responded that it had also been exactly three months. My question whether he had ever experienced this kind of pain at home was answered with no, and he then confirmed that this was indeed a condition that he had contracted at the college. Coincidentally, two leaders of the school happened to be present at this time. When I told the student now that his illness had been caused by these two people, the leaders laughingly responded: "How could his condition have anything to do with us two?" The graduate student also looked slightly confused and asked me to explain how he could have contracted this illness because of these two people. I explained: "Think it over carefully! You have been stewing over the fact that the leadership here is faulty behind their backs, and because you have been stewing over this, you have been dissatisfied. Tell me, is this the truth or not?" It didn't even take him five minutes to admit that this was right: "It is true! I came to this college knowing that tuition was 7,000 Yuan, which I paid. This is the standard amount. Nevertheless, the college now wants to collect an additional 600 Yuan from us, which I just don't think is right." I asked him why he thought that it was wrong for the college to charge this additional fee, and explained: "They have never before charged this extra money until this year. I just think the leadership is wrong to charge this fee." When the two leaders of the college heard this statement, they laughed and of course wanted to respond with an explanation, but I immediately took charge of the conversation and asked them not to respond right away and to allow me first to ask the student some more questions. So I continued to ask the graduate student: "Were you the only one charged with this fee or did all your colleagues also get charged?" He responded that everybody had to pay the fee. So I said: "Then that was right. If they had only charged you, it would have meant that somehow they didn't like your looks, in which case it wouldn't have been right for you to give it to them. But since they charged everybody, this means that they must certainly have had another reason. Tell me, am I right in this or not?" He responded: "It is I who was wrong. The fact that everybody was charged shows that this was just a general regulation of the college." Approximately twenty minutes later, this graduate student started pressing on his neck and then shaking his head. Expressing surprise he exclaimed: "How come that the pain in my neck is gone?"

Even though the division of illnesses that affect the head is very detailed in terms of the affected zone, we only have to seek out the correct cause of the disease, and they become easy to cure. If you know which elder you have felt anger towards, which leader you have felt anger towards, and you are able to humbly admit your fault and transform your heart with sincere regret, it won't take much time at all and this kind of disease will be healed just like this.

II.2 ILLNESS IN THE LEGS AND FEET

Illness in the legs or feet is due to anger that you are feeling toward someone younger than you but from the same generation, or toward someone from a younger generation. These conditions can be demarcated by using the knee as boundary, with conditions above the knee being caused by anger towards your younger brother or sister, and conditions below the knee being caused by anger towards your children. Conditions that affect the knee itself are due to both of these aspects at the same time.

There are some elderly people who are in their seventies or eighties and yet their legs and feet are still very nimble. Such older people generally do not feel anger towards their children. There are, on the other hand, also a great number of older people with particularly severe problems in their legs and feet, to the point where they are lame and crippled. It goes without saying that in most of such cases they don't get along with their children. Why is that there are so many old people in our modern age who are suffering from hemiplegia? When people reach old age and have grown children, such elders love to meddle and worry but their children don't listen. Even if they don't act in direct opposition to their elders, they disagree with them. But there is nothing these old people can do so they experience anger. One is an old child, and the other is a young child. If the older child pits him- or herself against the younger child, they can very easily contract hemiplegia. And while other conditions may still be easy to cure, this disease is not. Because as soon as a person contracts hemiplegia, their brain does not function well any more, and if you ask them to reflect on their past actions and make them repent their wrongdoings, they often fail to respond. Hence their treatment is difficult.

In 1998, a forty-year-old man came to see me from Kedong County in Heilongjiang Province. What was the disease he had contracted all of a sudden? He was unable to touch the ground with his right toes and heel. As he put it, "As soon as I touch the ground, I feel pain as if I were being pierced by a million needles." When I asked him whether he had contracted this condition all of a sudden, he affirmed: "Yes, all of a sudden. I have been receiving treatment for seven months now, going far and wide, from Tianjin in the south to Jiamusi in the north, but nobody has been able to help me. Now I heard about your ability to cure illness by explaining it, so I hurried to come here." I told him: "It is indeed true that I can explain illness away, but still, it is you who must cure your illness, by finding your own wrongdoings." So he asked me where he had done wrong. I answered, "You say that your problem is in your right foot? This means that you must have gotten furious with a girl. Is that the case?" He immediately confirmed that. So I asked him to explain in more detail why he had gotten so angry. He replied: "It is my anger towards my sister's daughter. I am completely involved in my older sister's family affairs. No matter what happens over there, they always keep me informed and let me make the final decisions. But when her daughter got engaged, which is such an important event, they for some reason failed to notify me. It was not until the very end, when they were preparing to meet the parents of the son-in-law, that they let me know and invited me to the banquet. Feeling great anger pent up inside me, I went to my sister's home and told her: 'This is not acceptable! This is such an important affair and yet you didn't notify me until now!' At this point, my niece spoke up: 'Uncle! In the past, you have had the final say in every major event in our family. But with this event today, you could not be allowed to have the last word. This is the most important event of my life, and you cannot control that.' This really made me blow up instantly! So I pulled her over, slapped her in the face, and turned around and left. But who would have thought that as soon as I got home, I was unable to put my foot down on the ground!" I explained to him: "You were overly controlling. You weren't even able to control your own daughter's engagement and yet you wanted to control your niece's engagement? And then you even felt all self-righteous about it! Please think this over carefully. Did you really act properly? Wang Shanren once said that controlling others is Hell, and blaming others is a Sea of Suffering. Isn't your current state just like being in hell? This illness of yours is nothing but the manifestation of your descent into hell." After mulling this over for a while, he responded: "I have indeed made a mistake. I will never be controlling again in the future. Now will you let me recover from my illness?" I told him: "If you sincerely and genuinely regret your wrongdoings, do you think you still have to worry about curing your illness?" And indeed, three days later he was able to touch the ground with his heels and delightedly returned home.

Since we have just raised the topic of engagement and how it causes worrying and irritation, I want to mention something that Wang Shanren had to say about this subject. When he talked about engagement and marriage, he also called it "grafting" and compared it directly to the way in which you connect a graft to a tree. If the graft is done well, no major trace of it will be left, but if it is not done well, it will leave behind a large knot. People nowadays fight after getting married, and so many of them end up in divorce. This is just the same as such a large knot, which is the result of a graft that was not connected well.

II.3. ILLNESS IN THE FOUR LIMBS

Illness in the arms comes from conflict with your older brother or his wife, or your older sister or her husband, or your husband's older sister, etc. Illness in the legs above the knees is related to issues with your younger brother, younger sister, etc. It is essential that we concern ourselves with our own business and fulfill all our duties to the best of our ability, rather than concerning ourselves with other people's business. Older people should take care of younger people, and younger people should respect older people. When you are the older person, do not concern yourself with whether a younger person respects you, but it is your job to take care of them. When you are the younger person, do not concern yourself with whether the older person takes care of you, but it is your job to respect them. Depending on the kind of vehicle, it must run on a certain kind of roadway. Trains must run on railroads and cars must run on highways. Older brothers are kind and younger brothers are respectful, each practicing in accordance with their Dao.

Where does periarthritis in the shoulder come from? It is the result of conflict with one's elder brother or his wife, or alternatively, it is caused by carrying too heavy of a burden, by being too concerned with too many things, and feeling like you have to manage everybody else's affairs. This can also cause your shoulders to feel heavy and contract periarthritis. I once met a woman in Harbin who was suffering from periarthritis in the shoulders. She asked me why her shoulders always felt so heavy, so I told her that she was carrying too heavy of a load. What load are you talking about, she asked me. I explained: "Regardless of who it is, you want to manage everybody else's business; you are involved in the affairs of too many other people. When they handle them well, you drop the issue, but when they do not handle them well, you blame them for it, and they blame you in turn. So you end up bearing a grudge afterwards." She responded: "This is true. In my family we are seven brothers and sisters. I have older siblings above me and younger ones below me and am right in the middle, but all of them let me handle their affairs for them. My older sister's family, my younger sister's family, my older brother's family, I manage them all for them." So I asked her, "Isn't it true that you are involved in too much? Let it go! Let it go, and allow yourself to relax! Every person has their own destiny, and regardless of much good fortune they have, let them enjoy their good fortune, regardless of how much misfortune they encounter, let them encounter that. How can you bear responsibility for all of that?" When I had finished speaking, I got up and left. She followed me, walking along with me, and after not even one sixth of a mile, her two shoulders no longer felt heavy. Cheerfully she said: "Both of my shoulders are all relaxed now, and my heart is also feeling free. In the past, my heart has always been burdened by other people's affairs and was exhausted." I responded: "That is right! Didn't the sage teach us, 'Before you straighten out others, first straighten out yourself'? First take care of your own affairs before you get involved in those of others. When the gentleman lacks virtue, he blames his own cultivation practices, but when a small-minded person has faults, he blames other people, if not in his words, then in his heart. And blame that lodges in the heart is precisely the core of all illness. Where does illness come from? Doesn't it all come within yourself?" These words pleased her greatly.

II.4 ILLNESS IN THE LOWER BACK

Where does illness in the lower back come from? It comes from anger between husband and wife. In the past, the man was considered Heaven and the woman was considered earth, so when women got angry with men, the illness manifested in the head. In our modern age, though, times have changed and women and men are now equal. Anything that a man can do, a woman can do likewise. So just like a man can mange the affairs of society or government, a woman can do likewise. For this reason, when a man now gets angry with a woman, the illness manifests in the lower back. And when a woman gets angry with a man, the illness likewise manifests in the lower back. Now where do diseases in the kidney or in the intervertebral disks of the lumbar spine, and gynecological diseases come from? In the vast majority of cases, they come from disharmony between Yin and Yang, disharmony between husband and wife. You look at the way I handle something and consider it wrong. I look at the way you are handling something and consider it wrong. You annoy me, and I annoy you. Under these circumstances, it is easy to contract such conditions.

In 2005, when my teacher Wang Yuanwu and I were on our way to Putuo-shan to give a lecture, we were met at the airport in Shanghai by a man, unknown to both of us, who held up a sign to meet us. When I asked him why he had come to meet us when he didn't know either one of us, he answered: "Dr. Liu Lihong told me to go and meet you here." When I asked him why Dr. Liu Lihong had sent him to meet us, he told us: "I have been suffering from an illness for three years already and have taken all sorts of medications and tried every method out there, all with no result. Then I happened to come across Doctor Liu's book "An Investigation of Chinese Medicine" (*Sikao Zhongyi*), read it, and found this doctor of Chinese medicine to be quite insightful. Therefore I pulled a lot of strings until I finally got to meet him in person, hoping that he would give me some medicine. Nevertheless, who would have thought that not only did he not prescribe any medication for me but instead told me to find you two in Shanghai! He told me that you would be able to help me with my illness." So I asked him what illness he was suffering from. He answered: "Lower back pain. Every single morning around four or five am, the pain is so severe that I can no longer stay in bed but have to get up and walk around, with my hands pressing against my lumbar area. I said: "Such a minor disease? You simply haven't found the root of your illness yet! As soon as you discover its root, you will be fine." He responded: "But I don't know where the root of my illness is." I told him: "Fine. Let me tell you where this illness has come from. It has come from your neighbor, from the person who lives closest to you." "But I don't have a neighbor," he responded. "I live in a building all by myself." At this point, Teacher Wang interjected: "Young man! Don't you have a wife? Isn't that the person who lives closest to you?" Surprised, he objected that they were divorced. So I told him: "This is indeed where the root of your illness lies. If you had not gotten annoyed with her, you would not have con-tracted this illness, and you also would not have gotten a divorce. Because you disdain her as being ugly and useless, you don't like her but like somebody else. And because of this, you have contracted this illness." He responded by asking what he could do about the situation at this point. When I asked him whether he or his ex-wife had remarried, he informed us that neither of them had found another partner but that they were still living in the same house, he in one room and she in another room. I said, "There is a thread between you two that is connecting you." "What kind of a thread?" he asked. I responded: "You still have a child together, who is running back and forth between this room and that room, torn between you two. As you two are fighting with each other, this thread is being pulled tighter and tighter, right up to the point of snapping apart. Now you two want to divorce, but what about this child who is caught in the middle? If he follows his father, he will not have a mother; if he follows his mother, he will not have a father. Think for a moment, don't you think your son is suffering greatly from this situation? You two have brought this child into this world. You were able to give birth to him but now you are unable to raise him. As a result you will leave a troublemaker behind for society to deal with. And as loafers and vagrants get out into society, without a solid education and proper guidance, they waste their life away, committing all sorts of senseless acts. What good does that do for society? Because you were not satisfied with a minor aspect of your life, you went selfishly looking for pleasure. And you might have found temporary happiness, but you have created limitless suffering later on." He agreed with me, "Yes, yes, yes! But what can I do about it now?" I told him, "Make the circle that has been broken whole again by reconciling with your wife. You two will be happy, and your child will also be happy. Go back to living in the same room!"

Like this, we had talked to him for about twenty minutes. Then we embarked on a boat and left for Putuoshan, where we stayed for three days. On our return, he came once again to meet us. Noticing how happy he looked even from a great distance away, I commented to Master Wang that he had most certainly recovered. When Master Wang asked me how I knew that, I answered: "Just look at how happy he looks and you know it. That day when he came to meet us for the first time, do you remember what his facial expression looked like? It was so full of pain and suffering." So when he walked up to us, we asked him how he was. And he told us that he had been completely pain-free for the past three nights and had been able to sleep until well into the morning. I commented: "This proves that you have restored harmony with your wife. Just look at yourself! Doctor Liu's medicine is surely working well!" Hearing this, he laughed out loud.

Between husband and wife, do not use reason to work things out. If you reason with each other to work things out, you will only explode in anger. These days, people all reason with each other, until they reason each other into the ground. If they don't end up separating, they end up getting a divorce. Between husband and wife, you must use your feelings to work things out. If you use your feelings to work things out, you will end up dearly loving each other again.

LECTURE THREE

The Causes of Illness and
The Methods of Treatment

I. The Causes of Illness

I.1 FIVE-ELEMENT INTERACTIONS WITHIN THE FAMILY

When I first began to study the Dao, I was told that to truly grasp the wisdom from the classics, you must walk 33,000 miles. Without walking that distance, you will not only fail to grasp the true wisdom from the classics, but you will not be able to enter the realm of Buddhahood either. I thought to myself, in our day and age, I fear that we will be unable to grasp the true wisdom from the classics or enter the realm of Buddhahood. It was only later, after studying Wang Fengyi's teachings, that I realized the meaning of this saying. In reality, these 33,000 miles are identical with the Five Relationships and Eight Virtues. The Five Relationships consist of the Ten Ways of Righteousness, namely between father and son, husband and wife, older brother and younger brother, friend and friend, and ruler and subject (i.e., the relationship between superior and inferior). The ten ways of righteousness here correspond to the 30,000 miles, while the Eight Virtues correspond to the 3,000 miles. Adding it all up, we get the sum total of 33,000 miles. Thus we can see that all we have to do is act in such a way as to make our social relationships complete, that there is no need to go out in the world to do great deeds, that we can truly grasp the wisdom from the classics, that we can enter the realm of Buddhahood, just by sitting here. On the other hand, if you are deficient in the Five Relationships and fall short in the Eight Virtues, you can walk around the entire globe and yet you will never get anything but bad results, much less grasp the true wisdom of the classics or enter the realm of Buddhahood.

As Wang Shanren has taught: "Don't talk of mysteries, don't talk of subtlety! Focus your teaching on the Dao of being human." And where does this Dao of being human start? It starts with the Five Relationships, it starts with the family. Family relationships are the crucial step in the Dao! The Dao of the family! What is the Dao of the family? The family simply is the Dao! Where can we find the Dao? We find the Dao in the family! Where can we find the Buddha? We find the Buddha in our hearts! "You may find the Buddha at Lingshan,[1] but you needn't seek far – Lingshan is right here in your heart. All of us humans possess a Lingshan pagoda, we simply must cultivate ourselves in the direction of this Lingshan pagoda." The human heart is nothing but this Lingshan pagoda. The heart is identical with the Buddha, and the Buddha is identical with the heart. Both come from the same root. How did the Buddha come into being? The Buddha came into being as a human. We must simply learn how to be human. If we can act as proper humans, we will be able to transcend the Three Realms.[2] If not, it will be hard to escape punishment.

Every one of us has a family. What is this family? The family is a shackle,[3] a shackle that is locked around our neck. And if we are unable to make this family whole, we simply allow the family to keep us shackled, until we die shackled in this family. How can we make this family whole? Each of us must practice our particular Dao to the best of our ability, each must correctly fulfill our duties in the proper role. When all of us practice our particular Dao and everybody returns to their role in society, we will naturally not work against each other and constrain each other. For example, if you are an elder, you must return to the position of an elder. It is the elder's responsibility in society

---

1   Lingshan is the location of the biggest statues of the Buddha in the world.

2   A Buddhist term, connoting the three realms of existence, namely the realms of desire, form, and formlessness. Sanskrit: Trailokya. In the Wang Fengyi system, however, the "three realms" (三界 sanjie) are identified as xing 性 (heavenly nature), xin 心 (heart), and shen 身 (body).

3   In Chinese, "family" and "shackle" are homophones, both pronounced "jia".

to exhaust the Dao of kindness. If you are a young person, you must return to the position of a youngster. It is the youngster's responsibility to exhaust the Dao of *xiao*. If we are able to act like this, this is what is meant by each person fulfilling their particular role, each being settled in their position. The result is peace and harmony everywhere under Heaven. If we cannot do this, there will be arguing and yelling, fighting and wrangling, disorder and chaos throughout the entire family.

Sometimes when I go to the hospital to see patients, at the very first glimpse, I truly feel pity. Some patients have gone through such great efforts, struggled so hard, and wasted so much money, and yet they are not cured. Why is this? Because they do not know the cause of their illness, because they have not taken the right medicine for their condition. In my experience, the roots of illness are actually very simple. In the vast majority of cases, it all comes from the members of the patient's family. Why do I say this? Because the family is a reflection of the Five Elements, and the human body is likewise a reflection of the Five Elements. The Five Elements all affect each other, and if the Five Elements do not function smoothly within the family, this naturally affects the way the Five Elements function within the human body. As I have mentioned previously, the Five Elements in the human body can be further subdivided into the internal Five Elements and the external Five Elements. The internal Five Elements refers to the five *zang* and six *fu* organs in the body; the external Five Elements refers to the four extremities and the trunk. Let us each examine very carefully which person we might have gotten angry at, and you will see, with no exceptions, that illness is planted in the corresponding part of the body. Wang Shanren often lectured: "All you have to do is to recognize it and reveal it and break the pattern, and the illness will invariably be cured. Please give it a try consistently!" Use this approach on a regular basis for comparison and let reality validate the efficacy of this method, just see if your illness is getting cured or not. If it works, you will continue to progress towards health; if it doesn't, it won't have delayed or impeded your healing either.

1.2 ILLNESS ORIGINATES FROM THE HEART: QI AND FIRE

The human body is created from the Five Elements, and the five *zang* organs are obviously also created from the Five Elements. When the five *zang* organs contract a disease, this is most often caused by the presence of the five poisons in the heart. The heart is the ruler of the body, the organ in charge of the five *zang* organs. How do these poisons manage to intrude? They intrude by being received by the heart. There is no end to the harm done when a person is stirred in their heart and aroused in their thoughts. As the common saying goes, "The heart is a monkey, the mind is a horse," in the sense that the heart is like a monkey, constantly scurrying up and scrambling down, and the mind is like a horse, galloping wildly to and fro. What is the heart? The heart is a monkey. If you don't watch it carefully, it just wants to run away. Like a monkey, as soon as it has climbed a mountain, there is no holding it back. If something catches its curiosity, it is almost impossible to control it.

Wang Shanren told us that the heart is the central axis around which the Three Realms revolve. As soon as the heart is stirred, the Three Realms are all stirred. If the heart is not stirred, the Heavenly nature cannot be stirred, and the body cannot be stirred either. As Chinese medicine theory teaches, "The hundred diseases all originate in the heart." Illness originates in joy, anger, grief, and sorrow. Feeling an excess of joy can generate illness, feeling an excess of grief can also generate illness. So what are we to do about this? Simply keep calm and hold on to your position in society. If you can hold on calmly, illness will not be able to grow inside you. If you are unable to hold on calmly, illness will be able to grow. If you respond in joy every time you witness something good and respond with sadness or worry every time you witness something bad, how can you not contract illness?

My own experience of explaining illness to people for over twenty years has certainly validated Wang Shanren's teaching that "Illness is formed by eating the pills of the five poisons (blame, hatred, irritation, anger, and annoyance)." From the perspective of Chinese medicine, poisonous Qi is always black Qi. I personally have never been able to see this black Qi, but once happened to meet a man who is able to see the Qi in the channels and network vessels of the human body. This man told me that when a person gets angry and unhappy, there is definitely black Qi that rises up in the body and bores directly into the corresponding channels and internal organs. You can do your own research on whether you want to believe this or not. But regardless, what is certain is that the effects of rousing your heart and stirring your mind are unspeakably harmful. As soon as you are stirred by bad intentions, as soon as you are not happy, poisonous Qi will bore into the insides of your body and bit by bit, layer by layer, bring you down. Building up over the course of days and months, you will have planted illness, without even knowing it.

In general, there are two ways in which people get angry and cause fire to rise up in their body. Some people remain unstirred on the outside and are only stirred on the inside, speaking nothing with their mouths but only in their heart. As soon as they speak in their heart, though, they start feeling uncomfortable because this means that they receive this poisonous Qi into their heart. Other people are stirred in their mouth but not in their heart, and as soon as they are done yelling, they are over it. This means that they have set that poisonous Qi free and gotten rid of it. While these kinds of people may not fall ill themselves, they have nevertheless lit a fire that will burn down a mountain, setting other people ablaze and acting unbearable towards others. Wang Shanren mentions a person like this in his book Record of Sincere Actions (Yan Xing Lun), an old lady who was constantly yelling and cursing at people. The people who she yelled at did not fall ill, but conversely, the people who she did not yell at fell ill. Even Wang Shanren was utterly perplexed by this and investigated this affair deeply for three entire days before he discovered the reason: Even though this woman had this old habit of yelling at others, when she was done yelling, people told her immediately: "You are still yelling at others! These people will all fall ill as the result!" So she would immediately go to the person and treat them with acupuncture or cupping, never putting them out of her mind. This is where her strong point lay. So you see, in our every-day interactions with others, we must learn that we may get stirred in the mouth or get stirred in the body, but we must not allow our hearts to get stirred.

What kinds of illnesses do people contract when they get angry or allow fire to rise up inside them? Illness of the heart, illness of the Heavenly nature, illness of the physiology (i.e. congenital diseases), yinguo (Karmic cause and effect)-related illness, fortune-related illness, natural illness, mental illness, moral illness, etc. etc.

Previously, when Wang Shanren had lectured on the "five demons stirring up trouble in a house," I had not fully understood his point, wondering why he was bringing up these five demons when he was unwilling to "discuss mysteries and subtleties." Wasn't he confusing things with this talk? It was not until many years later that I solved this puzzle. What does he mean by the "five demons"? When a person with a fire disposition gets angry, their face turns red – this is what is called a "red-faced demon." When a person with a wood disposition gets angry, their face turns green – this is what is called a "green-faced demon." When a person with a metal disposition gets angry, their face turns white – this is what is called a "white-faced demon." When a person with a water disposition gets angry, their face turns black – this is called a "black-faced demon." When a person with an earth disposition gets angry, their face turns yellow – this is what is called a "yellow-faced demon." What are these five demons? Aren't they simply the dark Yin aspects of the dispositions of the five elements, aren't they simply the five poisons? When the five poisons invade your five *zang* organs, since these five organs are just like your house, isn't this exactly the same as "five demons stirring up trouble in a house"?

Getting angry is the equivalent of a demon, allowing fire to rise inside you is the equivalent of a monster. Why do I speak like this? Let us look at an ordinary couple arguing with each other. As one side gets angry, the other might say: "Look at this! There is a demon taking shape again." What is a demon taking shape? Getting angry is precisely what this demon taking shape refers to. As one person's fire is getting aroused, rising straight to their head, causing dizziness in the brain, and making their face turn red, isn't this precisely the same as a monster? Rising fire is a monster, sinking anger is a demon. Getting angry means that you are getting knocked down by a demon; allowing fire to rise inside you means that you are getting knocked down by a monster. Qi and fire are the two demons of impermanence, both coming to take away human life. Humans who are able to transform their Qi and fire are living immortals. Why is it that as soon as Qi and fire are transformed the hundred illnesses disappear completely? Because illness depends on eating Qi for its survival, wounds depend on eating fire for their survival. The more you get angry, the happier your illness is. And the more it grows and gains strength the more miserable you feel. Stopping yourself from getting angry is the same as not giving your illness food to eat; not allowing the fire to rise is the same as not giving your illness water to drink. Simply spend each and every day happy and cheerful, and you will make your illness die from hunger and thirst.

It is not that medications do not treat illness; they most certainly are able to do so. Medications are able to treat diseases that are caused by the six exogenous factors wind, cold, summer-heat, dampness, dryness, and fire, as well diseases that are caused by factors related to physics and chemistry. They are merely not good at treating diseases of the heart or of the Heavenly nature. If you are happy and content in your heart, the medications that you take will work great and everything will be fine. But if you take medications while at the same time getting angry, the medication will not only not treat your illness, it will even cause you side effects. All medications are 30 percent poisons, so taking medications is the same as using poison to attack poison. And if you on the one hand take medications and on the other hand continue getting angry and thereby gather up yet more poison inside, how can your illness possibly get better? I was twenty-five years old when I first understood this truth, and I am now more than seventy years old. In the over forty years in the meantime, I have not received acupuncture or taken medicine even once. At times, when I have caught a cold or gotten a headache or felt hot in the head, what did I do then? I have searched carefully for the reason, for the thing that caused me to get angry or made the fire rise inside of me, and as soon as I have restored harmony and balance in my heart and Heavenly nature, the demons of illness have run away. If you don't feel anxious and don't allow fire to rise up inside you, a cold will have no way of entering your body. The human body is like a house, also containing doors and windows. If you do not open up these doors and windows, wind, cold, summer-heat, or dampness will be unable to enter. The saying "If there is no thief in the family, you will not encounter thieves from the outside," is exactly what I am referring to.

"When confronted with a good reason, not to let anger flare up is medicine for long life. In the presence of fire not to let it erupt is a pill for immortality. In the face of injustice not to seek retribution is to truly practice cultivation." These sentences are worth a lifetime of study. Who is able to stop anger from flaring up when they have a good reason? Who is able to open-heartedly accept anger and fire? A single person cannot cause a fire on their own. The Chinese character for "burn" (yan 炎) is made up of two fires (huo 火) on top of each other, just like it takes two people to make a quarrel. If between two people, one starts a fire and the other one does not, the fire simply burns itself out in a little while. But if your opponent starts a fire and you respond with another fire, you end up with a blaze. If you possess wisdom, when the other person comes at you with a fire, you do not respond with your Qi. You let your Qi dissipate instead of using it to blow on the other person's fire. In this way, you prevent that person's fire from flaring up. Therefore I say, you have to know how to employ this trick. If you don't, you are in great trouble.

II. Methods of Treating Illness

II.1 TRANSFORMING YOUR CONSCIENCE

I once met a lady who told me: "I have lived my entire life in utmost virtue. I have been virtuous towards my mother, towards my mother-in-law, and towards every one of my relatives. But now I have contracted an illness and none of my family members understand me. So in my heart, I feel great bitterness." I advised her in this way: "As we study the teachings of Wang Shanren, we do not speak of our own merit but we concentrate on finding our own faults. What is illness after all? Illness is a manifestation of our faults. The fact that you have an illness is direct proof that you have wronged somewhere. If you had not done any wrong, would you have fallen ill? Since you have lived such a virtuous life, how is it that you have still fallen ill?"

In my many years of observation and investigation, I have found that illness is always incurred by us of our own accord, that death is always the result of our own actions. For every one of us, our life spans should be very long, at least to age eighty or ninety or a hundred if we live long. But why is it that nowadays so many people die already at the age of forty or fifty? It is because they get angry, allow the fire to rise up inside them, they lose their temper and give free reign to their emotions. Obsessive pondering in the heart generates fire, stirring of Qi attracts cold, and when cold and fire compound each other, the roots of illness are drilled deep into the body. Wait until your trouble has reached a certain degree, and your body is packed full with the five poisons, just like a garbage can that is filled until it overflows. And at this point, guess what a physical examination will reveal? You are right, cancer! And by the time you get cancer, it is too late and there is nothing you can do about it.

Mr. Yi Zhi, the author of "Introduction to Wang Fengyi's System of Emotional Healing" composed the following poem: "An old pine, askew and crooked, standing upright amidst howling winds and torrential rains. No woodcutter or carpenter will cut it down, only there to point the way for passers-by." When we explain family relationships to people, we are just like the police directing traffic, to give you directions and show you the way, to give you a green light. When we explain disease, we simply match you up with your symptoms, to tell you in accordance with your symptoms which person in the world of the Five Elements you have gotten angry at. We make you look deep inside yourself to see which person you have wronged in the framework of these five relationships – this is what is called matching your seat to the number on your ticket. Like when you ride the train, if you clearly have a ticket for seat number 1 and yet sit down in seat #3, the person with the ticket for that seat will obviously not agree with you. Many people have asked me: "Why is it, when you lecture, that you always talk entirely about me? According to what you are saying, is it really always me who is at fault?" In reality, I hadn't even been talking about them, but they merely recognized a similar sort of fault that they themselves had committed. All you have to do is match the number and when you have found the person that you have wronged, there will be a response. If you are able to turn yourself around and bring out your true conscience, you will most certainly recover from your illness.

I am only able to explain illness; I am not able to treat illness. Explaining the illness lies in my hands, but curing the illness lies in yours. Illness is something that you have sought out yourself, and it is also something that you yourself must cure. If you yourself do not want to cure it, are unable to match the number and turn your conscience around, those of us who explain illness are unable to do anything because you have not yet done your part. It is just like the practice of self-cultivation, even though you may be practicing on the surface, if you have not plunged into it whole-heartedly, you will never be successful.

II.2 UNTYING THE KNOTS

When Wang Shanren once said that he wanted to change the whole world, somebody asked him, "Aren't you talking a little too big here?" Wang Shanren replied: "Great deeds are done with small actions. To carry out great actions, we have to start with small things." Where do we start? We start with people's hearts and minds. What do we call that? It is called "transforming conscience."

When people contract illness, it is most certainly related to their personality. There is not a sliver of doubt about that. Unconscious people don't know this, but conscious people know this right away. This is a great shame and funny at the same time. With all this money that people spend, their illnesses are still not cured. What is the reason for this? That they have not untied the knot in their heart. The saying in Chinese medicine that "The hundred illnesses are all engendered in the heart" means just that, that illness comes from being born in the heart. Having an illness in your body, you will know it in your heart, and for illness of the heart you must take medicine for the heart. When we explain to people about their illnesses, this is nothing more than opening the apertures of their heart. If you don't first open up people's heart, when you give them medication, there are generally no apparent results. But after you have genuinely opened up their heart, their illnesses are cured very quickly.

People come to my home from far and wide to ask about their illnesses, and most of them come with a look of pain and suffering but leave all happy and cheerful. What is the reason for this? Nothing but the fact that their hearts have been opened. In reality it doesn't matter whether I explain to them about illness or about family relationships, as long as I help them untie these knots in their hearts. When your heart is opened, doesn't that make you feel good? I once had a female patient from Suihua who had been feeling depressed and anxious in her heart for over twenty years. As soon as I explained things to her, she began to cry. She cried and cried, and when she was done crying, her difficulties had vanished. Why? Because she had untied a twenty-year-old knot of sorrows.

Many doctors of Chinese medicine have listened to my lectures and then afterwards gone on to use this method to treat their patients, all with good results. A Doctor Wang from a hospital in Beijing has come twice to visit me at my home. After doing lots of research on the five-element constitutions, this Doctor Wang has told me: "In each case, after I have determined the patient's disease, I devise a method for opening their heart and only then do I give them medication. As my experience has grown, I have become able to know from one look at the disease what kind of people my patients are in conflict with. With a little bit of pushing and guiding from me, they are able to speak their truth and tell me where their anger comes from. At this point I tell them that I will only give them medicine if they are sincerely able to admit their mistakes. And after patients have admitted their mistakes, I go ahead and prescribe medicine for them, which then works wonders! In reality, it is not the medicine that heals them but these few sentences that they spoke. But since these patients have come to me looking for medicine, it wouldn't do if I didn't prescribe any. Simply speaking a few sentences, with the addition of the force of a bit of medicine, is enough to cure most diseases."

As soon as people open up their hearts, how can they not feel joy? And as soon as this joy is shared in the family, how can they not all feel happy? There is no need to talk to the other family members, if only a single daughter-in-law can become joyful, can't you see how it affects the entire household? But if she is walking around pouting and with a long face, everybody else will feel downcast and nobody will dare to speak up. In this day and age, our greatest problems lie in the family, and the greatest problems in the family fall into two categories: One, between husband and wife, and the other between mother-in-law and daughter-in-law. These days, so many couples are divorcing, and after the divorce the health of the children suffers. When the parents hear that I can explain away illness, they come and see me, bringing their child along. How do I treat these children? First, I don't know medicine, and second, I don't know medications. I only know how to say a few sentences about the Dao of being human. But since they have already come this far, I may as well tell them something. After they hear these few sentences, if the parents are able to look inside, find their own wrongdoings, and transform their way of thinking, as soon as the knot in their heart is untied, their children's health also improves as a result.

When I had just started to explain illness, a woman came to see me from Liaohe County in Heilongjiang Province who was in very critical condition. Getting off the train, she was not even able to walk. As she arrived at my home, she was so sick that she frightened me. Her face was so swollen that it looked like a purple turnip, and she was unable to take off her trousers. How could I not have been scared, seeing this kind of pervasive swelling? What would I do if even one of ten thousand patients died at my home? I told her that her illness was most likely a condition of the heart caused by hatred and asked her whether she had been to the hospital. She told me that she had been examined at the hospital and received the diagnosis of mitral stenosis resulting from rheumatic heart disease. So I asked her: "Who is the person you hate? Your resentment is so ferocious! Quick, think about this really hard!" She answered: "I know the answer, but I cannot say it." At this time, I didn't have any idea what her circumstances were and why she couldn't tell me. So I responded: "Wherever you contracted this illness from, that is where you will have to find the cure. If you do not say it, you cannot recover." She remained at my home for thirteen days.

Even though this lady was originally from Liaoning, she had contracted her illness in Heilongjiang, at her older sister's house. Eventually, her sister saw no other way and finally told me the truth: My patient had originally contracted her illness as the result of her hatred towards her brother-in-law. I immediately went and told her: "You must confront reality! Up to now, you have continued to blame your sister's husband, but in fact it is you who has done wrong. If you had not done wrong, your brother-in-law would not have acted as he did." She replied: "If it is truly as you say, then does this mean that I have to get down on my knees and confess my wrongdoing to him?" I answered: "You do whatever you want to. If you want to survive, you must get down on your knees in front of him. If you don't care about your life, there is nothing anybody can do for you."

At last she surrendered, got on her knees, and acknowledged her wrongdoing in front of her brother-in-law. And as soon as she did that, her brother-in-law followed suit and acknowledged his fault toward her, with the result that the knot in both of their hearts was untied. So you can see, when we explain the Dao to people, this is nothing but untying knots in people's hearts, opening them up to kindness rather than blame. And as soon as these knots are untied, everybody feels so much lighter! When she came to my home for her second visit, before she even entered the house, she spent an entire day vomiting up froth in our courtyard (one form of response to expelling illness). Subsequently, she returned to her sister's and spent another four months there, having barely escaped alive from the threat of death, recovered, and never suffered another recurrence of her illness.

My many years of experience have taught me that it is impossible to mediate between two people who are arguing with each other until both sides have developed trust in you. Arbitrating between them is no use at all if they do not trust you. It is a question of grasping the opportunity when it arises. If you want to create harmony between two people, you must first criticize them and explain how they are both at fault. And after you are done criticizing them, you must point out how they are both right. Because no two people think alike, they also handle things differently. So how can you bring them together? Explaining their faults is helping them expel their Yin; explaining their right actions is helping them take in Yang. This is what is called pulling out Yin and receiving Yang. It is a key principle of Wang Fengyi's system of healing through the emotions.

It is quite often that I see children who have contracted physiological diseases and are brought to me by their mothers. How am I to explain this kind of illness to them? If I tell them that it is their mother who has given the disease to them, these children will hate their mother for the rest of their lives. If I keep silent, though, the mother will not understand the truth, and the child won't understand it either. There is no other choice but to talk to them separately and in private, not letting one hear what I tell the other. To the mother, I point out that there must have been some wrongdoing in her heart during the child's pregnancy. In accordance with the child's condition, I inform her of the specific area of her anger. And to the child I say that the disease is one that they contracted on their own, that they have carried this fault since birth and must simply suffer this burden. The mother must acknowledge her wrongdoing and the child must also acknowledge his or her wrongdoing towards the parents and older generations. If both sides try hard, there is hope for recovery.

11.3 *Bu yuan ren* (DO NOT BLAME OTHERS!)

Wang Shanren said, "Not to blame others is the root of the great path towards enlightenment." When cultivated persons lack virtue, they blame their own lack of cultivation, but when small-minded people have faults, they blame others.

If they don't blame with their mouths, then they blame in their heart, and as this blame lodges in the heart, it turns into illness. Just think about it. If you continuously butt heads with an individual above you, trample an individual under your foot, carry an individual in your heart, hide something from a person behind your back, how could you not fall ill? Because others are always wrong and you are always right, you will invariably make your illness grow.

Regardless of whether you encounter a good situation or a bad situation, do not turn your blame towards the outside but search within yourself for any shortcomings, look at yourself to see whether you might have done wrong. Events can get turned upside down, logic can get flipped around. So always consider other people's hearts in comparison with your own. Wang Shanren often lectured: "If you always blame others, no matter what happens, does that make you right?" If you are annoying to other people and they are irritated by you, you will not feel comfortable. In reverse, if they are annoying to you, will they be able to feel comfortable?

A manager from Dalian once told me the following: "Before I turned thirty, my entire body was diseased. Could I really let this happen? If I were to die, my whole large family business would be finished. And since then, whatever I deal with, I do not allow myself to get angry or to blame others. I have to start with my own actions, by looking inside and examining myself." And not only did he speak like this, he also acted like this. And ever since, regardless of whether an affair turns out good or bad, he never blames others. When something is done wrong, he simply says: "For this situation, I do not blame you, I only blame myself. It is all a case of me not guiding you well, of me not handling this affair correctly." After three years, the diseases all over his body were gone. Currently, he is in his fifties and his health is still excellent.

The three words "bu yuan ren" 不怨人 (don't blame others) work miracles. The practice of not blaming others has limitless strength. I have experienced the truth of this teaching not only directly on my own body but in my family as well. In 1992, my oldest son was involved in a tragic car accident in Changchun. He was hit in the head by a Dongfeng-model car that cracked open his skull and very nearly took his life. The accident happened at eleven at night and I was quickly notified by telephone. At that time, I told my wife: "This son of ours, he cannot die, just like true wealth cannot be lost. Let us prepare ourselves well in our minds. And one more thing, if the driver who caused the accident fled the scene, we will just treat our son ourselves. And if he didn't flee, we cannot hold him responsible either." And then we rushed off by train to Changchun that same night.

When we got there, we were unable to find the right hospital. After searching for a long time, we finally met my younger son and his wife. They wanted to take us straight to the hospital but I told them that we should not do that. They responded: "What else did you come here for? Your son is in very critical condition right now!" I said: "We still shouldn't go to the hospital right now. First, let us eat a little and sleep a little, and only then go." When they asked why I was so determined, I told them: "Regardless of whether I am there or not, he will be in the condition he is in." So we slept first and only afterwards went to the hospital.

At the time we arrived, our oldest son was still in the emergency room. Even though he had undergone brain surgery that had removed any shards from his skull, he still had not regained consciousness. For nine days, he stayed like that in Critical Care. On the tenth day, he finally woke up and was able to speak but still did not recognize anyone. It was not until the eleventh or twelfth day that his mind began to clear up and he was able to ask me to help him get up. But as soon as I began propping him up, he immediately yelled out in pain to make me stop. When I asked him why, he responded, "Pain in the waist!" My intuition told me right away that this was bad news, that he had to have some broken bones in his waist. So I found the doctor and had him do a physical examination and take X-rays. As expected, the X-rays showed that the small bones on both sides of his body above his waist were all broken. The doctor wanted us to sign immediately to prepare for another operation. At that point, I wondered whether my son would really be able to handle another operation right then. He had not regained full consciousness yet and if, after the completion of the surgery, he were unable to follow instructions, he could cause paralysis in his lower body with a mere twist of his body. So I consulted with the doctor: "Let us wait another two days, until he has fully regained consciousness before we take action. Is that an option?" The doctor understood my reasoning and left without saying anything else.

At this point, the following thought came to me: "This is no big deal! These bones will grow back together quickly."

The first time I had tried to help my son get up had been in the morning. At noon, after he had had the x-rays taken and returned to his room, he asked me again to help him get up. But the nurses would not allow me to do that, worried that if I propped him up, this might compress nerves and cause even more serious injury. I told them that it couldn't possibly be that serious and went ahead, helping my son to sit up. After he sat up with my support for two minutes, I made him lie back down. After what seemed like an eternity, he could not stand it any longer, so when evening came, I once again helped to prop him up. At this point, an old man who was standing nearby came over in fear and, grabbing my hand, tried to stop me from supporting my son. I told him: "Old grandfather, I know that you are concerned for him. But please rest assured. Everything is fine." Then I once again propped up my son, this time allowing him to sit up for half an hour. When I asked him how he felt, he told me that he merely felt a little numbness but no pain. So I told him that everything was going to be all right. Now I knew with certainty that we should just let the bones heal naturally.

Around midnight, he got up all by himself. Lifting his feet, he sat up in bed and spoke: "Father! Just look at me. Am I awesome or not?" I asked him what he meant and he replied: "This morning, when you tried propping me up, I could only howl in pain, but now I feel no pain at all. I am able to sit up all by myself, and I am even able to walk." I told him not to walk, though, and to only sit a while and then lie back down. This time he sat up for an entire hour before I could make him lie down again. On the morning of the following day, he was able to sit up by drawing his feet back and promptly asked me to help him go for a walk. So with my support, he went for a walk along the corridor, covering a distance of more than a hundred meters.

After my son had stayed in the hospital for a total of nineteen days, the doctor would not let him stay any longer and insisted that he go home with us. I said: "The other patients here next to my son have also sustained head trauma, and some of them have been here for two months, some even for three months. This old man here, who was run over at the department store, has been here for four months and is still lying there. How come you are making my son leave the hospital?" The doctor answered: "I am the head of the department of Brain Surgery here and have worked in this hospital for forty years. In all this time, I have never seen any other patient like your son. He is truly extraordinary! He has been recovering so rapidly from one day to the next, you tell me, what point is there in me giving him more medication? It makes no sense to prescribe more medicine so I may as well just make him leave the hospital." After the doctor had spoken in this way, there was nothing I could respond, all I could do was ask him: "Fine, so we will bring him home. But would you please give us some medication to take with us?" The doctor thought this over for half a day and then gave us twenty sleeping pills. Taking the medication from him, I asked the doctor:"Director Wang, why did you choose to prescribe this medication for him?" And he replied, "When your son is unable to sleep, give him one tablet at a time, in this way his brain will be able to recuperate."

After such a serious traffic accident, I certainly hadn't expected to come home just like this, without any medication or anything. What would we give him to eat when we got home? I suddenly had a stroke of insight: Eat fruit. What fruit should he eat? Peaches! So I asked my son what fruit he might like to eat. He initially responded that he didn't feel like eating anything, but when I listed one fruit after another and finally got to peaches, he replied: "Yes, peaches are delicious. I will eat peaches." So I made him eat peaches, five *jin* of peaches a day, so for two whole months he was never without peaches, eating them continuously. When we had first brought him home, he had still been a little foggy and incoherent in his mind. But after eating peaches for two entire months, both his waist and his skull were fully healed.

Thinking about this situation afterwards, I found it a little strange myself. We had paid 3,400 Yuan in hospital fees for my son, while among the other patients on his ward one had spent 40,000 Yuan and another 170,000. The old man who had gotten run over at the department store had spent 320,000 Yuan, and had already stayed there for four entire months, still not ready to go home. How could my son have recovered so quickly? Later on, I found the answer: *Bu yuan ren* - Do not blame others! This situation truly serves as the perfect testimony for how great the power of *bu yuan ren* is. If we are able to not blame others, the poisonous Qi is unable to enter into our body, but can only exit out of our body. And in that case, how can recovery from illness not be quick? In our modern times, there are so many people, where all you have to do is bump into them once, and they will blackmail you, force you to pay them a large sum of money, make you deal with them for any number of years. These kinds of people indeed lack conscience. They think that they are taking advantage of you, but in reality they have planted an evil seed, and an evil seed will invariably end up with an evil fruit. In addition, there are so many people who fall ill and end up in the hospital. Their relatives go there to serve them and take care of them, but they not only fail to feel gratitude, they even harbor resentment. Doesn't this mean adding illness on top of illness?

In 1996, a mentally ill person came to our home. Can a mentally ill person behave normally? Whenever his insanity would erupt, there was nothing we could do, and nobody was able to control him. One day at the time of the afternoon nap, my older son was squatting on the ground, repairing a shovel. Out of the blue, this mentally ill patient took an ax and hit my son on the back of his head five times, to the point where the left side of his skull collapsed. This time, I really got scared stiff. For the first time ever, my wife got angry with me and yelled: "Old man! This time, you are really going to be our ruin."

We rushed our son to the county hospital, hoping that they would suture up his wound. But when we got there, they did not dare to touch him at all but immediately had him transferred to the municipal hospital in Bei'an City for a CT scan of his skull. The results showed that the left corner of his head had collapsed by the width of a finger. In addition, my son was missing a piece of bone on the right side of his skull. Fortunately the five ax strikes had not all hit the hole in his head. If they had, would he still be alive?

After Professor Zhang from Bei'an hospital evaluated my son's condition, he told us that he would have to operate and cut open the skull. As soon as I heard him mention opening up the skull, I received such a shock that I was on the verge of fainting. Opening up his skull yet again? Wouldn't that cause his skull to collapse? At that time, I thought that if my son really had to undergo another surgery, we wouldn't have his skull opened at that hospital but would take him back to Changchun to find the doctor who had treated him there previously.

We stayed in Bei'an that night, and as soon as I woke up the next morning, I was quite shaken. While I personally thought that this head injury was not that serious after all and shouldn't cause problems, I still had to explore my son's and his wife's attitude. It turned out, though, that as soon as I spoke to them, they did not have a single word of blame for me. They did not resent me and did not tell me that if I hadn't been explaining illness to people my son wouldn't have gotten injured. Any normal daughter-in-law would have been yelling insults at me at this point and would never have been able to forgive me. But my relatives didn't say anything, not a single word. When I asked my son how he had slept that night, he responded that he had slept through the night without any pain and had no complaints. So I said to them: "Please talk it over between the two of you. Will it do if we do not go ahead with the surgery? The doctor did say that if you do not have this operation he is afraid that you might develop epilepsy in three years." Being a wood-type personality, my son is very obstinate. He responded: "It's nothing! I don't feel pain or itching, so why would I develop epilepsy? Father, if you say that I shouldn't have this operation, let's just go home." I agreed, so in this way we just went home. And three days after his return, my son was planting and tilling right along with everybody else as usual.

Why was he able to recover so quickly without any surgery? This is one more example of the power of not blaming others (*bu yuan ren*).After this incident, the relatives of the person with the mental illness wanted to give us money but I refused to accept their gift. I told them that my son had recovered and that this was a cause of great joy. Furthermore, the mentally ill patient also recovered after he returned to his family, perhaps because the incident had frightened him into recovery. Whenever his illness did break out, it would be utterly strange: He would perform somersaults, thrash around, and twirl.

On April 27 of 2006, my second nephew went to the city, hauling fertilizer. While he was loading the truck, there were three bags left on the ground, and right when he was bending over to pick them up, all the other bags unexpectedly fell over and collapsed on top of him, squashing and breaking his leg. His boss took him to the hospital for an X-ray, and the X-ray showed that the ligament in his right leg was torn and his kneecap had a crack in it as wide as the tip of a chopstick. The doctor told him that he would have to stay in the hospital and have his leg stabilized with a cast for 28 days. My nephew responded that 28 days was impossible because he still had more than two hundred *mu* of land that he needed to plant. The doctor exclaimed: "You are still thinking of farming? Even if your injury heals well, you will not be able to work at all this year." But my nephew responded: "This just won't do. I will not stay in the hospital, I must go home." At this point, my nephew's boss broke out in cold sweat and asked: "Don't you want to keep this leg of yours? Do you want to force me to support and feed you for the rest of your life? How much money do I have to pay you?" My nephew answered: "I couldn't let you pay me money. You didn't intentionally let the fertilizer bags collapse on top of me after all, it is purely my own fault that I was not careful. Please just take me home, and whether I later recover or not is not your concern at all." The boss said: "In that case, we must put this down in writing, with signatures from both of us." My nephew agreed and told him to write something up. After they had signed their agreement, the boss took him home.

At this time, my second nephew was still living at my home. When he arrived and was unable to get out of the vehicle but had to be carried by two people, I went up and asked him what had happened to him. He said that he had squashed his leg. When I asked for details, he explained that the ligaments in his leg were torn and his kneecap had a crack as wide as the tip of a chopstick. When I heard how serious his injuries were, I asked him whether he knew the reason why he had gotten squashed. He simply answered that he knew. So I said: "If you know it, that is good enough. Come inside!" So we carried him into the house. My relatives challenged me, asking why I hadn't made the boss pay for medical treatment, but I answered: "What is there to treat! Wasn't this an incidental misfortune that his leg got squashed by accident? Why should he be held responsible?"

My nephew rested on the *kang* for a whole day and night, and on the second day was already able to get up again. How could he recover so quickly? I myself was quite astounded so I asked him: " Does your leg feel like it is emitting a cool wind or does it feel hot?" He answered that it was emitting a cool wind, that it felt like a cool breeze whistling right out of it. I told him: "This is nothing to worry about, it is just the poisonous Qi leaving the leg. Your condition is improving quickly and you will recover in just a few days." On the third day, he was able to walk but still relatively slowly. This incident occurred right in the middle of the planting season, and my family was entirely dependent on him to plant the more than two hundred *mu* of land. So on the fourth day he began all the preparations to start the planting work, and on the fifth day really did get up on his planter and planted.

The doctor who had examined my nephew and happened to be my son's father-in-law, scolded my nephew at that time: "What kind of a fool are you? Even after he squashed you, you still won't make him pay for your treatment? Isn't this going to cost you money?" In fact, though, my nephew's leg didn't cost us a single cent. What power did this come from? From the power of *bu yuan ren* (not blaming others). For this reason Wang Shanren once said: "*Bu yuan ren* (not blaming others) has limitless power. *Bu yuan ren* enables you to reach enlightenment." No matter who we encounter, no matter what situation we are faced with, we must never blame others but instead focus all our efforts on deeply transforming ourselves, on deeply criticizing ourselves. This is precisely how we can reach enlightenment.

II.4 SELF-REFLECTION WITHOUT DELUSION

What is the Dao? The book "Talking About Transforming the Heavenly Nature" contains the following quotes: "Minding other people's business is to be a fake; minding your own business is to be genuine. Before rectifying others, we must rectify ourselves. This is the meaning of the Dao." "It is only by rectifying ourselves and cultivating the heart, with no thoughts of anything else, that we have a boat to carry us across the bitter Sea of Suffering." Thus we must concentrate wholeheartedly on cultivating our own heart and Heavenly nature as the only path to escape from suffering and find joy. Wang Shanren talks about self-reflection without delusion in the same way that the Buddhists talk about it. It is only by reflecting on ourselves that we can be free from delusion, but when we reflect on others, freedom from delusion is impossible.

In the context of our every-day life, however, how many people do in fact mind their own business? Everybody minds other people's business. Looking at other people's shortcomings is nothing but collecting garbage; looking at other people's strong points is nothing but gathering inspiration. If you look at other people's shortcomings, this will stir the heart, it will make you angry, and that's why I call it "collecting garbage." When you take filthy trash and store it inside your body, illness results. A whole lot of people who have studied the Dao are like this. They have reached great heights in their study of the Dao, but then they take this Dao to measure others, to place demands on others, to control others. This being wrong and that being wrong, isn't this a completely displaced way of studying the Dao? As long as you rectify others, they will not listen to you. And as they resist you, you will not be happy and will become angry. And what is this anger? It is poison, and when this poison enters your body, won't it harm you and cause illness all over your body? Why did Wang Shanren suffer from chronic ulcers and consumption for twelve years? Because he could not stand to watch the way in which his fellow villagers treated their elders without proper *xiao*. I personally have also suffered serious illness for twelve years and it was also because I always focused on other people's wrong-doings and wanted to mind everybody else's affairs. Even when I didn't dare to interfere with my mouth, I still interfered in my heart, ultimately turning myself into an invalid, with disease all over my body. Thus, we cannot make demands of others but must instead turn the focus on ourselves, examine ourselves, transform ourselves, cultivate and rectify ourselves. Once you have genuinely transformed yourself, there is no longer a need to mind other people's business. Others will transform themselves on their own.

One of Confucius's disciples named Zengzi is known for his practice of the three self-examinations, for which he reminded himself three times each day. We want to model ourselves after the ancient sages and hence should practice introspection at least twice each day. As we get up every morning, we want to call out our own name and ask ourselves: "Do I still blame others or do I no longer blame others? Will I be able to treat others right or not?" If you are a daughter, ask yourself whether you will be able to act as a good daughter. If you are a daughter-in-law, ask yourself whether you will be able to act as a good daughter-in-law, as a good wife, and as a good mother. And after asking yourself like this in the morning, then answer yourself in the evening, after you are done with the day's work. Calling yourself by your name, ask yourself again: "Did I fulfill my intentions? Are there any areas where I transgressed? Why did I transgress? Where does the cause lie?" If you act like this, over a long period of time you will indeed change your Heavenly nature.

II.5 ADMITTING OUR FAULTS

We always look at other people's wrongdoings, and as soon as we do that, we get angry. This is the equivalent of emptying out a garbage can into your own body. If you do this for a long time, your body turns into a bucket full of dirt. Our current practice of explaining the Dao and explaining illness is a way of helping everybody to clean out their dirty bucket. How do you clean it out? By searching for the precise root of your illness, by recognizing the precise origin of your illness. By means of the Dao, you find one aspect. The aspect that you find through the Dao is exactly what the Daoists refer to as "to turn the light around to reflect back on oneself," which is the same as what the Buddhists call "self-reflection without delusion," namely that we look deep within ourselves. Among the people in your family, who all have you let down? Who all have you gotten angry with? Are you able or not to admit your wrongdoings? Are you able or not to face the truth? If you believe in the Buddha, you can express your remorse in front of the Buddha. If you believe in Christ, you can express your remorse in front of Christ. If you don't believe in any religion, you must still have a mother and father, or relatives and friends, so you can express your remorse in front of them. This magnifies the effect of your repentance. As soon as you admit your wrongdoings, you allow a stream of Yang Qi to enter your body. And as soon as Yang Qi comes in, Yin Qi is inevitably forced to leave. This is what we call eradicating Yin and choosing Yang, or Yang returning and Yin fleeing.

When Wang Shanren heard the story of San Niang teaching her son and saw three generations admitting their faults to each other, he was moved to also admit his faults. And when I read this story, I was equally moved to admit my faults along with him. The chronic ulcers and consumption that Wang Shanren had suffered from for twelve long years were thereby cured in a single night. I myself vomited for seven and a half days and nights until my illness was all vomited out and I recovered. Heaven does not condemn those who regret their transgressions. Even the greatest faults under Heaven, as soon as you repent, they disappear! Do not fear the transgressions you have committed, but only fear that you know your transgressions and still fail to change. If you know your transgressions and yet fail to change, there is nobody out there who can help you. Over the years, I have encountered quite a number of such patients.

In 1997, a lady came to me who was suffering from brain cancer. Twenty-seven years old, she was forced to just lie in bed, unable to get up, so she asked me to help her by explaining her illness to her. I asked her: "I have come to explain your illness to you, so please think carefully. Who among your elders have you transgressed against?" She glanced around at all the people in the room, thought about my question for a long time, and replied with a single sentence: "I have never gotten angry at any of the elders in my life." "In that case," I explained, "there is nothing else I have to say to you." When she asked why, I told her that I could not cure this disease of hers by explaining anything else. With these words, I got up and left the room. Her husband followed me out and asked what they should do then. I told him that she did not want to continue living. Why, he asked. I told him: "She does not trust me. She is not willing to admit her faults. As a matter of fact, she contracted this disease as the result of getting angry at an elder. But she is unwilling to acknowledge this, and in this way she has pulled the door shut in one swoop. She herself has closed this door and nobody else is able to enter, nobody else is able to help her now." And in the end, seven days later she indeed passed away. People should not be afraid of committing mistakes but of not knowing their mistakes, and of not changing their ways after they have committed mistakes. If you know your mistakes, you will inevitably change, and once you have changed, you become a good person. And this means that we are able to cure your illness.

In 2005, a women's school for self-cultivation from Beijing organized a series of lectures in Hangzhou. When they invited me to give a lecture, I declined. Why did I do that? Because I lecture on the Dao as a public service. I am not in it for fame or for money. But since this lecture series was a for-profit event, I was not able to participate. Nevertheless, they called me repeatedly, more than ten times, and what the person in charge explained to me was quite convincing, so eventually they changed my mind and I attend, together with Zhang Xiuying.

Upon my arrival, I looked around and noticed that every one of the 42 participants was female, so I decided to speak specifically about the Dao of women. After the conclusion of my talk, one of the students with the last name Meng immediately sent an e-mail to her husband. What for? To acknowledge her fault and reverse her wrongdoing. Her husband replied: "What kind of an excellent place have you gone to? You have never before admitted any fault towards me, so why is it that you are acknowledging your fault today?" She responded that she had attended a lecture by me and thereby for the first time realized her own wrongdoing. "My husband," she said, "I have truly wronged you!" Her husband then asked how much she had paid for this lecture series. When she told him that she had paid a fee of 5,000 Yuan for four days of instruction, he responded: "Not expensive! That e-mail that you wrote me just now is well worth those 5,000 Yuan! With one sentence, you have warmed my heart and filled me with joy and affection. It is not that you, my wife, have wronged me but that I as your husband have not treated you right." So you can see, when husband and wife admit their mistakes to each other, how can a family not become warm and harmonious? From this moment on, whenever this couple needed to discuss a certain matter and one of them disagreed with the other, they put the issue aside for a time, with neither of them getting angry. Then they would wait until their hearts calmed down and their thoughts were in agreement again, before they continued their discussion. This husband and wife now truly treat each other with sincerity and respect each other like honored guests.

There is a saying: "Men don't shed tears lightly, and they have gold under their knees.[4] They kneel down in front of Heaven and in front of their parents, so how could they kneel down in front of a wife?" But if you have wronged your wife, you must also kneel down and admit your mistakes. Nevertheless, there are things that should be said and must be said, and there are other things that are better left unspoken. If you have had an extramarital affair, for example, it is best not to speak of it in your wife's presence, because as soon as you discuss it, her heart will turn cold and she might divorce you in the end. If you know that you have wronged, that is enough; if you have changed, you become a good person. If you hold in your heart the awareness that you are her husband, you will fulfill this role as a proper husband. Why do we refer to a married man as a husband? Because your wife has come to you to lean on.[5] Think about it for a moment. Your wife has left her relatives, the people she was closest with in

---

4   A traditional expression, to convey the significance and preciousness of men's ritual of kowtowing.

5   This is a play on words: The character *zhang* 丈 in the Chinese term for husband used here, *zhangfu* 丈夫, is etymologically related to the character *zhang* 仗 that means "to lean on".

her life, and come to join you by your side. Given how much she has sacrificed for you, how do you really want to treat her?

11.6 LOOKING FOR THE GOOD IN EVERYTHING

I am going to share yet another method with you here. If you apply it well when you get home, your family will certainly be harmonious, your body will enjoy perfect health, and your affairs will go smoothly. This method is concerned with looking for the good in everything. If you look at people and see only goodness, if you look at them and see only Buddhas, this means that you yourself are a living Buddha. Conversely though, if you constantly look at people's wrongdoings, if you look at everybody and see only demons, then you end up being even more demonic than demons. And eventually, you will see that your entire body is afflicted by illness. Isn't this the same as turning into a demon?

Some people have told me things like this: "There is nothing good about him at all. I truly am unable to find even the smallest place of goodness in him." If you cannot find it on one side, you must look for it on the opposite side. A man looked me up once who was suffering from kidney disease, telling me that both of his kidneys were diseased. I told him: "Isn't this a sign that you are annoyed by people full circle?" He asked me what I meant by "being annoyed by people full circle," so I explained: "All the people in your periphery, all the people subordinate to you, you are annoyed by them all." He responded, asking: "How can you speak so accurately? I do truly feel annoyed by them." I told him: "It is precisely because of this fact that you have contracted this disease. Why is it that you are so annoyed by them?" He responded, "They do not do their job well. They do not fulfill my expectations." "Ha," I said, "that's exactly right. This is precisely the root of your disease. You must look until you find their strong points." To this he responded: "But where do they have strong points? I am unable to find them!" I informed him: "You are the leader, and when the people under your charge don't do a good job, you hold it against them and consider them worthless." He agreed with me, so I continued: "This is indeed precisely where their strong point lies! If they were all like you, maybe even to the point of being stronger than you, would you still serve in this leadership role? They would quickly push you down to a lower position." After he heard this perspective of mine, he genuinely understood the situation and said: "What you say is correct. Why didn't I think of this point myself? I previously assumed that they were worth nothing, nothing at all." I asked, "If they really were good-for-nothings, they would have tried to push you down from your position earlier, saying 'Step down! Let me handle this, as I am stronger than you!' Isn't this really where their strong point is found?" He agreed with me emphatically and told me that he wouldn't get annoyed with them any further. On the morning of the next day, he returned to tell me that his condition had truly responded to my treatment and that he had felt no pain for the entire night.

11.7 EXPERIENCING JOY

Humans are not saints, so who would be able to live without transgressions? We are not saints, so who is able to be faultless? It is only a question of whether our wrongs are big or small. When other people make mistakes, we must not only stop ourselves from blaming them but we must forgive them and help them change by our example. Whenever Wang Shanren witnessed other people's wrongdoings, he invariably gave them a smile. What is smiling? Smiling means welcoming the good spirits. What is anger? Anger is demonic. As soon as you smile, the good spirits come. As soon as you get angry, demons come. And as soon as the good spirits come, the demons are forced to run away. This is what is called "bringing out the spirits and making the demons disappear." You must live each and every day with great happiness, joy and laughter, to starve your illness to death. As we have already discussed above, illness depends on eating the Qi of anger for its survival; skin sores depend on eating fire for their survival. One is their water, and the other is their rice. If you don't get angry and generate Qi, and if you don't cause fire to rise up inside you, this is tantamount to not giving your illness water to drink and rice to eat, until the illness, without food and drink, will naturally starve to death.

If you live your life in joy, there is a seat for you in paradise. But if you live your life in sorrow, you will journey to hell. Being consistently happy, you won't get sick and, moreover, your affairs will go smoothly. What is this if not paradise? On the other hand, though, if you live your life in constant worry, this means that you are making illness grow, so you will have to go to the hospital, have surgery, and have your chest or abdomen cut open or your arm or leg amputated. Is this not exactly what we refer to as hell? People with illness are living in hell. Do you really have to wait for death to descend to hell? No, this is living hell, living hell, this is living in hell right here!

There is an old saying: "30 percent medicine, 70 percent nurturing health. Skill in healing is not as good as skill in nurturing health." What do we mean by "nurturing health"? Nothing but consistently maintaining a joyful attitude, which has a much faster effect than taking medications. When patients are able to truly understand this way of thinking, they are able to open up their heart and chest and get rid of their diseases, from that point on living in joy. The Bodhisattva Maitreya is always full of joy and laughter, and it would do us well to learn from him and also be full of joy and laughter each and every day. This is the only way in which you can study Buddhism.

Some people might say, "I am unable to be joyous. What am I to do?" So let me teach you a trick. Every day, place a small mirror in front of you and take a good look at yourself, this poor creature suffering from ten thousand years of unhappiness. And this will allow you to become happy. If you don't feel genuine joy at first, just fake it. When your family members witness this, they will think: If a sick person can be so happy, how could I still be unhappy? In this way, everybody will become happy. And when everybody is happy together, isn't this enough Yang Qi? As the Yang Qi enters the body, the streams of Yin Qi that arrive as the result of you getting angry must flow straight to the outside, with no other place to go but away from you. This is precisely what we call "making Yang return and Yin flee." A lady from Harbin once came to see me with her son, and the mother said: "Wang Shanren, from the moment I first saw you, my heart disease has been cured!" How could her heart disease be cured just from her seeing me? Because she felt happiness in her heart, which allowed Yang Qi to flow into her body and caused the Yin Qi to be expelled instantly. Nothing but "Yang returning and Yin fleeing"! You all can perform an experiment when you go home: As you enter through the front door, when you see everybody happy and content, within one or two months all the illness in your body is guaranteed to disappear!

A woman once told me that she was unable to be joyful because her husband looked down on her. In fact, though, it is not that he looks down on you, but that you look down on him, you dislike him in your heart, and for that reason you are unable to be joyful. You must "turn the light around to reflect back on yourself," so take that mirror and have a close look at yourself. As soon as you look at yourself, you will understand. The wife should be like a star of happiness, radiating constant joy all day long. This long face of yours, always somber and Yin, who is happy to look at such a dark star of bad luck? If you are happy and in high spirits all day long, will your husband be able to dislike you? With nothing but joy in your heart, there will be a space for you in Heaven. With nothing but sorrow in your heart, it is a journey to hell. Always feeling sorrow, aren't you simply running straight to hell? You must turn your heart around, flip it over completely, and you will be able to let joy rise inside of you. If you cannot turn it around, then you cannot let joy arise.

In 1999, a lady came to see me from Kedong County. As soon as she crossed the threshold, she started crying. I wondered to myself what was going on with her that she started crying as soon as she came through the door. Taking a closer look at her, I realized that among all the women in the room, she had the fairest complexion of anybody present. How could she have such a fair complexion? How could she look so exceptional? I waited until she had finished crying and then asked her why she had come in here crying like this. She responded that she was being mistreated. When I asked for details, she explained: Previously, I found myself a husband but as soon as I married him, he started beating me." I interjected: "If he started beating you right after you got married, this means that you failed to be a good wife for him." She objected: "How could I have failed to be a good wife? Of course I was a good wife." I asked her: "If you had been a good wife, would he have beaten you?" She continued her story: "I left him. I did not want to suffer under him. Later on, I found myself another man. Eventually though, as soon as we got married, this man again started beating me!" I told her: "Just from looking at you, I can tell you that it is your fate to suffer abuse. You must simply endure being beaten." She cried out: "How could I have a fate to suffer abuse? How should I simply endure being beaten?" I explained: "Glancing at your sad face, expressing ten thousand years of unhappiness, I see that you are more beautiful than most women but your face is full of unhappiness. If you are able to cheer up, he will no longer beat you." When she asked me how to do that, I told her: "As soon as your husband comes home, even if there is no joy in your heart, you must force yourself to be joyful. And as your joy grows, it will come to you naturally." When she heard this, she asked, half believing and half doubting me: "If I am joyful, he truly will not beat me?" I told her: "If you don't believe me, just try and see what happens."

After staying with us for several days, this lady went home. Three months passed, and then she returned. This time, as she entered the house, she didn't cry but smiled instead. I commented: "Just look at her! That lady has surely not been beaten!" When everyone else asked her whether her husband was still beating her or not, she told us that he was no longer beating her. Everybody wanted to know why, so she said: "Didn't Liu Shanren here tell me that it was just a question of being joyful? Every time he came home, regardless of whether I was joyful or not, I welcomed him with a smile." I explained, "A raised hand doesn't beat a smiling face. Who would be able to beat a cheerful person? As soon as you became cheerful, he stopped beating you." She agreed with me: "For these past three months, he has not beaten me even once." I told her: "When your husband comes home, he may have something on his mind that is bothering him or he may be preoccupied with something. And in that situation to be greeted by a gloomy face like yours, who would want to look at that? What else could he do but let out his anger at you and beat you!" So you see, the wife is truly the spirit of joy in a family. If the wife is always full of joy and laughter, a family can indeed enjoy peace and harmony.

III. The Stages of Reversing Illness

III.1 REVERSAL OF ILLNESS MANIFESTS DIFFERENTLY IN DIFFERENT PEOPLE

The way in which we treat people by explaining illness to them must change with each individual. We must look at their personality, their illness, and their situation in the family. After we clearly understand each of these factors, we can then deduce where the person's illness came from and who else is involved.

We all differ from each other in our disposition, and we all differ in the way in which illnesses arise within us. So of course the way in which illnesses leave also differs. Illness is caused by joy, anger, grief, or sorrow, and so it must be expelled by joy, anger, grief, or sorrow. An illness that has arisen by crying must leave by crying. An illness that has arisen by laughing must leave by laughing. An illness that has arisen by sobbing and yelling with bouncing and with leaping must leave by sobbing and yelling with bouncing and with leaping. To summarize, the ways in which illnesses leave are utterly strange and bizarre. One person may be moved by their illness to crawl around on the ground while another may run around endlessly in a circle. It is worth studying some of the causes for such behavior.

III.2 THE STAGES OF REVERSING ILLNESS

III.2.a Crying Out Past Hardships First

The sagely Wang Fengyi has taught us, "Illness enters through the mouth and also exits through the mouth." Why is it that we always make patients give voice to what is inside their heart? Giving voice to what's inside the heart means releasing Qi, releasing the grief that they harbor inside their heart. Patients may give voice to the losses they have experienced, the wrongs they have suffered, the abuse they have endured. At this time, you must definitely let them speak, speak until at long last they say: "I have nothing else to say. I am done speaking." Then I tell them: "So you are done speaking. You have given voice to all the wrongs other people have done to you. But have you given any thought at all to yourself? Have your actions always been right?" At this point, patients might agree with me that they have also committed wrongs. So I say: "Yes. In this round, please speak about your own mistakes. Now that you have finished talking about everybody else's mistakes and have scrubbed every one else clean, speak again to give yourself a good scrub next." What is that you are supposed to scrub clean? Scrub your own heart and spirit, scrub your internal organs, or in other words, dump out your own bucket of pigswill. If patients want to vomit, or hiccup, or belch or break wind, this is precisely the manifestation of dumping out their bucket of pigswill.

When we explain illness to people, some patients respond with joy, some patients cry. Cry about what? They cry out their whole life's suffering, their whole life's grievances. It is only when they are done crying that they are able to repent. If they repent right from the start, then it is not real. Because people must first suffer grievances before they become angry. They must first feel like they have accomplished much and done great good deeds, in order to get so angry. When patients cry, if they are able to release all their suffering and express all their grievances, this is best. Nevertheless, crying alone can also have a releasing effect. If there is genuine transformation inside them, the crying alone can also work without any speaking.

People who are unable to be joyous have a Yin quality to them, and people with a Yin quality are unable to be joyous. If you don't get rid of this Yin quality, the illness cannot improve and you cannot find joy. Once you have truly cleaned out this Yin quality and gotten rid of it, whatever you look at will make you laugh. Isn't this truly a sign that their joy is limitless?

III.2.b Repentance

When Wang Shanren had completed the hundred-day mourning period for his father, he suddenly reached an enlightened understanding of our Heavenly nature. So he gifted a treatment method to the poor who could not afford treatment for their illnesses. This is precisely the Wang Fengyi system of treating disease through one's disposition and emotions. This treatment method is truly wonderful, able to cure diseases with no need to take medications, no need to get acupuncture, no need to spend money. I myself was once so sick that I was about to die, and I used this method to recover from my illness. At that time, I made a vow that I would no longer live for my own sake. That I would take this treatment method and transmit it to the world, that I would not allow it to get lost. What is this treatment method? It is to deeply practice repentance in silence by oneself. If we want to recover from illness, we must recognize our mistakes with sincerity, set our intention on changing and repenting, thoroughly correct past wrongdoings, and become a new person.

Repenting With Sincerity

When the heart is sincere, miracles happen. For repentance to be effective, it must certainly be genuine and thorough. Some patients tell me when they come to see me that they have already prayed to this Buddha or that Bodhisattva. As I explain to them, "If you don't repent with sincerity, your illness will not be cured, even if the Bodhisattva Guanyin were standing right in front of us. Yes, Bodhisattvas may want to rescue you, but if you don't recognize your faults, don't change your wrongdoing, how could your illness improve?" There are others who act with wonderful repentance on the outside but are in reality all closed off on the inside, sealed off really tightly so that you have no idea what is inside of them. With people like that, it is impossible to cure their illness.

It is a commonly heard expression in China that "illness arrives like an avalanche but departs like reeling silk thread."[6] Nevertheless, Wang Shanren told us the opposite, namely that "contracting illness is like reeling silk thread but getting rid of it is like an avalanche." On the basis of my experience of many years of explaining illness to people, when I consider this issue carefully, I see that this is the truth, that it is truly like this. Regardless of how many years we may have suffered from a disease, as soon as we discover our conscience, we are cured with a single word. Even the greatest crime under Heaven dissipates as soon as we repent. There are truly too many examples to tell them all. I once encountered a young boy from Dalian who was suffering from pulmonary edema that was so advanced that you could not see his lung in X-ray pictures. How did he contract this disease? By being deficient in his practice of *xiao*. *Xiao* is able to nurture the lungs, while *ti* (love and respect for siblings) is able to nurture the heart. Lacking *xiao* injures the lungs; lacking *ti* injures the heart. This boy subsequently came to realize the truth and woke up, recognized his wrongdoings with a genuine heart, and the accumulated fluids in his body were quickly discharged.

I remember the first time I met Dr. Liu Lihong, which was in Changchun. There were two ladies present at that time. One of them had come from far away and had a large tumor under her right armpit, the size of an egg, that had been there for three years already. In fact, she had come to Changchun to have surgery. As soon as she saw me, she told me: "Liu Shanren! What great timing. I am scheduled to have surgery tomorrow, but now I may no longer need to do that." I replied: "With such a large tumor, do you really think you

---

6   This refers to a slow laborious step in the production of silk.

will be able to recover without surgery? If you really are determined to avoid this operation, this will require a whole lot of hard work." She responded that she was willing to work hard. I then turned around to chat with Liu Lihong. What was the topic of our conversation? We focused on discussing the Dao of the daughter-in-law, on how a proper daughter-in-law should conduct herself, how she should act towards her mother-in-law, towards her husband, and towards her sisters-in-law. While we were talking, this lady suddenly kneeled down in front of us and began to cry. Soon, though, her crying turned into laughing, until she was laughing so hard that she was rocking back and forth. After laughing for a while, she went to the bathroom and vomited with an uproar. She vomited and vomited until her intestines were turned inside out and her stomach flipped upside down. Because this was the first time that Liu Lihong witnessed this kind of a scene, he was a bit alarmed. Very early on the next day, as soon as the lady with the tumor got out of bed she exclaimed elatedly: "Look at that! My tumor has shrunk, shrunk by a whole lot!" When Dr. Liu examined her, he confirmed this finding, that it had truly shrunk, down to the size of the tip of the thumb. How is it that in a single night a tumor that had been the size of an egg could have shrunk that much? It was quite unthinkable indeed!

Seeking the Target With Precision

A whole lot of people practice repentance. But it is essential that you seek your target with precision when you do so. It is just like when you have lost something. If you have lost something in the east, can you find it if you go looking for it in the west? Likewise, if you have contracted your illness as the result of an interaction with a man, you won't be able to cure your illness by repenting before a woman. Or if your illness was contracted in connection with an older person, doing repentance before a young person will do you no good. If you got angry right in front of somebody, you must admit your mistake right in front of them. And if you got angry behind somebody's back, you must admit your mistake behind their back as well. This is the only way that you can make sure that you hit the target with every single shot.

I once treated a lady who was suffering from uterine fibroids. When she realized that her disease had been caused by her feelings of annoyance toward at her husband, she went and kowtowed to her husband under tears, acknowledging her fault. This is to say, there is no use in acknowledging your fault to anybody else, you must admit it precisely to the person with whom you got angry. Some people don't understand this principle and they kowtow in front of an image of the Buddha and pray: "Buddha! I have done wrong! I implore you to make my illness go away." But the Buddha did not cause you to do wrong, so the Buddha will not cure your illness either. There is no use in kowtowing to the Buddha. If you have an illness in the uterus or lower back, you must kowtow to your spouse. Between husband and wife, what need is there to save face or to hold back for any other reason? How could it hurt you to bow your head?

Repenting Every Single Instance

The poison in our bodies is like the pages in a book. Every time you get angry, you press a layer of poison into it. If there is a single page that you have not turned over, the poison will remained pressed in there. Thus if we want to eradicate all illness, we must turn over every single page, to get rid of all the Yin qualities in our belly in their entirety. Otherwise these Yin qualities will tie you down and your nature will not be easy to change, your heart will not be easy to transform.

The diseases that everybody asks me about, like hypertension, heart disease, nephritis, lower back and leg pain, liver cirrhosis, I have had them all. How did I get rid of these diseases? With a lot of hard effort in my heart. Going back to the very beginnings of my memory, by searching for them, one by one, by going through them, one by one. Among all the people in our village, whoever I had gotten angry with in the past, I went to each and every one of them and acknowledged my wrongdoing. And when I was facing them, if it was truly too embarrassing to kneel in front of them, I kneeled and kowtowed to them in my heart and acknowledged my wrongdoing in silence. This is how I cured my diseases.

Some people might comment: "From childhood up through my entire adult life, I have gotten angry at too many people. How could I possibly remember all of them?" If you cannot remember all of them at one time, you can always take a piece of paper and write them down to help you remember. Didn't Zhang Xiuying fill so many pages with names? She actually searched through several years of registers of people who had worked at the factory with her, looking them up one by one, thinking about them one by one, repenting to them one by one. Only in this way was she able to cure all the diseases in her body and completely transform her personality.

III.3 DO NOT FEAR THE REVERSAL OF ILLNESS

A lot of people have physical responses when listening to my talks or watching me on video because they turn their attention to their own mistakes. Some get loose bowels, some start vomiting, some belch or break wind. Some ask in confusion: "Before I heard Master Liu lecture, I did not feel like anything was wrong with me. Why is it that as soon as I have listened to you, illness has come?" In fact, though, this response does not mean that illness has just come but it is rather the response of a pre-existing illness in you. It is the manifestation of the poison being expelled from inside your body. When you heard me lecture, you were stirred profoundly, you were hit by a great stream of Yang Qi. And the poison of the illness that you harbor inside your body is nothing but Yin Qi. When this Yin Qi encounters Yang Qi, there will be a reaction, and these are simply its normal manifestations.

When you experience such physical reactions, you absolutely must not be afraid or suppress them. If you take medication to suppress the symptoms at the time when these poisons from your illness are being expelled to the outside, the poison of the medicine will push them deeper into your body so that the poisons of your illness can no longer leave the body. For this reason, when you are stirred by any illness in your body, it is best to not suppress it but to allow it to naturally release and be expelled to the outside.

Even though it is common to vomit when you are expelling illness, this method of vomiting is fundamentally different from any vomiting you may experience as part of your illness. The vomiting associated with the reversal of illness can at times be ferocious, like making rivers flow upstream or turning oceans upside down, like turning your intestines inside out and flipping your stomach upside down. But in spite of the ferociousness of this vomiting, you will generally not throw up food, not even a meal that you may have just consumed. In most cases, what people vomit when reversing illness is phlegm, mucus, or in more serious cases black blood, or anything in the five colors and five flavors. Why is it that people vomit up substances in these colors or flavors? Because the poisons of disease are hidden away in the internal organs of your body, your various channels and vessels, your four limbs and hundred marrows, as if in hibernation, unbeknown to you under ordinary circumstances. It is only when you reflect, when you repent with a sincere heart, that these pathogenic poisons will flow from every channel and vessel, to gather in the lung channel. Why is this? Because the lung holds court over the hundred vessels. After passing through this connection between the lung and the hundred vessels, the poisons from every location throughout your body gather together by the orifice of the lung, from where they are then expelled. If it is a poison that has come from the spleen channel, the vomited substance will be yellow and sweet. If it is a poison that has come from the lung channel, the vomited substances will be white and acrid. This is identical with the five elements, five colors, and five flavors of traditional Chinese medicine. Sometimes, the internal organs respond as if you had taken the lid off a boiling pot. Some people vomit so intensely that their chest hurts as if they had a fire burning inside and they don't dare to drink even water. If you are not somebody engaged in this method of emotional healing, if you have not personally experienced this, this can truly be frightening. Because I have reversed my own illness in this way by expelling it, I do not get frightened. Quite to the contrary, the more a patient vomits, the better they will recover; the more they vomit, the happier I am.

The reason for this is that it is only when you turn your conscience around and get rid of the five poisons in your body that the illness can be cleared away from the roots on up, that you can transform your heart and nature, that you can transform the basic quality of your Qi. If you do not turn your intestines inside out and flip your stomach upside down, you may think that you have cured your illness, but you have not succeeded. Why? Because the Yin qualities are still suppressed inside of you, the roots of the poison are still tying you down on the inside, as if in hibernation, hidden away inside your body. And as soon as somebody lights a fuse underneath them, they will flare up with a vengeance, and you will suffer a relapse of your illness. It is only when you have truly dumped out all the poison that your heart can stay level and you remain unmoved. What is the Buddhist concept of enlightenment? It is precisely to have a Heavenly nature that is unmovable like a towering mountain. If you do not dump out your Yin qualities, your nature will invariably want to move. And even if you say that you don't get moved, this just means that you have not encountered the right situation. As soon as you encounter something, you will certainly be moved. For this reason transforming the quality of your Qi is not something that you just talk about on a rational level, you must have thoroughly washed away your Yin qualities. And when your Yin qualities are washed away, Yang Qi can come in, and it is only then that the quality of your Qi can truly be transformed.

III.4 DRASTICALLY TRANSFORM YOUR LIFE

In my thirty years of experience in lecturing about the Dao, I have encountered a great number of people who have drastically transformed their lives after studying the Dao, who have become a completely different person. In truth, people are all the same. Don't be afraid of illness. If only you are able to truly and drastically transform your life, how could you not recover from it?

In 2000, a young fellow came to our home. Rubbing his chest, he asked me: "There is an area right here where I feel sharp pain, as if from a thousand fires. Can you tell me what this is all about?" Rather than answering him directly, I asked him in return what this place was called. He answered that it was the esophagus. Correct, I said, that was the medical term, but what did the common people call this location? The chest, he replied. I said: "Yes, calling it the chest is correct. Calling it the thorax is correct as well. But there is one more name by which that area is known, and that is 'conscience'!" The young man objected: "But my conscience is not bad!" I replied: "Then why have you contracted this illness? Think about this carefully." He had to think for half a day before he told me: "Perhaps I have indeed committed a wrong. I was hanging out with a gang of my friends, with nothing to do, so we went out in the evening to have fun. On the outskirts of town, we caught two large geese, butchered them, cooked them up, and ate them with some vegetables while also drinking. Could I really have gotten my disease from this particular incident?" I confirmed: "Yes indeed. Raising these geese and feeding them until they were so big was surely not an easy task. But you and your friends stole them with no effort at all and simply ate them. Where is your conscience in this?" As a result of our conversation, he then repented publicly in front of everybody:

"I have stolen chickens and geese and my conscience was bad. From hereon out, I will no longer act like this." Not long after he finished saying this, this feeling of intense burning pain in his chest simply vanished.

People's habitual nature is certainly not easy to change. After the young fellow had mended his ways for a while, he once again fell in with his old friends. So eventually, they once again asked him to go out with them and have fun. Have fun doing what? Stealing geese again. He told them that he was no longer interested in stealing, so they asked him to watch their bicycles instead. So he helped them by watching their bicycles, and when they returned with another goose, he ate it with them, just like the last time. And as soon as he was done eating, his illness flared up again. So he came to see me again. I told him: "The illness has flared up because the person has flared up. If the person doesn't flare up, neither will the illness." He replied, "You don't say! I thought I could get away with this because I didn't steal again, but my friends came back with the stolen geese and invited me to eat with them, and sure enough, I ate with them." "I see," I said, "the person has indeed flared up again. Last time, when you recognized your fault, it wasn't all that easy to dump out your bucket of pigswill and scrub it clean. And yet, after you finished all that scrubbing, you once again poured pigswill into it. So this bucket of pigswill went right back to where it was last time." The young man exclaimed: "This time, I truly know that I have done wrong. I did wrong once, and I did wrong twice. But there will not be a third or fourth time. I will never ever do wrong again!" And from then on, he was completely reformed and never committed another wrong.

There was a lady with the last name Gao who lived in the town of Wangshi, in Haicheng City, Liaoning Province. In 2003, her four-year-old son developed liver cancer, which was first diagnosed at Haicheng Municipal Hospital and then confirmed at the large Shenyang Military Hospital. Eventually, the hospital would treat him no further and did not allow him to stay there any longer, so his mother called me up on the phone. At that time, I happened to be at our teacher Wang Shanren's home in Beijing. After I listened to her explaining her son's condition to me, I told her: "Liver cancer is truly devastating! I don't think I can save your son." She responded, "Liu Shanren! Can you at least give me a little bit of advice?" I said: "Because your son is still so young, if you can find the root of the illness and admit your fault directly face-to-face to the person, there may still be a sliver of hope." "Even with just a sliver of hope, I must try!" she responded. So I told her that her son's disease was an illness planted by anger and then asked her who she felt such great anger towards. Without the slightest hesitation, she responded that it was her father-in-law. I explained to her: "Regardless of whether your father-in-law was at fault or not, for you to get angry with him means that you wronged him. If you are able to step in front of your father-in-law, face him, bow your head, and admit your mistake, the child still has a chance of survival." At this point, she began to cry and then told us that she was able to do so and would go right now. She hung up the telephone and immediately went to see her father-in-law.

Her father-in-law had just gotten up and was preparing his breakfast when this Mrs. Gao entered the roomed, kneeled down in front of him, grabbed his leg, and started crying. Because he was used to having her always fight with him, when he saw her crying and holding his leg like this, he was quite startled. So he asked her gruffly, "You there, with the last name Gao, have you come yet again to fight with me?" She replied: "No! I have come to apologize to you. In the past, I have yelled at you and gotten angry at you, my elder relative. I have wronged you. It is all my fault for I have been unable to conduct myself as a proper daughter-in-law." This apology of hers was so sincere, such a genuine admission of her fault that she cried until she was half dead and kowtowed so hard that her forehead started bleeding. After she cried like this for three rounds, her son was able to get up from his bed.

Later on, when she heard that I had returned home, she brought her son to my home, prepared to stay with us for two months. What did she do the whole time while she was staying with us? She sought out every single person who she had gotten angry with in the past and apologized to each one of them with kowtows and utmost sincerity. After eight days of this, I told her that she was ready to go home and that her child had recovered. When she was still a little doubtful, I assured her: "Yes, he is cured. Your son is able to eat and drink, he is able to sleep, and he is even able to play. Nevertheless, his treatment is not completely finished yet and it all depends on how you act once you return home to your family. If you have genuinely changed, your son's cancer cells will disappear completely, otherwise they will recur. Everything depends on your behavior." So she returned to her home. Not long thereafter, she took her son to the hospital for an examination, which showed that the shadow on the right liver had disappeared completely but that there was still a slight shadow on the left.

Half a year later, I went to her home. Her mother-in-law greeted me, saying: "Our family has received a new daughter-in-law!" This statement confused me quite a bit. I wondered to myself whether Mrs. Gao had gotten a divorce. So I asked the mother-in-law to explain her statement. She responded: "This new daughter-in-law of ours is not at all like our old daughter-in-law. She is a completely different person. The way she acts and talks is completely transformed. She treats me more dearly than she treats even her own mother." When I heard this, I exclaimed happily: "This is what is called 'shedding the mortal body and exchanging the bones,' or in other words, completely rebirthing yourself and drastically transforming your life."

As Wang Shanren has taught us, to save somebody's life is to save them from temporary suffering, but to save somebody's Heavenly nature is to save them for eternity. After we have saved somebody's life, we still need to save their Heavenly nature, we still need to guide them to transform their personality, transform their inner quality, to truly drastically transform their life. If people are genuinely able to reach this stage, their illness will be cured just like that. If you are unable, on the other hand, to truly transform your outlook on life, if you haven't transformed your personality, and after your illness is cured you are still not a good person yet, your illness is bound to return sooner or later.

LECTURE FOUR

Illness and Human Relations

I. The Dao of *Xiao*

I.I REPAYING THE KINDNESS OF OUR PARENTS

The path of *xiao* is the root of humanity, and we must never forget this root. Just as we must not forget the person who dug the well when we drink water, from the moment we were born into this world, we must not forget our parents' kindness in nurturing and providing for us. Even if we practice *xiao* to the utmost degree, we can never completely repay this kindness. Because your body is literally a part of your parents' bodies, because your limbs and trunk are formed from your mother's Qi and blood. How do you repay your mother for her blood and Qi? As I have read in the "Sutra on Repaying Mothers" (*Bao Mu Jing*), during ten months of pregnancy and three years of breastfeeding, each of us has consumed 1,407 *jin* of our mothers' blood. So you see how truly wonderful our mothers are!

In our present age, however, some people look down on their mothers in contempt: "This old woman is dirty and lazy, with her runny nose and all." There are also many young people who think that because their parents are unable to earn a lot of money or run a big company they are incapable of anything and therefore dislike and avoid them for their poverty. Such people have not turned their gaze inward to ask themselves: "When I came into this world, with nothing but my stark naked body, did my parents dislike and avoid me for my poverty?" Let us deeply reflect on the fact that our parents have raised us and brought us up with such utmost care. Let us ponder over how we could ever begin to repay them.

1.2 PRACTICING *XIAO* TOWARDS THE BODIES, HEARTS, AND HEAVENLY NATURES OF OUR ELDERS

When we practice *xiao* in the care of our elders, we must attend to three aspects, namely their physical body, their heart, and their Heavenly nature. Nurture their physical bodies, act in alignment with their heart, and practice deference to their Heavenly nature.

Let us first discuss expressing *xiao* towards the physical bodies of our parents. Our parents have raised us from infancy to adulthood, and now that they have reached old age, we shoulder the responsibility of caring for them in their old age. This is the law of Heaven and order of nature. In addition, the elderly all receive social security and have retirement savings so they don't need your financial support or depend on you for their livelihood. From the economic perspective, they no longer depend on their children, which has already lessened the burden substantially for the children. Nevertheless, there are still many people who cause their parents unhappiness because they lack *xiao* in terms of the physical care of their parents. It is only because I have seen so many cases like this that I know that there are problems even in this aspect of *xiao*. Some children spend lots of money on their parents for food, for clothes, and for other things for them, or they even just give them money. But the parents have many children and remember and care for each of them with great concern. As the old saying goes, "When you stretch out all ten fingers of your hands, regardless of which finger gets bit, you feel the same amount of pain." Regardless of whether it is a son or a daughter, whenever one of their children is in trouble, parents will worry about them and give them the gifts that they themselves have received. This is fine as long as the son and daughter-in-law who gave the parents the gifts don't know, but as soon as they find out that their parents have given their gifts to another one of their children, they turn against them saying: "I am telling you, if you again take the things that we have given you and pass them on to others, we will not give you any more gifts from now on. And then we will see who you give things to!" This frightens the parents. This is controlling your parents, it is not acting in *xiao* towards them. If the parent then is about to put some food in their mouth and just when they are about to do so they see one of their grandchildren standing next to them, they of course want to give the food to them but are afraid of upsetting the person who bought the food for them. So they don't give the food to the grandchild but can't swallow it down themselves either, causing even more suffering all around. Let us consider this carefully: If you want to truly act in *xiao* as a son or daughter, you must simply deliver the gifts to your parents but then may not concern yourself with who they might give them to. Whoever they like to pass them on to, let them do it. If they don't want to eat your gifts, let them give them to others to eat. Just allow them to feel happiness in their heart and nothing else, this is truly the utmost fulfillment of the Dao of *xiao*.

Next, let us talk about expressing *xiao* towards our parents' hearts. *Xiao* means to show obedience, to act in alignment with their heart. The person who is obedient practices *xiao*. So we must be in alignment with their heart, allow them to rest assured, and make sure they are not worried or upset by us. As the "Classic of *Xiao*" (*Xiao Jing*) says, "Our bodies, our hair, and our skin, we have received all from our parents, so do not dare to injure them." If you injure them, it is the same as injuring your parents' heart. Because the body of the children is the heart of the parents. I have witnessed so many occasions when a child was suffering from illness and the parents were so deeply worried! Some mothers have even asked me whether I could transfer the illness over to their own body. So you see, we truly must feel pity for the hearts of all parents in the world, for all parents have hearts like this.

Some children, however, are not willing to serve their parents and feel like they have enough money and can hire caretakers to attend to their parents. But how could this be what the parents want? Parents want their children by their side, to chat with them about what is on their mind. There is a song titled "Often come home to see us!" The composer of this song is clearly somebody who has found the Dao. For children to come home all the time to see their parents, this is what parents desire. But if we in our role as sons and daughters don't understand our elders, don't understand their hearts, this is called having a heart that lacks *xiao*. Who among us is able to oblige our parents? Old age is lonely! Without their children right by their side, frequent phone calls certainly give our parents great happiness. I am presently in my seventies and I always feel like this. Whenever my son calls from far away, I am overjoyed.

The last point to discuss is how to practice *xiao* towards our elders' Heavenly nature. If our parents' nature is not good, if their personality is not good, do not blame them. If they are strict towards you, this is an opportunity for you to practice the Dao of *xiao*, this means that they are giving you the gift of the Dao of *xiao*! If you can carry out all sorts of meritorious actions and thereby change your elders, transform their bad nature, this means practicing *xiao* toward their Heavenly nature. In this way, you help your parents succeed, and you also allow yourself to succeed.

1.3 THE MANY DIFFERENT FORMS OF *XIAO*

The practice of *xiao* can be divided into many different kinds. There is great *xiao* and small *xiao*, there is genuine *xiao* and false *xiao*, and there is distant *xiao* and near *xiao*.

1.3.a Small Xiao and Great Xiao

The "Classic of *Xiao*" contains the following quotation: "*Xiao* is the root of virtue and the starting place for education." We can say that all educational change starts from *xiao*, and *xiao* is therefore not such a simple affair after all. For example, if we are not treating our elders badly but care for them attentively, and yet we don't take good care of our own health, can we consider that practicing *xiao*? As Confucius said, "Parents only worry about their children's health." Or as Wang Shanren said, "The children's body is the parents' heart." If children are not in good health, is this not the same as constantly injuring their parents by causing them to worry in their heart? If husband and wife don't live in harmony, can we consider that practicing *xiao*? Causing four elders to fret about both of you all day long. Conflict between siblings, can we consider that practicing *xiao*? Peace between siblings means *xiao* among them, but conflict between siblings will invariably make the elders upset as well. Moreover, *xiao* is not only limited to our parents, but we must also care about and pay attention to the people and things that our elders cherish. If we are able to practice everything that I have discussed above wholeheartedly, this is what is called *xiao* in the family. Even though this *xiao* in the family is the "small *xiao*," if we can fully execute it to perfection, it an extraordinary kind of *xiao*. Both Yang Yi and Wang Shanren received deep inspiration when they mourned their parents' passing. Can we follow their example and accomplish the same?

"Great *xiao*" refers to the practice of *xiao* towards all the elders in the world. If we are able to treat other people's parents as if they were our own parents, this is indeed "great *xiao*." In our modern age, there are a great number of people involved in the care of elderly who have nobody else to depend on, in retirement homes. There is a nursing home in Shenyang that houses more than 300 elderly people. In Anshan, there is a charitable institution that not only provides for many elderly people but in addition takes care of a number of mentally ill patients and unwanted children, giving them the opportunity to live a stable and happy life. Why do people make such sacrifices for others? This is an expression of their heart of mercy and compassion, which is precisely this "great *xiao*." I have paid visits to both of these homes and have been deeply touched by the power and radiance of the caregivers' virtue.

I.3.b Distant Xiao and Near Xiao

"Near *xiao*" refers to the one-time practice of *xiao*; "distant *xiao*" refers to *xiao* that lasts for eternity. To be remembered and honored throughout history because of a heart of *xiao* and because of actions of *xiao*, this is "distant *xiao*." The above-mentioned acts of *xiao* by sons like Ding Xiang and Yang Yi, these are examples of "distant *xiao*."

When I first began to lecture on the Dao, I used the same book that Wang Shanren had used when he first started lecturing on the Dao, called *Xuanjiang Shiyi* ("Omissions from Preaching"), which contains 24 stories about *xiao*. I told these stories to people who were deficient in *xiao*, to help them turn around their heart and nature and first transform themselves and then the other people in their families. During my lectures, I always observed their illnesses first and looked for their shortcomings, and then I told them an example for that particular step of the Dao that they were deficient in, changing the content of my lecture in response to each patient. As my patients compared their own situation to these examples from the ancient past, they gained an understanding of where their conduct was incorrect. Once their conscience was triggered, most of them cried their eyes out, gradually feeling remorse and transforming themselves. This is what is called "following the example of the ancients." This is the power of "distant *xiao*."

Moreover, I feel that there are a lot of people right now who lack a sense of basic moral principles and premarital education. If young men and women are able to understand the Dao of human life before getting married, they can certainly leave behind a good legacy for society, a legacy that can be transmitted from one generation to the next. This is another aspect of "distant *xiao*," this is the application of *xiao* towards our ancestors.

I.3.c Genuine Xiao and False Xiao

Genuine *xiao* expresses virtue (De 德, the manifestation of the Dao). What do we mean by "genuine *xiao*"? To fully express *xiao* with all your heart and all your intent, with no thoughts of anything else. To completely dedicate yourself to the Dao of *xiao*, to overcome your selfish desires and return to morality. Regardless of how much suffering you personally might experience, to practice *xiao* to its utmost. In times of abundance, if you give your parents something but this is nothing in comparison to what you give to your children, this does not count as genuine *xiao*. In times of poverty, on the other hand, if you nevertheless treat your parents truly well, giving them more than what you give your own children, this counts as genuine *xiao*.

It is a common sight around here that one old person is able to support eight to ten children but eight or ten children are unable to support even a single old person. Nowadays, if an older parent has two children, they take turns providing for the parent, but a parent with three children becomes homeless, because they all shirk the responsibility. The youngest may say, "This parent has not given birth to one child only, I still have older siblings." And the oldest might say, "I have so many younger siblings below me, so why should I carry a special responsibility?" In this way, they go around and around, setting up a system of taking turns in shifts and pushing the parent back and forth between their families every few days. What is a parent to do in such a case? He or she has no choice but to go along.

There once was a family with a situation like this, where they had a system of shifts for taking care of the old mother, which caused her to become greatly enraged. The fire of her anger flared up so strongly that she turned blind in both eyes, so nobody wanted her. After this old lady's daughter-in-law heard me lecture on the Dao, she knew how they had wronged her in the past. She mentioned to several of her sisters-in-law: "I now see how we must not continue caring for our old mother-in-law by taking turns like this." Her three sisters-in-law responded: "If we don't take turns, do you want her all the time?" So she replied: "If you in fact don't want to take care of her, I want to." The others said: "At present, while she can still earn a living, you want her. But if she later might become paralyzed, will you still want her?" To this she replied that she wanted to take care of her, even if she were to become paralyzed. The others therefore said: "Fine. We shall send our mother-in-law to live with you if she ever becomes paralyzed!" So this first daughter-in-law said: "Yes, please send her to my home. I can take care of her then." This woman lived in Baiquan County in Heilongjiang Province. She was completely illiterate, unable to recognize even a single big character. Why do you think we often say that the Dao settles in fools? In our day and age, clever people are often misled by their own cleverness, and quick-witted people often eat the fruit of their own quick wit. Such clever and quick-witted people may be able to give great speeches on the principle of the Dao, but they fail to act in accordance with those principles, and only know how to take advantage of others by unfair means. Even though this daughter-in-law here was illiterate and could not have given a fancy speech on the principles of the Dao, she still knew the meaning of *xiao* and was able to truly put it into action.

Strange things happen in this world! If you truly want to practice *xiao* to its fullest, you will be presented with the opportunity on your path of *xiao* to see whether what you are practicing is ultimately a case of genuine *xiao* or of false *xiao*. Three months after the conversation above, the old mother-in-law did in fact become paralyzed at the home of one of her daughters-in-law. This woman now called her sister-in-law, saying: "Didn't you say that if our mother-in-law were to become paralyzed we should send her to you? Now please come over to take her home with you." And indeed, this good woman went and brought the old lady home with her. After she took her in, nobody else provided any financial support for the old lady. The daughter-in-law thought to herself:

"Even without any outside help, I can take care of her. Isn't it only one old lady? How would I not be able to take care of her? I may not be able to earn a living for a year or two, but I will wait on my old mother-in-law and treat her well. I will make every effort to allow her to regain her health and be able to walk again." Just look, everybody, at how determined she was!

When the old lady first became paralyzed, she suffered from such anxiety that she became severely constipated and was unable to defecate. This good daughter-in-law helped her mother-in-law by extricating the feces with her own hand. I asked her whether the smell hadn't bothered her. She replied: " No, I didn't mind the smell at all. I couldn't smell it. If had smelled it, I might not have been able to help my mother-in-law."

If your practice of *xiao* is genuine in the heart, it is able to move mountains. Half a year later, she had attended to her mother-in-law so well that the old lady did in fact regain her health. And even though the wives of the other sons again mocked her and attacked her, she remained steadfast and ignored what they said. At long last, when they ran out of other things to say, they had a final showdown with her, saying: "From now on, you just take care of our mother-in-law! Since you were able to provide for her so well when she was paralyzed, now that she has recovered, you really don't need our financial support or assistance in taking care of her." The good daughter-in-law replied: "Whether you give support or not is an issue of *xiao* in your own heart, it is none of my business." In this way, she attended to her mother-in-law for another three years until the old lady passed away.

To practice *xiao* to its fullest, we cannot only rely on what our mouths speak but must follow up with action. Dao is expressed in actions, De (virtue) is something that you do. If you don't act on it, you don't have Dao; if you don't do things, you don't have De. I have met so many people like the devoted daughter-in-law in the story above. After these people grasped the principle of the Dao, they truly did practice what they preach and profoundly changed their lives. This is what it takes to practice genuine *xiao*, and it is only with genuine *xiao* that you can possess De (virtue).

False *xiao* is harmful. What do I mean by "false *xiao*"? It is empty vanity on the surface and falseness in the heart. It is calculating in the mind that if we do not treat our elders well, other people might laugh at us. This means to only fulfill the responsibilities of *xiao* to save face, not to practice *xiao* with a genuine heart. Even though false *xiao* may not be visible on the outside, your actions are feigned, and Heaven cannot be feigned. Heaven's law works in cycles.

In 1998, I encountered a lady like this. She lived in Yi'an County in Heilongjiang Province and was known near and far for her devotion to the Dao of *xiao* in her actions. In her entire village, there was not a single person who would have said that she was not *xiao*. Later, though, she fell ill and came to our clinic for emotional healing in Bei'an. As soon as she arrived, she began to cry, and continued crying for three whole days. When I asked her why she was crying like this and where her difficulty lay, she told me: "I have two children. The youngest is only eight years old. Whenever I wake up at night, I always feel like choking him to death. One time, I even put my hands around his neck, when I realized in shock that this is my own child! How could I do this! How could I choke him to death? So I pulled my hands back. This has happened a number of times, so now I don't dare to let my children sleep at home but I make them go to their grandmothers to sleep there. I am so afraid that I might not be able to control myself one of these times and truly choke my own child to death!" When I asked her why she would act like this, she said that she had no idea. I told her: "You must speak the truth. What are your thoughts that ordinarily pass through your mind, what are your ordinary actions? There must certainly be hypocrisy in your conduct." She answered: "Everybody always says that I am a daughter who acts with great *xiao*. But since I have come here to listen to you, I have realized that I am the very opposite of that." So I encouraged her to speak about this to everybody in public.

At this time, she did not care at all about saving face but stood up on the platform and began to speak in front of everybody: "All the people in my village, even the little children, say that I am a paragon of *xiao* and obedience, but in reality I do not have *xiao*. My attitude of *xiao* is all feigned. Why is it feigned? Let me tell you. My mother and my mother-in-law both live in my village. One time, I prepared a special meal and then pondered in my mind: 'If I don't let these two old ladies know that I have prepared a special meal, they will surely find fault with me, and my good reputation as a daughter with *xiao* will be ruined. So how can I let them know but without letting them eat all my food?' Glancing at the clock, I realized that it was almost noon. I cooked a quick lunch and went over to my mother's. Entering her home, I told her that she shouldn't cook lunch today. When she asked me why, I told her that I had cooked a special meal and invited her to come to my home to eat. My mother responded: "But it's just about noon now. The workers and students are about to come home for lunch now. The pigs are also coming back and I have to feed those as well." I told her: "Let's go! Come eat at my place and when you are finished, you can come back here and take care of all that." My mother replied: "How would that work? The workers are exhausted, and they must eat as soon as they come home. But I've got an idea, which almost counts as me having eaten your meal. The fact that you came over here to invite me, this attitude is enough. Even though I was unable to actually eat your food, I have gotten the same amount of joy.' When I heard her say this, I turned around and left. Oh how happy I was, you see, because even though I had invited her and made her very happy, she had not eaten with us. Afterwards I went to my mother-in-law's home and played the same trick with her, with the same effect. And then at last the four members of my family got to enjoy all that good food. While eating, I was secretly pleased with myself, thinking: 'If you two old ladies had joined us, wouldn't we have had much less to eat?'" So you see, everybody, this is what we call false *xiao*!

By acting in such a scheming manner towards her parents, her conscience had become corrupted. And this was the reason why she had this kind of a problem. After she finished sharing her story, she cried and cried, wailing loudly until she was more dead than alive, and yet she felt somehow that all her efforts were in vain. When she anxiously asked me for advice, I told her: "Go home and face your real life. Step in front of your mother and your mother-in-law and explain everything to them. Do not cover up your face with rouge or powder but take that mask off and let them see your true face and eyes. Reveal your human face." When this lady had returned home, she knelt down in front of her mother-in-law and told her: "Esteemed mother-in-law! The way in which I have shown respect to you in the past with an attitude of *xiao* was utterly false. The reason why you were happy even though you did not get to eat the food that I cooked was because I tricked you with my words." Then she went to face her own mother and said the same thing. After saying these things, after she had completely dropped her fake mask, she felt great relief in her heart. Later on, she publicly spoke of this situation in front of everybody many more times. Why did she do that? This is called "airing out one's personal affairs." In airing out your personal affairs, you must not be afraid of disgrace, just like you must not be afraid of pain when docking a tail. If you want to sever all your bad habits, you must not be afraid of pain. And from this time on, the lady never again suffered from the bad thought of choking her child to death.

So here you can all see how truly wonderful this way of thinking is. A genuine person is genuine to him- or herself, and a fake person is fake to him- or herself. This is the law of nature. The daughter-in-law in particular must scrupulously carry out the Dao of *xiao*. At home, she must act in *xiao* towards her father and mother, and after marriage she must serve her in-laws with *xiao*. With a true heart and true intention, drawing out the truth by being true.

Don't waste time in practicing *xiao*. If you serve your father and mother at home with *xiao*, why do you need to travel far to burn incense? In reality, we don't need to burn incense in the South and pray to the Buddha in the North. Each one of us has a living Buddha in our home, our father and mother are precisely this living Buddha. Are we able or not to serve these two esteemed living Buddhas well? If you spend all day bowing and praying in worship but don't revere your parents in *xiao*, what Buddha is it that you are worshipping? One act of kindness is superior to chanting Amitabha's name a thousand times. One bad deed makes burning ten thousand incense sticks useless, and praying to the Buddha will then bring misfortune instead.

How are we as sons and daughters to repay our parents for their kindness of having raised us? What is the best way to express to them our heart full of *xiao*? This is the most basic and the most important thing. It is not hard to act in *xiao* when our parents are still alive. But to complete *xiao* when our parents have passed away is much harder. So when our parents are still alive, we have to make good use of this time and hasten to practice *xiao* to its fullest. If you wait until your parents have passed away and then you think of acting in *xiao*, it is too late!

In the ancient past there was a man named Yang Pu. His father had died early, leaving him and his old mother behind to depend upon each other for survival. Because of his dedication to the Dao, Yang Pu was committed with heart and soul to studying the art of longevity and therefore prepared to leave his home and travel the world. When Yang Pu's mother heard about his plan to travel far away in search of techniques for prolonging life, she exclaimed brokenheartedly: "Oh my son! You are wrong in your thinking. As the ancient sages said, 'As long as your parents are still alive, do not travel far, and if it is necessary, have a clear direction.' How come you don't know this? If you absolutely must go far away, you must first get my permission, but at present I am not giving you my permission. I am alone, an old widow, and who is there for me to lean on if you leave?" Yang Pu, however, ignored his mother's words and left secretly, after hearing that there was a great Wuji master on Mount Emei who possessed a method to prevent aging and prolong life. After he left, his mother thought about him day and night and cried continuously until she just about ran out of tears.

After traveling for two months, Yang Pu at last reached the foot of Mount Emei where he met a Daoist master with hair white as a crane and a child-like complexion, holding a horsetail whisk[1] in his hand and with the air of an immortal. As soon as this Daoist master saw Yang Pu, he asked: "Aren't you Yang Pu?" When Yang Pu heard this, he thought to himself: "How strange! I have never met this Daoist master before, so how can he call me by my name? He must surely not be an ordinary person." So he immediately stepped forward, bowed respectfully in front of the master, and said: "Yes, I am Yang Pu. Who are you, esteemed Daoist master, waiting for?" The master answered, "I am waiting here specifically for people who have lost their way." Upon hearing this, Yang Pu thought to himself that he surely was somebody who had lost his way, so he immediately performed a kowtow in front of the master and asked him to transmit his method for longevity to him. The master replied: "To prolong life, surely there is a life-prolonging method. To avoid aging, surely there is an anti-aging pill. But why should you have to travel so far west to Sichuan? If you want to learn about longevity, go home and ask your Buddha there." Yang Pu objected: "There is no Buddha at my home. The Buddha lives in the

1   A Daoist emblem of immortals.

Western paradise!" The Daoist only said: "Far away in the Western paradise, close by in your home. Go home and see for yourself! Wearing clothes inside out and shoes pointing backwards, this person truly is an old living Buddha. Go on now!" When Yang Pu heard this, he was greatly perplexed but kneeled in front of the master to express his gratitude. By the time he got up, the master had already wandered off.

At this point, there was nothing else for Yang Pu to do but to go back home. He walked and walked until he at last reached his home in the middle of the night. Disregarding the fact that it was the middle of the night, he urgently stepped forth and knocked on the door. Mrs. Hu, his mother, had been up all night, unable to sleep because she had been thinking about her son, so when she all of a sudden heard her son calling and knocking at the door, she responded with great joy. In her rush to open the door, she ended up putting her clothes on inside out and her shoes pointing backwards. As soon as she opened the door and her son saw her like this, he realized all of a sudden that this person wearing clothes inside out and shoes pointing backwards was nobody other than his own mother! So he kneeled down in front of her and, weeping bitterly, told her: "As your son, I have failed to act in *xiao*. I have failed to listen to my mother's words and travelled far away, causing you to worry. From now on, I will most definitely stay by your side, my mother, and carry out the Dao of *xiao* to its fullest." And after this, Yang Pu cared for his mother from dawn to dusk, following her every wish with total and sincere obedience. When one year had passed, during which he had come full circle in perfecting the Dao of *xiao*, his mother peacefully passed away.

After his mother's passing, Yang Pu was free of obligations and once again left home to wander in search of the Dao. This time he did not pursue longevity but instead went looking for another old widow on her own, like his own mother, in order to support and wait on her. But three years passed and yet his search had not met with success. Should he go home or should he continue in his search? Right at this most difficult point of his journey, he encountered an old woman begging for food. At this time, Yang Pu had turned into nothing but skin and bones, plagued by worry and illness. Glancing at this beggar woman, he realized with surprise that she bore a great resemblance to his own mother. Arousing himself, he insisted that this beggar woman accept him as her son and allowed him to take her home to take care and wait on her. Left with no other choice, the old woman agreed, but under one condition: As she told Yang Pu, "If you insist that I accept you as my son, you must obey me in everything. Whatever I order you to do, you must do it." Without saying anything else, Yang Pu agreed.

After they returned home, this new mother acted truly strange. In February, when it was time to sow and everybody else was busy sowing, she would not allow Yang Pu to sow but made him wait until April. He obediently followed her orders. As a result, when there was a drought in the spring and a flood in the fall, everybody else's crops that had been sown in the spring dried up and died while the sprouts that he had planted prospered and grew. After a perfect rainy season followed, he enjoyed a bumper crop. Of this abundant harvest, he only kept enough grain to feed himself and his mother and gave all the rest away to the people whose harvests had failed.

For the next three years, Yang Pu's household continuously enjoyed harvests of double ears of grain and horses that gave birth to twin foals. This third year happened to be the year for paying tribute to the emperor in the capital, who asked Yang Pu why his horses were giving birth to twin foals and his grain producing twin ears. Yang Pu answered, "Because I have a heart of *xiao* towards the elderly." The emperor responded, "If you have such *xiao* in your role as son in your family, you are certain to be a loyal subject to my country. In my authority as the sovereign, I will therefore make you a county magistrate." But Yang Pu declined: "Your majesty! I am unable to serve you in that position. I still have an 80-year-old mother at home. I will not accept an official position until after my mother has left this world." When the emperor heard this response, he praised Yang Pu as a son who was showing true *xiao*. And ever since, Yang Pu's tale of adopting a mother to serve and support has become a much-told story of virtue.

II. The Dao of *Ti*

The relationship between siblings exemplifies the model of the Five Relationships of Confucianism, in that the older sibling must act in friendship, and the younger sibling must show respect. Siblings are born from the same mother and must not argue with each other over anything. You cannot cook beans by burning beanstalks, and the love between siblings is a fact of nature. It is only when they get along in perfect harmony that the Dao of the family can prosper. Siblings are like hands and feet, and the Dao of *ti*[2] creates Great Unity.

Wang Shanren's book "Record of Speeches and Actions" (*Yan Xing Lu*) recounts the story of how he gave away his family's fortune three times to support his brothers. His fourth brother spent his days gambling instead of working for a living but Wang Shanren never resented him. Seeing how his younger brother showed no willingness at all to mend his ways, he told him: "Fourth brother! I would not get angry even if you gambled away my very own wife." These words moved his brother's heart so deeply that he kneeled down before Wang Shanren, saying: "Older brother! Please rest assured. From today on, I will turn away from evil and return to what is right." And from then on, his brother was a changed person.

Nevertheless, the world is full of siblings who only think of money and who fight with each other over material possessions, even to the point of life and death. This causes their parents great anxiety and breaks their heart so that they cannot spend their remaining years in peace. This is the greatest offense against *xiao*! Why did Confucius emphasize that *xiao* and *ti* are the root of morality? Because *xiao* and *ti* are linked together inseparably. If you are unable to follow the Dao of *ti*, it is simply impossible to have the Dao of *xiao* come full circle. For the Dao of *ti*, the relationship between sisters-in-law is of the greatest importance. Or to put it differently, it is only when sisters-in-law get along harmoniously in accordance with the Dao that brothers can treat each other with *ti*. When sisters-in-law treasure each other and live in harmony, the Dao of friendship can prosper in the family. Together, they serve their parents in utmost *xiao* and help each other to raise their children. Even

---

2   *Ti* 悌: The virtue of being a true sibling, expressed in respect, care, reverence, and love for your sibling.

though they were born with different last names, after death they are buried in the same grave. For people with two different last names to come together in a single household, there would appear to be some distance, but I am telling you, there shouldn't be any. After death, they are all buried together in the same grave and before that, they give birth and raise children for the same ancestors. Why would there be a need to be stingy and count pennies?

"Harmony among relatives and amity in the neighborhood." To truly become a wife with the virtues of wisdom and *xiao*, you must have harmony in all of these areas of your life. By helping your husband and generating virtue, you are able to ascend to Heaven; by burdening your husband and generating vice, you are bound to descend to hell. In your role as wife, you must help your husband and support him in his role of being a proper son and brother to the fullest, you must fulfill the Dao of the wife and the Dao of the sister-in-law. When your husband's relatives come to visit, you must warmly greet and serve them enthusiastically, treating them even better than your own relatives. This is what is called helping your husband.

Nowadays, however, many women not only fail to help their husband but on the contrary burden him. How is it that they like to do this? By whispering irrelevant rumors and nagging in their husband's ears to incite him: "What is it your mother did? What is it your brother and his wife did? And what about your sisters?" As if not a single decent person existed in his entire family. And then they watch their husband get angry with his family members and fight with them. This kind of nagging is unbearable. How many men are able to ignore it? And as soon as they listen and believe, they get overpowered by the strength of these words. As men, we must be very careful, because this is like a typhoon. The arrival of a typhoon is something we all fear, it is something we all try to hide from.

In 1988 I encountered a female patient who had married into a family with six daughters-in-law, of whom she was the youngest. As soon as I started explaining about illness to her, she got up and began to spin in place. Nobody knew why she was acting like this. She explained: "I can't stop spinning. It feels like there is a machine blowing air on my back, blowing so hard that it is making my buttocks cold." I immediately got the picture and responded: "Now I

understand! Is it true or not that every night, as you lie in bed with your husband, you nag him and incite him, turning him against your five brothers-in-
law and their wives or complaining that your mother-in-law is being partial?"
She smiled and admitted: "You are correct, and I do in fact act like this.
Every night as I lie in bed, I complain to my husband, if not about my eldest
sister-in-law, then about my second sister-in-law. I complain about every one
of them. I tell him that I am the only proper wife in this family, the only one
who does not cause any trouble, and that I am his eyes and ears." What kind
of eyes and ears is this? This is rather like a poisonous arrow or a poisonous
snake! She is turning her husband into a son who lacks *xiao*, into somebody
who is deficient in the Dao of *xiao* towards his mother and deficient in the
Dao of *ti* towards his siblings. In my eyes, the entire family has failed in two
aspects of the Dao, namely *xiao* and *ti*, and whose fault is this? The fault lies
with this wife. So I turned to ask her, "do you know now or don't you?" She
responded by saying: "Since you still haven't explained anything, how could
I know?" I replied: "So you are still blaming somebody else, in this case me. I
should have explained everything to you earlier, and if I had explained things
to you earlier, maybe you wouldn't have committed these transgressions. You
are still blaming me for acting wrong. Nevertheless, from today on you can
no longer commit any transgressions. And if you commit another mistake,
you won't be able to blame me."

For this reason, women must be extremely careful. While chitchatting, you
must not talk about other people's mistakes. Under no circumstances, spread
rumors to complain about other people to your husband and family members.
If you really must spread rumors, make sure that you are not blowing cold air
on your buttocks but transform it into warm air, hot air, and talk about all
the positive qualities of your family members instead. If you do blow warm
air like this, everybody will be happy, but as soon as you blow cold air, everybody will be harmed.

III. The Dao of Compassion

III.1 TEACHING BY GUIDANCE AND NOT BY FORCE

What is this so-called "Dao of Compassion"? To guide our children to study the Dao, to teach our children by guidance. Our children succeed because we have taught them, and fail because we have not taught them. After children are born, they are like small trees, in need of a good gardener and of proper pruning when their branches grow out, in order to turn into usable timber.

Those of us who are older must be able to provide guidance, to teach by guidance and not by force. The way in which prisoners are treated in jail, this is what I mean by "teaching by force." Today's children can no longer be taught by force. In the past, when you forced children, they were unable to run away. But if you force them today, they may do just that. Wang Shanren understood this truth and therefore told us: "To try to force people is just like grabbing a stick and then calling a dog. The more you call it, the farther it will run, because it is afraid of you beating it."

In that case, how should we educate our children? We must teach them by guidance. Teaching by guidance and teaching by force is not the same. Teaching by guidance means that you yourself set an example first. The parents are the child's first teachers, and their every-day words and behavior, all their actions in their ordinary life, are branded deeply into the child's brain. Parents are like the vehicles that went before, and after these vehicles have passed, there are tracks left behind. Children hence have very clear impressions in their mind. You don't have to deliberately go out of your way to teach them, they will naturally on their own follow in the tracks that their parents have left behind. This is exactly what Wang Shanren meant when he said: "If parents' characters are good, the children will be good as well. If parents' characters are bad, the children will also be bad."

Those of us who are parents had better reflect very carefully: How are we doing in our role as our children's first teachers? Are we able to fulfill this responsibility or not? What kind of an impression are we leaving on our children? Have we taught our children well by guiding them or not? I once heard Dr. Liu tell a story about a father and his son: One day during working hours, this father unexpectedly had to return home to pick something up. When he opened the front door, he noticed that his twelve-year-old son had not gone to school but was home watching a pornographic movie. We don't need to go into details about the extent of the father's rage. As he raised his hand and was about to beat his son, the son only said one sentence: "How come you are the only one who can watch these and I can't?" It is therefore essential that we as parents ponder deeply what direction we want to guide our children in. To lead our children in the proper direction for the rest of their lives, to raise them with direction and purpose, to teach them to be honest and wise, this is what all parents should be doing. In your role as parent, do not concern yourself with whether your child acts in *xiao* or not, but instead carry out the Dao of Compassion to the fullest of your ability. In your role as son or daughter, do not concern yourself with whether your elders act with compassion or not, but instead carry out the Dao of *xiao* to the fullest of your ability. This is what is called each person being proper in their particular position, each person returning to their particular position. Only when we each carry out our own Dao can we avoid collision and create peace instead. This is the meaning of the following quotation from the *Zhongyong*:[3] "Heaven and earth are positioned in this, the ten thousand things are raised in this."

III.2 INCREASING OUR EFFORTS TO FOSTER VIRTUE IN CHILDREN

The Dao of Compassion has many different aspects. We must not leave behind debts for our children to repay, but neither must we save up riches for them. This is the Dao of Compassion. In our role as parents, we must raise our children to be independent and cannot dote on them too excessively and drown them with our love. Generally speaking, once we have raised them to adulthood, given them an education, and enabled them to partake in society, establish a family, and have a job, our responsibility is finished.

At present, however, a great many parents do not know when they have fulfilled the Dao of Compassion. Many of them drown their children in love and

---

3   The *Zhngyong* 中庸 ("Doctrine of the Mean") is one of the four sacred texts of Confucianism.

are only able to spoil them with material things or money, rather than using their spirit to teach them by guidance or, even less so, using their own good qualities to guide their children (in the majority of cases because they don't have any). Ultimately, they end up causing their children to cultivate all sorts of vile habits, too fond of delicacies but lazy in their actions, wasting their life with debauchery and drinking, doing whatever they please and committing countless sins. This situation is one in which the more deeply they love their children, the more deeply they harm them, to the point of pushing their children straight towards hell with all their might, but still thinking in their own minds that they are carrying out the Dao of Compassion to its fullest extent.

If you give your children a lot of money, is this really the Dao of Compassion? This is not necessarily compassion but most likely harmful to them. Because material wealth is the root of disaster, and without virtue, if you use it unwisely, you actually stir up a fire that will burn you.

As parents we must ponder very carefully how we can act in such a way as to truly benefit our children. We can use money to gather merit and do good deeds, to rescue people in difficulty and offer support in critical situations, to cherish the elderly and provide for the poor, to build bridges and repair roads, to overcome the self and guard the Dao, to build schools, to make our elders comfortable and take care of our young. When parents use their money to do these kinds of good deeds, this is what we call fostering virtue. When we provide a foundation for our children, this virtue blesses our children and grandchildren. This explains the following sentence: "Children don't need to be forced; everything depends completely on responding to their parents' virtuous actions."

If you are of noble character, the Gods and ghosts will admire you, let alone your children. Nobleman Wang has said, "If the parents change, the children will surely change. What example the parents have set, the children will follow." When your virtue is great, even the spirits admire you, and your children even more so. As Wang Shanren once said, "When the parents change, the children change as well. In whatever way the parents change, the children change in the same way."

In our age, many, many parents hope that their children turn out well, hope that their children change for the better, and use all sorts of methods to obtain this goal. Some use force, some use arguing, some yell at and some even hit their children. To use these kinds of methods in the hope that your children will turn out well is a mistake on the part of the parents. Where are the parents at fault? Their mistake lies in only using money and material things to raise and support their children, instead of using virtuous behavior to raise and support them. To wait until the child has cultivated bad habits and then use a bad attitude to force them, this is most certainly not compassion!

When we send children to school, the teachers' sentiments are identical to those of parents. So as parents we must teach our children to respect their teachers. What is it that teachers do? Teachers educate children in special skills. What parents foster is virtue, and what teachers educate in is special skills. It is only when these two aspects are combined that children can be well-rounded with both virtue and special skills. If children only receive moral cultivation but do not enjoy good teachers to educate them, they cannot develop special skills. On the other hand, when there is no virtue, the root of virtue cannot grow, and regardless of how much effort the teachers waste on trying to teach, they are not guaranteed success either. Many parents have great expectations for their children's future success in life and go to great lengths, like the farmer who pulled the sprouts up to help them grow more quickly and thereby killed his crop. The pressure they exert on their children is too severe, the demands are too heavy, they discipline them too strictly. In realty, though, as parents having such expectations and applying such pressure is useless. You only need to understand what I have outlined above and foster sufficient virtue in your children, and that is enough. If parents have virtue to begin with, and teachers have special skills on top of that, children will immediately be able to receive those skills. For this reason, if you want to raise your children as future pillars of society, parents must certainly begin by fostering virtue in them. This is the prerequisite, this is the key!

Furthermore, there are some older people who do not understand their children's hearts and are overly critical, to the point of blaming and hating them. Such people are extremely likely to contract heart disease. One time, when I was in the middle of giving a lecture on illness, a doctor with the last name

Yan stood up and asked me: "Good Man, I suffer from heart pain. I am a doctor myself and I have taken a lot of medications to manage this heart pain, but nothing has had any effect." I asked him how many children he had in his family. He told me he had three, and I then asked which one of them he disliked the most. He told me, the youngest one. I asked him to explain why, and he responded: "The first and second of my children have both passed the entrance examination for university, but the third one is not good at studying." I asked him, "And that is why you hate him?" He said: "Yes. I hate the fact that he is not good at studying. I hate the fact that in his case the iron will not turn into steel." So I told him: "You are wrong in your thinking. If a mother gives birth to nine children, of course they are all different from each other. Are they all going to be able to attend university? In my eyes, having two children who are going to college is not bad at all. You should be satisfied with that! In addition, you are also too selfish. The university has a limited number of places for enrollment. Try hard to develop your heart of compassion and leave one of these places for admission for somebody else." When he heard me talk like this, he cheered up and said: "What you are saying truly does make sense. How could every one of them attend college? On top of that, there are the children of other families. From today on, I will no longer resent my son." And strangely, about twenty minutes later, his heart pain had disappeared.

In subsequent years, we frequently met up in Bei'an. When I once asked him whether his heart was still giving him trouble, he answered: "It has stopped hurting. From the moment you finished explaining illness to me, I have not experienced any more heart pain. I have let my son go his own way. I no longer worry about him." I replied: "This is good. As the ancients said, 'Children have their own fate and you cannot turn them into horses or cows.'[4] Let it go, let it all go! Let it go from your heart! Why do you always worry about them? Are we old people ever going to be happy if we always worry about others? Clinging to your worries and being emotionally entangled is wrong. It is harmful."

At this point, I would like to point out one more thing: As parents, we must learn how to plant good seeds for our children.[5] What are these good seeds?

4   Or in other words, you cannot change them into something that they are not.

5   These "seeds" are a reference to the Buddhist notion of Karmic retribution (Yin guo因果), the concept that any intentional action is bound to produce a harvest of fruit, whether

Every thought and sentiment is such a seed. You absolutely must never say things like, "my son is such a failure" or "my daughter is totally worthless." If you really want to plant such a seed, they will really turn into failures. In your heart, you must cherish a single thought: "My child is not bad at all. He or she will certainly be able to succeed." And as a result, he or she will do just that. As Wang Shanren said in the Yan Xing Lu (Record of Words and Actions), "I never went to college, and I will definitely let my son go to college. And after I have let him finish his education, he will benefit the country and benefit all the people." And indeed, Wang Guohua (Wang Shanren's son) eventually became a teacher. This is an example of the good seeds that Wang Shanren planted for his children.

III.3 DO NOT FEED YOUR CHILDREN POISON

For those of us who are parents, especially for mothers, it is essential that we never ever feed them poison when they just begin to understand things. What do I mean by "poison"? Hatred, blame, irritation, anger, and annoyance are precisely what I mean. How do we feed these to our children? By talking bad about the grandfather or grandmother in front of the child, putting down the father, or the uncle or the aunt...

Some mothers do talk to their children about their father's shortcomings. And because the children are old enough to understand, they immediately accept this. If you tell them that their dad is no good, they hate their dad. If you tell them that their grandma is no good, they hate grandma. And as soon as children feel blame and hatred, you have poured poison into them, muddling their brain and impairing their physical and mental health, with great negative effects on their studies. We all hope that our children are good students but if you don't give them sufficient psychological support, how can they study well?

What do I mean by psychological support? In front of our children, we should concentrate on discussing our relatives' good qualities. And the most important aspect of this is that the father and mother must never ever speak about the shortcomings of the other parent in front of the child. Even if a couple has

---

in this lifetime or later on.

disagreements, they must never allow the children to see this, much less fight in front of them. In front of the children, we must only say positive things about dad or mom, about all the other relatives, regardless of who the other person is, we much always speak of their good qualities. In this way, we instill an attitude of respect and of compassion in our children toward their father and mother and towards all their elder relatives. This is the best psychological support we can possibly give to children.

I once encountered a child of this kind, a girl just old enough to understand things. Her mother had frequently told her bad things about grandma because she didn't get along with her mother-in-law. Even after the grandmother had passed away, the child still continued hating her grandma. Eventually, this girl became mentally deranged and was therefore brought to our home. Because she was my third sister's daughter, I did not feel comfortable telling her the truth outright. But my fourth sister couldn't contain herself and asked directly: "This child is really deranged! You won't sit still, can't stand calmly, as if something is gnawing at your heart. Where does your hatred come from? How is it that you are so hateful?" The child answered: "My mom used to tell me time and again how my grandma is wrong in this regard or in that regard, so I simply hate my grandma. And at those times, I always thought how I wanted to reign in my grandma when I grow up." After she spoke several sentences like this, the girl started bleeding from her nose and her mouth, fresh red blood. We treated her like this three times, and her condition was cured. Luckily this was my niece. If it had been an ordinary person, bleeding like that from the nose and mouth would have frightened everybody greatly. So you see how big her hatred was! And who was it who had planted this hatred in her? The mother planted it. Those of us who are mothers should take this as a stern warning!

IV. The Dao of the Girl

IV.I GIRLS ARE THE ORIGIN OF HUMANITY

Wang Shanren once said: "Every person is a single Heaven and earth. If you have made one person good, you have made one Heaven and earth good." You see, each person is really that important, truly more precious than Heaven and earth, and we ourselves don't even know it. What are Heaven and earth? Heaven and earth are Yin and Yang. What are Yin and Yang? Yīn and Yang are one man and one woman. One man and one woman together form a family, and from the family they form one society.

Water has its source, trees have their roots, and the roots and source of humankind are nothing but our girls. It is only when we have good girls that we can have good wives, and only when we have good wives that we can have good mothers, and only when we have good mothers that we can have good children, that we can have a beautiful future for humanity. So you see, this is how important girls are!

Girls must be pure. The birthplace of humankind is just like the source of any river. If the water springing forth from the source is clear, the water will always be clear. If the water springing forth from the source is turbid, the water will always be turbid. If the birthplace is not good, the root of humanity tends toward badness. If girls are not good, they turn into wives that are not good, into mothers that are not good, and they raise children who are not good. Regarding today's girls, what I have to say may be a bit excessive, but they are not pure, they are not white, but they are muddied, and therefore the root of humanity has become bad. Wang Shanren wants us to educate starting from the root, and for this reason we must first make girls understand the Dao of the Girl.

IV.2 A DISPOSITION LIKE COTTON

Girls must have a disposition like cotton. Cotton has five good qualities:

1. Cotton blossoms are pure white like jade, and girls must likewise be pure white. Pure white in the heart, pure white in character, and even more importantly pure white in the body. Their feet must not touch devious ground, their ears must not hear devious sounds, their eyes must not see devious things, and their heart must not harbor devious thoughts.

2. The thread that is spun from cotton is so long that it has no end, and girls likewise must have a long and constant disposition, instead of being loose and fickle.

3. Cotton is warm, making you feel nice and cozy when you wear it, and girls likewise must be warm and cozy in their disposition.

4. Cotton is particularly soft, feeling like fluffy cake when you pat it, and girls likewise must be soft and gentle.

5. Cotton treats everybody the same, neither despising the poor nor adoring the rich, regardless of what kind of a person wears it, rich or poor, young or old, whoever wears it on their body always feels warm and cozy. Only when a girl achieves all these five points do we consider her a girl with a good disposition.

Girls must have their will and intention as their root and elevating their family as their role and responsibility in life. If they can constantly praise the positive qualities of everybody in the family, they will be the shining star among all the family members. When a young woman after marriage returns to her parents' home, her position will be half guest and half host. A lot of young women, however, after marriage continue to return to their former family to manage affairs there. Considering themselves as so highly capable, they even run the homes of other families. In reality, though, this is wrong. If you meddle too much, your elder brother and his wife, your younger brother and his wife, all will have objections to you and you are not even aware of it. The members of your old family are the hosts, and you, having married out of this family, are merely a guest when you return there. A guest who loses her temper and starts foaming with rage, interfering in family affairs, leaves the host with no way out.

Promoting the good qualities of your family members is to gather inspiration, also called gathering Yang sunlight. Today's households only have one child, who is doted on by the parents, pampered and spoiled, and therefore develops a lot of bad habits. So many girls and young women are only able to look at other people's faults. This is called collecting garbage, or collecting Yin. If your belly is stuffed full of Yin Qi, how can children born from this be good? Why is it that some young women, after they get married, give birth to children who suffer from serious physiological problems? Because their congenital preconditions are not good, because the mother did not develop a good character when she was still living in her parents' home. After leaving her old home to get married, at the beginning of her new life, she was unable to work for a living but only able to enjoy herself, turning the Dao of family relationships upside down. For this reason, Heaven has given her a "counterfeit bank note," has given her a "counterfeit child," to play a trick on her, to sound the alarm for her, to undermine her. And when enough is done, enough is undermined, the child will close his or her eyes and pass away.

Young women must still "work more and spend less." Do not be greedy! Today's young women turn Wang Shanren's teachings upside down, working less and spending more. The more money they spend, the happier they are, always filling their gluttonous mouths. This is the exact opposite of the Dao of the Girl.

Another aspect of being a proper girl involves knowing how to have self-respect and self-worth. Nowadays, many girls walk around scantily dressed, wearing skirts that are way too short. A few years ago, when I went to a big city, I had to close my eyes. How can these girls be so ignorant and without reason? Why do I say this? When we are out in broad daylight, we must have a pure and proper heart and set a proper example for the world, instead of leaving behind a stain. When girls wear insufficient clothing and bear their arms and legs, or even worse, their lower back and navel, young men will get lewd thoughts, if they are not careful. Be aware that of the ten thousand evils lewdness is the worst! And who should take responsibility for this vice? Isn't it you yourself who have lowered your own worth like this?

V. The Dao of the Daughter-In-Law

V.1 A DISPOSITION LIKE WATER

Let us discuss once more the Dao of the daughter-in-law. If girls should have a disposition like cotton, what should daughters-in-law be like? They should have a disposition like water. If there is no water in the world, nothing can survive. Everything depends on water for its growth. Water runs towards the lowest place, serves as the bottom and accommodates itself below. The disposition of the daughter-in-law should be just like this, not struggling for success, but making herself lower and lower, shorter and shorter. This is the basic position and role of the daughter-in-law. She must not be like sewage water, enclosed and rotten, but like an endlessly flowing spring, flowing far and wide.

The daughter-in-law's disposition must be just like water, blending the five colors and harmonizing the five flavors, changing its shape in accordance with its surroundings. Becoming salty when you add salt, becoming sweet when you add sugar, turning red when you add red coloring, and turning yellow, when you add yellow coloring. This is what I mean by "blending the five colors and harmonizing the five flavors." When poured into a square bucket, it becomes square; poured into a round bucket, it becomes round. This is what I mean by "changing its shape in accordance with its surroundings."

The daughter-in-law's water-like disposition means that she must work hard and not pout in anger, accepting it as her role in life to hold up the family. What do I mean by holding up the family? After a young woman gets married and enters her new family as daughter-in-law, she must take on the responsibility of shouldering the household chores of this family, serving and respecting her in-laws with reverence, assisting her husband, raising and educating her children, and taking care of all the household chores, without sparing any effort. This is what I mean by holding up the family. In our modern times, so many young daughters-in-law pout angrily at the smallest amount of work, even to the point of pouting when they haven't done any work. Regardless of what you give her, of how you treat her, she is never satisfied. Some even turn the Dao of family relationships upside down so that the old mother-in-law becomes the young daughter-in-law and the young daughter-in-law becomes the old mother-in-law. Isn't it true that many modern households are run like this now? The old mother labors from dawn to dusk to take care of the household, while the young daughter-in-law sleeps in until late before she gets out of bed. She may even be served her breakfast in bed! Isn't this exactly the opposite of what it should be? Are you really loving such a daughter-in-law, or are you harming her? You have caused her to violate her Dao of being a daughter-in-law, and you have caused her to violate her Dao of being *xiao*.

V.2 RECEIVING A DAUGHTER-IN-LAW IN MARRIAGE MEANS WELCOMING GOOD SPIRITS

Wang Shanren has taught us that a daughter-in-law in marriage means welcoming good spirits. If a young woman understands the principle of being a proper young woman, to welcome her into your home brings great happiness, joy, and laughter. Courteously taking care of all the household chores, with a smile of satisfaction in her face, she is indeed a "spirit of joy." Because the daughter-in-law is full of happiness, all the other members of the family are happy. Some girls do not want any dowries from their old family, and do not want any betrothal gifts from their in-laws' family either. As husband and wife, man and woman manage their marriage with thrift and respect, without one side being indebted to the other side. The wedding ceremony is not done with ostentation and extravagance, allowing the two families of the bride and groom to avoid becoming entangled in arguments over finances. And after she has entered her new family, she is not contentious or greedy but of one heart and one mind with her new family. This is what is called "spirit of riches." After her arrival in her new home, she is able to carry out all the housework, taking it as her role to hold up the family, so that the entire family can enjoy her good fortune. This is a "spirit of good fortune." If a daughter-in-law is able to truly achieve this degree of perfection, we can say that she has brought out nobility. The entire family respects and values her, and therefore she is a "spirit of nobility." So you see, a spirit of joy, a spirit of riches, a spirit of good fortune, and a spirit of nobility: Receiving a daughter-in-law in marriage truly means welcoming four good spirits.

Nevertheless, some daughters-in-law are not like this, but as soon as they enter the door they get angry and start pouting, never being satisfied, always arguing and causing upheaval until the family is all stirred up in a total mess. What kind of spirits are these? The spirit of bad luck has arrived, the spirit of pouting, and who would not fear for their soul! Quickly distance yourself from her, the old mother-in-law, her sisters-in-law, none of them dare to get too close to her. Thus you can see how a single daughter-in-law's goodness or badness can directly affect the goodness or badness of a household. Why else would the ancients have said: "A good daughter-in-law can make three generations prosper; a bad daughter-in-law can make three generations fail." This saying is absolutely correct.

V.3 RESPECTING THE PARENTS-IN-LAW WITH *XIAO*

Even though a woman may be quite plain, in the environment of her family she can serve with *xiao* as an obedient daughter-in-law. The influence of this single word, *xiao*, can be very deep, it can cause great benefits for all the people around her. Nevertheless, nowadays many women don't know how to be a good daughter-in-law, don't understand *xiao* and obedience, or only practice *xiao* towards their own parents but not towards their parents-in-law and have conflict with their mother-in-law in particular.

I have encountered a number of women like this. They stand around talking about all the areas where their mothers-in-law are at fault and even give each other suggestions on how to manage and control them. Oh dear! Today you are a daughter-in-law, and tomorrow you will be a mother-in-law. Today you don't respect your mother-in-law, and tomorrow your daughter-in-law won't respect you. Don't you see this? To treat your parents-in-law with *xiao* is just as important as it is to treat your own parents with *xiao*. This is the path to cultivating happiness for yourself and to cultivate virtue for your children and grandchildren.

From the ancient past until today, there have been people who have gained great fame even though they never carried out heroic achievements. How did they do that? Because they practiced *xiao* with such sincerity and commitment. We all know the story of Ding Xiang serving her mother-in-law with *xiao*. Among all women, Ding Xiang stands out as a truly obedient daughter-in-law. She was able to cut off her own flesh to nourish her mother-in-law. Who among us is able to emulate that?

In her husband's family, Ding Xiang was the last one among the three daughters-in-law and suffered a lot of abuse. Nevertheless, all she wanted was her mother-in-law's happiness so she endured hard labor and blame. When her husband saw how she got beaten and yelled at again and again, he asked her whether she wasn't hateful towards her mother-in-law for all the beatings. Ding Xiang replied, "No, I don't hate her. I only want the old lady to be happy, even if it means getting beaten." Ding Xiang was thus able to carry out the true Dao in the midst of abuse, without hatred and resentment in her heart. This is difficult indeed!

Later on, her mother-in-law fell ill and suffered from constant heart pain, which no doctors were able to cure. The old lady herself believed that she would not be able to recover and therefore said: "This time, I know clearly that I am going to die. My last wish before I die, the only thing I can think of at this moment, is to eat one more mouthful of meat and to drink one more mouthful of soup." In these times long ago, living standards are not what they are now and people were starving. Where would they find meat for her? When Ding Xiang found out about her mother-in-law's wish, she cut off a piece of flesh from her own arm and made a meat broth from it for her mother-in-law.

This extreme level of sincerity was so powerful that when the mother-in-law ate the meat and drank the soup, she felt great joy in her heart and the pain went away. As the old lady looked around, she saw her oldest daughter-in-law serving her the meat, and her second daughter-in-law serving her the soup, but what was the third daughter-in-law doing? She went to Ding Xiang's room to have a look at her and found her lying in bed. The old lady flew into a rage: "Look at that! The eldest daughter-in-law is serving meat, the second daughter-in-law is serving soup, and the third daughter-in-law is just lying in bed pretending to be ill. She should be beaten!" And she was just about to beat her, when Ding Xiang asked her: "Old mother-in-law! Whose flesh have you eaten? Whose soup have you drunk?" The old lady responded that she had eaten the eldest daughter-in-law's flesh and drunk the second daughter-in-law's soup. Ding Xiang then asked her to take a close look to see whose arm had been injured. When the old lady looked carefully and realized that Ding Xiang's arm was still dripping blood, she was so moved that she fainted. Later on, as she woke up, she told Ding Xiang under tears: "It is hard to imagine how I could have treated you like this and yet you have maintained such a heart of *xiao* towards me!" And ever since, this story of Ding Xiang's filial treatment of her mother-in-law has become a famous and much-praised tale. This is the meaning of "distant *xiao*."

This is a tale from the ancient past and there is no need for you to practice *xiao* in this manner in our modern times, with much higher living standards. You only must be one heart and one soul with your elders, and we elders are satisfied and happy. Don't say anything else, just give your mother-in-law a few kind words, and she will be so overjoyed that she won't know left from right. These days, it is not very difficult to make our elders happy because their needs and demands are not that high. Are we able to accomplish this aspect of the Dao or not?

V.4 LOVING YOUR HUSBAND

Wives! Wives! You must appreciate your husband! If you do not appreciate your husband, then who else is there to appreciate? Whether your husband is rich or poor, high or low, the kind of person who you married is the person who you must be comfortable with. Your husband is your support, who you rely on and lean on. If you always complain about and blame him, always say that he is not as good as somebody else's husband, this is wrong.

To be a good wife, you must appreciate your husband and you must respect your husband. Especially in front of other people, you must never cause him to lose face. I have seen many wives who don't care whether there are other people around or not, when the husband says something slightly inaccurate or does something slightly wrong, they immediately criticize him viciously, to the point of yelling at him, with no understanding or consideration towards him. They think of themselves as highly capable and control their husband, even advising other women to never let their husbands dominate them but to control them so that their husbands fear them.

These wives are not thinking carefully. There are so many people in the world, in China alone around 1.3 billion. Among all these people, why did they choose their current husband? Didn't they marry him only because he seemed right to them? But after they are married, they look at him differently and view themselves as a beautiful flower planted in cow dung. Aren't they just making fools of themselves? Ultimately, they are simply discontent, and people who are discontent have no joy.

I once treated a young wife who was suffering from depression. When I asked her how she had contracted the disease, she replied that she didn't know. I told her that she had contracted depression because she hated somebody and then asked her whether she knew who it was that she hated. "Yes," she replied, "that I do know. I hate a former male classmate of mine. I took a liking to him but when I pursued him with words, he rejected me. Later on, he became a judge. No matter how many letters I wrote him, he never answered. How can I not hate him? For this reason, I have gradually developed this depression." When I commented that her present husband was a good person, she agreed that yes, he was a good person, but told me that she didn't like him. I asked her why she didn't like him since he was an excellent young man. She replied: "I feel like I am a beautiful flower planted in cow dung." I told her that she had to drastically change her way of thinking and encouraged her to think very carefully whether her current husband was treating her well. She had to agree, that her current husband treated her well indeed, never losing his temper regardless of what she said, but then said that she imply couldn't respect him. So I told her: "You must turn your thinking around and look for his strong points. This time, think of yourself of a beautiful flower planted in a great palace hall. As soon as you become content, you will be happy, and your depression will be cured." Upon hearing me say this, she turned around to take a good look at her husband and then said to me: "You are right. He really is an excellent person." Looking at him again, she then told him: "You truly are good-looking. How come I haven't noticed this before?" Then she went up to him, embraced him, and said crying: "I am so very sorry for how I have treated you! For all these years, I have wronged you greatly." After crying for a good while, her heart and chest felt much freer and open and from this point on, her depression was cured.

Another time, I met a female patient in a hospital. All the electric lights in her room had been turned off and the only light came from a small candle. She said to me: "I am dying. The hospital has given up on me. Soon I shall have no more voice left to speak. The light inside me cannot be relit." I asked her whether she trusted me, to which she replied: "What would you be able to do if I believed in you?" I replied, "If you want to live, I can save you. If you don't want to live, I cannot save you." She said: "Who doesn't want to live? But I cannot go on living."

This patient had been yelling for a whole day and night because she was in such unbearable pain. I asked her why she had been yelling like this, and she replied: "I am in pain! Starting from the pit of my heart, going about a hand's width to the left and back, it feels like a hot iron is pressing down on me. Why else would I be yelling like this?" I told her: "Please trust me! Give me an honest answer to a single question. If you are able to answer this one question, I will be able to save you." She told me to go ahead and ask, so I asked her: "What is going on between you and your husband?" This single question caused her to start crying, quietly at first but then gradually louder and louder, until she cried so hard that her husband couldn't bear it any longer and had to leave the room to stand outside the door. At last, she called out to her husband: "Husband, please come back. Come back in the room!" And her husband indeed came right back and told her: "Don't cry. Take care of yourself so that you can recover." But she said: "Oh no! My husband! I must apologize to you!" Her husband replied: "What is there to apologize for! Just take care of yourself so that you can recover!" She said: "I truly must apologize to you. I remember when we were engaged and you went off to serve as soldier in the army. I thought in my mind that I was just a poor farmer but that you would be able to find well-paying work when you got back from the army. After you came back, though, nothing like that happened. You became a soldier transferred to civilian work and I was unable to break off our engagement, so I was forced to marry you. And ever since we got married, I have been quarreling with you." When her husband told her to stop talking, she again repeated herself: "I am so sorry, my husband, so sorry…."

I had gone to see her at 8 pm in the evening and she cried until 10 pm, for a full two hours. I finally told her to stop crying and then asked her how long it had been since she had been able to sleep. She replied: "Seven days. The pain has been so bad as to drive me insane, preventing me from catching any sleep at all." I told her: "Alright. Let us see if you are able to sleep tonight. If you are able to sleep, I can give you an 80 percent guarantee that you will recover." Then I left without saying anything else.

And indeed, she slept from ten that night until seven o'clock the next day. The next morning, she opened her eyes, saw that the sun had risen, got herself dressed, and without even combing her hair got out of bed with the help of a cane, to go see me. So afraid was she that I had already left. When everybody saw her, they all said this time they believed she might survive after all and quickly led her up into the room. As soon as she got up on the *kang*, she ate two pieces of cake. After this, she recovered gradually and lived on for another twenty-one years.

Why is it that Wang Shanren has said that explaining the Dao of human life has the power of raising people from the dead? From my perspective of encountering patients and explaining disease to them for thirty years, the Dao of human life does in fact have this effect of raising people from the dead. Nevertheless, after you have recovered from your illness, you must still transform yourself in your daily life, change yourself down to the very essence of your being, and make yourself into a new person. If you cannot become a good person, you will go right back to the way you were in the past, and your illness will be able to attack again.

V.5 PROPER SOCIAL RELATIONS MUST NOT BE TURNED UPSIDE DOWN

What do I mean by proper social relations? Proper social relations means that there is order between children and adults, that children respect adults, and that adults obey their elders with *xiao*. This is the root of Chinese culture and of all education. When we stress the importance of *xiao* and of proper social relations, we stress precisely this root. Why do we say that "*xiao* comes first among the hundred virtues"? Because *xiao* is tied to this root. Regardless of the situation, as long as this root has not rotted away, it can be rescued. But if the root has rotted away, you will not be able to rescue it. During my many years of lecturing about illness, I have encountered lots of children who have had problems from the moment they were born. What is the reason for that? In the vast majority of cases, it came from this root, from the fact that social relations had been turned upside down, that *xiao* had been turned on its head.

I remember one particular case when I was in Bei'an. Three members of a family, the mother-in-law and the daughter-in-law and her husband, brought a child to me asking: "This child is two years old. Why is it that he does not have a gallbladder?" After taking one look at the child, I told them that it was because their family relationships were turned upside down. When they asked me what I meant, I told them: "The mother-in-law is acting as the daughter-in-law, and the daughter-in-law is acting as the mother-in-law." The old lady disagreed: "That is not the case. My daughter-in-law calls me mother, after all." I told her that her daughter-in-law might call her "mother" but that the old lady was the one waiting on the younger woman, instead of the other way around. Listening to our conversation, the son had been standing by, but now commented: "Liu Shanren, you are correct! From our wedding day until today, my wife has never prepared a single meal for my mother. It is always my mother who is cooking for her." I said to the wife: "There you have it. What do you say now? Isn't this indeed a case of family relations being turned upside down? And then, when you were pregnant, you were even less helpful, you had even more of an attitude, saying that you were pregnant and had to nurture the fetus. So how come you haven't nurtured this fetus well?"

Hearing me talk like this, the daughter-in-law began to cry. She rushed up to kneel down in front of her mother-in-law and said to her: "Mother, I have been so wrong. I will work hard when I get home. I will cook for you. Please don't try to do things for me any longer." I then told the mother-in-law: "Old people also have a Dao of Elders to follow. Do not strive to do things for your children. Don't tell them, 'Ah, you are so young. You have been working for so many long days. Let me take care of things for you. I am still in good health.' What are you doing this for? This is causing your children to commit wrongs. You have reached old age, and now is the time when you should give your children the opportunity to serve you. This is allowing them to cultivate happiness. This is also allowing them to cultivate happiness for their descendants."

I met another daughter-in-law like that, who pouted as soon as she entered the room and never did any work at all. As a result, even though she gave birth to three children, every one of them died. The first one died right after birth but the woman never realized her wrongdoing. Even though she lived right across from her mother-in-law's room in the same house, she never entered her mother-in-law's room. When the mother-in-law was cooking, she would only hold the kindling to tend the fire, without doing anything else. And when dinner was ready, she'd fill two bowls with food, and she and her husband would take them up to their room to eat. Then she'd bring the empty bowls back, put them down, and not care about anything else.

When the second child was born, he suffered from abdominal swelling right after birth. Thirty-seven days after the birth, the woman brought the child to me, and I asked her to open the baby's diaper to let me have a look. I saw that the baby's stomach was swollen as if it were covered by an upturned bowl, and it made a hollow sound when tapped. So I told her: "This baby is suffering from a swollen stomach. It is a congenital condition, and he won't be able to recover." Hearing me say this, she took the baby back home with her, and he did in fact die a few days later.

Even though at this point she had lost two children already, the woman still did not realize the reason. Her next child was born suffering again from the same condition, a swollen stomach. She waited until fifty-seven days later before she brought that child to me. As soon as I saw the baby, I asked her: "Why have you yet again given birth to such a baby?" She told me that she didn't know the answer either. So I said: "It is because you wont' change your personality. As long as you don't change, none of your children will be able to reach adulthood." Under tears, she replied: "Please make him recover! Please make him recover! I just want him to recover, I will do anything you ask of me." This is the perfect time, I thought, to give her a little advice. So I told her: "Take your baby home with you. In the past, you never did any work and always just let your old mother-in-law serve you, and furthermore, you didn't allow her to hold your baby. This time, when you get home, take the baby to your mother-in-law's room and let her play with him while you take care of all the household chores: Feed the pigs, procure feed for the livestock, cook, take out the ashes, and whatever else there is to do. If you do as I tell you, this child may still have a chance to recover." When the mother doubted that this was possible, I said: "If you don't believe me, just go home and give it a try. Your mother-in-law is more than sixty years old. Even in the deepest cold of winter, don't you feel sorry for her? I fear that all reason has been flipped inside out, all affairs been turned upside down! View the other person's heart through your own and place your own mother side-by-side with your mother-in-law, and you will know what to do." She then agreed to go home and do exactly as I told her.

After this woman returned home to her family, she indeed brought the baby to her mother-in-law's room. The mother-in-law was delighted and said: "You have given birth to several children already but have never allowed me to hold them. What happened that you are now bringing this child to my room?" The daughter-in-law told her: "Liu Shanren has told me to let you play with the baby while I go and take care of the household. When the baby needs food, I will nurse him, and then I will continue on with the chores." In this way, she worked for three days, and sure enough, the swelling in the baby's belly did in fact disappear.

Wang Shanren once said: "Life! Life! Only when you work for a living are you able to live!" If you do not work for your living, isn't this the same as dying? These days, many people who work for a living don't actually "live" for a living but rather "die" for a living, creating a roadblock for their own future. According to the ancient saying, "The gentleman prepares a road for walking in the future." If you don't give all your heart and strength in your work, who will want to use you in the future? Isn't this just like placing a roadblock on your road to the future? For this reason, the meaning of this phrase, "work for a living," is deep indeed and is worth pondering in great detail. The woman mentioned in the story above was exactly like this. Because she had not truly worked for a living, she had placed a roadblock on the path to her children's future. As soon as she started to work, after only three days, the swelling in her baby's belly simply disappeared. She herself found it really strange, and her mother-in-law felt likewise: "How could the child's illness of the swollen belly simply have disappeared?"

Nevertheless, "it is easier to move rivers and mountains than to transform a person's nature (xing)." As soon as the child's swelling had disappeared, the mother once again returned to her lazy habits. Because she was unwilling to work, she left the mother-in-law alone with the chores at home while she brought the baby to her own parents. After she stayed with her old parents for three days, the baby again started suffering from abdominal swelling. Rather than going back to her husband's family, she brought the child directly to me. This was in the year 1990. I asked her: "Why are you bringing the child back to me yet again? After you went home, didn't he recover?" She told me that yes, he had indeed recovered, but only for three days and then had fallen ill again. I explained: "The child recovered for three days because you worked for a living for three days." She asked: "Could it really be this powerful?" I replied: "You see for yourself whether it is effective or not. You worked for three days and the child's swelling disappeared for three days. Now the child's belly is distended like a small bowl and sounds like a drum when you tap on it. This is nothing but your drummed up Qi, because you are not willing to work for a living, you don't know how to be content. You view yourself as a beautiful flower that is planted in cow manure." She agreed: "You are right. I did not agree to marry my husband. I did not fancy this husband of mine." I told her: "If you did not fancy your husband, then you should not have married him. By being forced into this marriage, much grief has been brought on the next generation." So she asked me what she could do about the situation now and promised to conduct herself much, much better when she returned home this time. I told her to go home and see how the baby responded.

From this point on, she never again avoided work but truly labored with sincere effort. The baby recovered but failed to grow tall. The reason for this is that the mother had collected too much dirt inside of her during her pregnancy, thereby causing a congenital defect in the fetus. And when the child was six years old, the old illness returned and the swelling in his belly returned. Once again, she brought the child to see me. After looking him over, I told her: "The swelling in his belly has erupted once again. While you and your husband have most certainly changed your ways, this time your child is passing." She asked me if there was nothing we could do. I replied: "Even if he doesn't die, look at how short he is. No matter how you nurture him, he has difficulty growing. Seeing how severe his congenital defect is, how can you cure this after birth? He is like a counterfeit coin, and he is going to die. If you get pregnant again, you might give birth to a healthy child." After that, she left, taking the child with her. And indeed, not long thereafter the child died.

This time around, the situation truly frightened the mother. She had given birth to three children already but none of them had survived, so she did not dare to get pregnant again. After two years had passed, she once again came to see me, telling me that she had to have a child. I responded: "This really is making me laugh! Here you come, asking me about having another child. I am not a magical grandfather who can send down children. You and your husband must take this matter into your own hands. If you feel that you have transformed your character, you will bear another child. If you haven't transformed your character, you will bear a child just like the others. Just ask yourself whether your personality has changed or not!" She replied that she felt like she had transformed herself, so I told her that in that case she could have a child. Later she gave birth to a daughter who is now already going to school and is growing up to be a bright and intelligent girl.

V.6 BEARING A HEALTHY CHILD

When we set out to evaluate the worth of a daughter-in-law or wife, the crucial point to consider is what kind of mother she will be. Her aptitude as a mother is extremely important! If you want to give birth to a good child, you must concentrate your efforts on this role of the mother. Otherwise the children she will give birth to will not be good, and you will leave behind a root for future disaster, passed down from one generation to the next, which is a terrible thing! Why do I say this? Because the hearts of the mother and the child are connected. From the beginning of pregnancy, the fetus grows by consuming the Qi and blood of the mother, and all the mother's joy or anger, cold or heat, activity or rest influence the child. The mother plants the seed, and the child bears the fruit. If the child has an illness, the most important thing for the mother is to look inside herself and examine herself to find which kind of Qi she has generated with whom. She must find the root of the illness, face reality, confess her own mistakes, and look for all the good points in everybody else. If she can be earnest and sincere, miracles can happen with the health of the child.

The most obvious example for this situation is a daughter of my wife's younger sister. When the girl was three years old, the right ventricle of her brain expanded and her walking was therefore unstable. She'd make two steps and inevitably fall over. I told the mother: "The illness of this girl is caused by your conflict with your mother and your mother-in-law. You are not willing to submit to those two." When my wife's sister heard my words, she did not evade the issue but responded: "I never agreed to this marriage. It was my mother who forced me to marry into my present husband's family. I had no choice, I could not disobey my mother, so I acted in accordance with her orders. And since I have moved in with my husband's family, I have had constant hidden conflict with my mother-in-law. I don't say anything out loud, but in my heart, there is no peace."

As she was explaining this situation to me, she started crying, overcome by her grievances. She had three crying fits like this, in the course of which she gradually experienced a change of heart and realized her own wrongdoing, her own lack of *xiao* toward her elders. When the mother had finished crying and transformed her consciousness, the child was able to walk with stability again and stopped falling over. What does this explain? It explains how strong the influence of the mother is when children are still young (under the age of twelve). All you have to do is to transform the mother's disposition and their Heavenly nature will return on its own. The power of the Heavenly nature is so great that if you only restore it to its original place, it is able to change the universe and to reverse the previous unfavorable influences on the child. My wife's younger sister realized where her own fault lay, made a firm commitment and vowed to correct her errors, acknowledged her wrongdoing in front of her mother and her mother-in-law, mended her ways with utmost sincerity, perfected her practice of the Dao of *xiao*, and as a result her child directly recovered.

Let me recount another example: There was a young lady who was studying traditional Chinese opera. When she got engaged to her boyfriend, the young man's parents objected because they did not want a member of their family to be involved in popular entertainment. The girl had successfully passed the entrance exam for the opera school but because of this marriage, she did not pursue her opera career. And she secretly made up her mind: "You don't agree with our engagement? But I am determined to get engaged with your son, so let's just see how I can settle up with you after we get married." And because the feelings between her and her boyfriend were so strong, he at last persisted and married her. After the wedding, this girl thought of all sorts of ways in which she could make her mother-in-law's life miserable. She had a bad relationship with her mother-in-law, as well as with her older and younger sisters-in-law. And over time, they turned into real enemies.

Later on, this woman gave birth to a baby boy who right from birth suffered from liver disease as well as from spasms so bad that half of his face twitched continuously and the spasms sometimes affected the entire body. This situation went on without change until the boy was about fourteen years old. And the mother herself also suffered from liver problems and then contracted a lung condition, both of which became quite serious.

In 1995, this woman brought her child to see me at our Clinic for Emotional Healing in Bei'an. After listening to one of my lectures, she began to sing opera, and said, singing and crying at the same time: "I am so sorry for having wronged my mother-in-law. I have turned my mother-in-law into my enemy. Previously, I always believed that it was my mother-in-law who was disrespecting me, but now I understand that it is in fact I who am disrespecting my mother-in-law." And at this moment when the mother admitted her fault, the child's eyes, ears, and whole half of the face immediately stopped twitching. Seeing these effects on her child, the mother cried even more intensely and said under tears: "As soon as I get home, I will admit my mistakes in front of my mother-in-law. I vow to change our relationship until we connect with each other heart to heart.

After spending another seven days at our clinic, she returned home and, without speaking a single word, kneeled down in front of her mother-in-law. Seeing her daughter-in-law like this, the mother-in-law was quite surprised. What was her daughter-in-law doing, coming home and kneeling in front of her like this? Finally the younger woman spoke: "Mother! I am so sorry for how I have wronged you! I have failed to act as a proper daughter-in-law. I have continuously held grudges against you and have accused you of being wrong, but in fact everything has been my fault." The more she spoke, the more remorse she felt, and the more she cried, the deeper her anguish became. Hearing her cry like this, the old lady hugged her daughter-in-law and also began to cry. The two women cried together for a good long while and thereby resolved many years of difficulties so that the family finally became peaceful and harmonious.

This lady's name is Hu Shuxia. After this change of heart, she wrote lyrics to go with the tune of "Iron Window," which she titled "The Tears of Regret." This song is written so masterfully that when the lyrics are combined with the music it expresses the deep sadness of true regret so strongly that it is impossible to sing this song without crying yourself.

VI. The Dao of Husband and Wife

VI.I HARMONY BETWEEN HUSBAND AND WIFE

Where do we find the Dao? The Dao is right here, by your side, so there is no need to search for it far away. You can explore it in the following two words: *dong* 動 "movement" and *jing* 靜 "stillness." The man is movement and the woman is stillness. Movement is *Qiqn* 乾, Heaven, and stillness is *kun* 坤, earth. The difference between *Qian* and *kun* is the difference between Heaven and earth, the difference between Yin and Yang. Man is *Qian*, the sun, while woman is *kun*, the moon. When we combine the Chinese characters for "sun" (*ri* 日) and moon (*yue* 月), they form the character for *ming* 明, meaning "brightness." In other words, it is only when there is harmony between husband and wife that there can be brightness. And isn't this harmony between husband and wife exactly what Confucius was talking about when he said: "One Yin and one Yang, this is what we call the Dao."?

The Dao of husband and wife is the foundation of all family relationships. Like the wheels on a cart, it keeps rolling on and on without stopping. As the popular saying goes, "A thousand years of cultivation are needed to enjoy sleeping together on the same pillow." Everybody, look at how deep this bond truly is! Why do we say that the bond between husband and wife is so extraordinary? Because when the limitless (*wuji*) transformed to give birth to the great universe (*taiji*), Yin and Yang were born; and with Yin and Yang, *qian* and *kun* were born; with *qian* and *kun*, male and female were born; and with male and female, husband and wife were born. How could we not treasure such a bond of fate? This bond is of the greatest significance indeed.

The man is *qian* and as such must lead his wife without controlling her. The woman is *kun* and as such must assist her husband without troubling him. In leading his wife, the man carries out the Dao; In assisting her husband, the woman manifests the Dao in her virtue (De). If they can really achieve this state, this means that Yin and Yang are in balance. The first sentence of the "Great Learning"[6] states: "The Dao of the Great Learning lies in making bright virtue bright, in treating the people like relatives, and in stopping only at utmost goodness." My level of education is not that high and my understanding of this sentence is limited, but still, I know a little bit about this topic. The Dao of Great Learning lies in making bright virtue bright – how do we make this bright virtue bright? It must be by attaining harmony between man and woman. Because man is the sun and woman is the moon, it is only when these two are placed together that you have brightness (*ming* 明). And it is only when we truly possess this brightness that we are able to make bright virtue shine all throughout the universe. Or in other words, husband and wife must live in utter peace and harmony, working together like Yin and Yang. And harmony between Yin and Yang means harmony between Heaven and earth. "In the harmony of Yin and Yang, you can refine pills of gold." What are these pills of gold that you can refine? This is nothing but a future generation of descendants who will contribute to the benefit of the world. For this reason, we say that the husband-wife relationship is the beginning of all family relations and the root of all creative change. Before we do anything else, we must carry out this Dao of husband and wife.

VI.2 MAN'S HARDNESS AND WOMAN'S SOFTNESS

The man rules with hardness and rectitude; the woman is valued for her softness and gentleness. If the man is not hard, the household will fall into complete chaos. What is this hardness? It is right knowledge and right perspective, it means having the right standpoint. Men must be hard, but this hardness must not be a violent hardness, but it must be the hardness of an upright disposition. He must have rectitude in all aspects of life, not only in the heart, but also in the body, in his words, his bearing, and his actions. Only this can be called the genuine hardness of a man. These days, many men misunderstand the

---

6   *Da Xue* 大學: One of the most important Confucian texts in classical China.

meaning of this "hardness," they think that a man should have a hot temper, should shout and yell in fights. How wrong! A man who hits and yells at his wife displays physical hardness turned upside down. And as soon as this physical hardness is turned upside down, the entire household collapses and sinks into a hellish sea of suffering. Men must have sincerity. If they cannot act in sincerity they will leave behind a legacy of suffering for future generations. As humans, we must absolutely act in sincerity, we must absolutely not act in falsehood, speak false words, commit false acts. We must speak with sincerity, act with sincerity, be truly sincere in everything we do.

If a woman lacks softness, there will be sorrow in the household. If a woman is too hard, with her mind all over the place and her fire burning too hot, a cat one day and a dog the next, wind now and rain tomorrow, lacking perseverance and a steady disposition, the household will be in utter disorder. According to an old saying, if a woman is too hard, if she doesn't overcome her husband, she overcomes herself, and if she doesn't overcome herself, she overcomes her children and grandchildren. In the end, either her husband will leave or her children will scatter. The softness of women should not be a softness that makes you weak and incapable but one that makes your disposition gentle and warm. The man being hard and the woman being soft, hardness and softness being perfectly matched, this is the only way that husband and wife can find harmony and give birth to children marked by *xiao* and virtuous grandchildren.

Men must not control women. The fact that a woman is a man's wife does not give him the right to control her. Controlling a woman like this is abusing the woman. At the same time, women must not control men either. The fact that a woman is married to a man does not mean that he is controlled by her or that his relationship with his parents is severed. This kind of control is called bullying the man. Why is it that one man is often able to command a powerful army with thousands of soldiers and horses and yet is not able to command his own wife and children? Because such a man is able to exert control but does not know how to lead. For this reason, the wife and children will not listen to him. Men must be able to lead their wives and learn the Dao, and women must be able to assist their husbands and manifest the Dao in their virtue (De). This is the only way to achieve harmony and joy in the family and to leave behind a good root for future generations to grow on.

VI.3 THE FOUR GREAT REALMS OF HUSBAND AND WIFE

There are lots of people right now who are studying Buddhism or Daoism. So many people wholeheartedly want to cultivate themselves, constantly telling themselves that they can no longer remain in this mortal world but want to transcend it and enter paradise. It is unfortunate that none of them know what this so-called paradise is. Where is this paradise? It is as far as Heaven but as near as our home. Our home is nothing but this paradise. If you look at this paradise and regard it as the realm of suffering and hell, do you still want to go to paradise? You can't go there!

Cultivate yourself! Cultivate yourself! And to cultivate ourselves, we have to practice diligently in our every-day life. Where is this Dao? The Dao is right here inside of us. Don't always look for it outside. Outside of us, there is no Dao. The more you seek, the farther it will be. Doing that is nothing but abandoning the roots to search for the tip. Everybody hopes to go to paradise in Heaven and to enter the realm of the Buddhas. But what people don't understand is that this paradise and realm of the Buddhas is right here, right in front of our eyes.

People who are able to live their daily life and get along with people by embracing whatever happens to them, regardless of whether it is good or bad, not saying anything, not focusing on other people's shortcomings or picking fights with them, such people have entered the land of the Buddhas. A husband and wife who no longer speak of worldly things are a couple who lives in the land of the Buddhas, a couple in the realm of enlightenment (*zhijie* 志界). And a couple who lives in the land of the Buddhas gives birth to Buddha children and grandchildren.

Couples who live in the realm of consciousness (*yijie* 意界) know contentment and constant joy. They feel deep gratitude towards each other and treat each other with courtesy and respect. The man loves and protects the woman, and the woman reveres the man. This is what is called mutual respect. Isn't this paradise indeed? Where else would you go to look for paradise? Two people who live in constant happiness, this is paradise right before your eyes. And couples who live in paradise give birth to children with *xiao* and to virtuous grandchildren.

Couples who live in the realm of the selfish heart (*xinjie* 心界) constantly lock horns and fight for personal gain, scheming against each other. As Wang Shanren said, "Husband and wife must not reason with each other when they talk; if they reason with each other, they will drive each other crazy. Husband and wife must use their feelings when talking with each other. If they talk by feelings, they will love each other dearly." Nowadays, so many couples argue and fight, until they strangle each other with all this reasoning. Husband and wife are like teeth and tongue, who will always have to stay together. Why would they always butt heads? Contradicting each other over every little thing, their bellies are swollen from all the bad Qi, and yet they continue to quarrel. Isn't this going to drive them to their death? The ancients argued over transgressions, and modern people argue over logic. They scheme painstakingly, employ tricks and strategies, and connive with intrigues. You tell me whether this is suffering or not. Quarreling and bickering all day long, as if they are living under a dark cloud, isn't this a Sea of Suffering? And couples who live in this Sea of Suffering give birth to disobedient children, children who don't listen, who fight with their parents and handle things contrary to their elders' wishes.

Couples who live in the realm of the body (*shenjie* 身界) only know about pleasure, about eating and drinking with self-indulgence, wasting their life away in debauchery and hedonism, with no care for anybody else. In the family, they constantly yell and argue, beat up and fight with each other, with not a single day going by in peace and quiet. Isn't this hell on earth indeed? And then they only wait until they die to go to hell in the other world. They already are living in hell while they are alive! Even though they may eat well and dress well, if their hearts have already sunk deep into hell on earth, what meaning is there to their lives? Couples who live in hell on earth give birth to children who demand payment of a debt, who have no other purpose in life than to ruin their families.

These are the lives of couples in the four great realms: The land of the Buddhas in the realm of enlightenment, paradise in the realm of consciousness, the Sea of Suffering in the realm of the selfish heart, and hell on earth in the realm of the body. The land of the Buddhas, paradise, the Sea of Suffering, and hell on earth, where do we find these places? Right here, in human society! They manifest right here in our homes. From this perspective, we must take a very close look at ourselves, to see where we personally reside. Do we reside in the realm of enlightenment, or in the realm of consciousness? Is it the realm of the selfish heart, or is it the realm of the body? In our modern way of life, the number of people living in the realms of the selfish heart and of the body is fairly large, while there are fairly few people who live in the realms of enlightenment or of consciousness. And corresponding to this, what kind of a family do we live in? Is it a family in the land of the Buddhas, or a family in paradise? Is it a family in the Sea of Suffering, or a family in hell on earth? Based on our own judgment, we can see what kind of a family we are living in.

If you can understand the meaning of the teaching above, you can instantly transform your family, you can instantly transform a hell on earth into a paradise, a Sea of Suffering into the Pure Land. Why is that? Because when a single person changes, the entire family will change as well. How do you achieve this change? All you have to do is to stop blaming (*bu yuan ren*). This practice of not blaming others is truly extraordinary, it is the root of the Great Dao of reaching enlightenment and becoming a Buddha! In all things, do not turn outward to blame others but instead think carefully whether you yourself have acted correctly or not. The wife blames the husband, the husband blames the wife; the mother-in-law blames the daughter-in-law, and the daughter-in-law blames the mother-in-law. In this sort of family, all you see is long faces and worried looks, with no way out for anybody. Isn't this going to turn into a Sea of Suffering? But if we turn this kind of a situation around, admit our own faults and mistakes to each other, focus more on finding our own shortcomings and on looking for the strong points in the others, criticize and change ourselves more, and cultivate ourselves, we can turn this family around into a family in paradise. Isn't this exactly the same as turning hell on earth into paradise, transforming the Sea of Suffering into the Pure Land? For this reason, it is all up to us alone to decide how we want to spend our days and what kind of a family we want to create.

VI.4 DO NOT DOMINATE EACH OTHER

Who is the reason that we fall ill? We fall ill because of our relatives and loved ones. Who is the reason that we might die? We might die because of our relatives and loved ones. For this reason, Wang Shanren taught us: "You want to keep those who are close to you at a distance, and you want to keep those who are distant to you, close to you." How can you keep those who are close to you at a distance? You don't want to be overly concerned about them. Being overly concerned is a terrible thing, and it is a sin. In regards to the people and affairs in our household, we must accept them as they are and then let them be, do our best but not wear ourselves out. Once we have done our best, don't worry about them any longer. If we continue worrying about them, we will be overly concerned and we will be overly controlling. The more you control a person, the more they resent you, the more they oppose you.

Between husband and wife, you must not dominate each other. You must learn to let things go. If the husband is fine, the wife will also be fine, and even if one of them is a thousand miles from home, they will both be at ease. If you are unable to do so, if you keep worrying about this or having doubts about that, this is the same as ordering the other side through your thoughts to do wrong.

Nowadays, so many women are unable to trust their husband, fearing that their own husband will be stolen away by some other woman. So they always doubt him: "Oh! What is my husband up to now? How come he hasn't been very loving towards me recently? Could it be possible that he has feelings for somebody else?" Other women constantly tell their husband: "When you are talking to others, you are full of glowing smiles, and yet when you talk to me, you always pull a long face. Why are you doing that?" In this way, they have just produced a stream of resentment in their heart. In reality, should we really talk to other people in the same way as when we talk to our own wife? When talking to others, we must respond with a smile in our face, but between husband and wife, we must be matter-of-fact. We must not pick arguments with each other and reason, or we will reason each other to death. Husband and wife must focus on their feelings when they talk to each other, focusing on feelings will make you love each other tenderly.

In addition, it won't do if I only ask something of the women here but not of the men. When women lower themselves, the men have to lower themselves as well. Your wife has given birth to and raised your children, has stoked the fire and cooked your meals, made your bed and folded your blankets. For you to not love and protect her but instead to think that all of this is just what she is supposed to be doing, this is wrong. There must be mutual understanding, mutual caring between husband and wife, you respect me, and I cherish you. This is the only way to have harmony in the household. Wang Shanren always said: "Men, you have to set your wives free and must not control them! Women, you must not control your husbands either!" And when a man and a woman are apart, no matter how long they are separated, you must not feel any doubt in your heart. If you can be without doubt, your partner will do no wrong. But if you begin to feel doubt, you have created a problem. If you have stirred up a thought inside of you, I guarantee that you have also stirred up a thought inside of them. You have planted a bad seed in them, the fruit of which they will then have to harvest. And the relationship between husband and wife will no longer be harmonious.

I once had a patient who was suffering from uremia. Because she lived not very far from us, only about a hundred miles, her husband brought her to see me by car. After I had taken a look at her and found out about the state of her illness, I asked her what her husband did for a living. She told me that he was a military leader. Just from looking at him, I had the feeling that her husband was a very capable person. I said: "Your husband is a general in the army. You are the wife of a general. What a pity that you are unable to trust him." This one sentence caused her husband to burst out laughing and to agree with me wholeheartedly. So I told this lady: "This is how you have contracted your illness. You make demands on your husband by the clock. As soon as his time is up, you wonder why he hasn't come home yet. Even if he is only two minutes late, you get anxious, and if he hasn't come home after five minutes, you rush to the telephone to ask him where he has gone, who he has gone with, and when he is coming home. I guarantee you that it is like this." Her husband agreed: "Yes, this is indeed exactly how it happens." Everybody, look at this story. The deeper our love is, the deeper our resentment is as well. In the end, this woman produced uremia in herself because of her resentment.

VI.5 TREAT EACH OTHER WITH WARMTH

How should husband and wife act towards each other in order to practice the Dao of husband and wife well? There must be respect between husband and wife as there is towards a guest of honor. When a man and a women who haven't known each other before come together as a couple, as if one were from the south pole and the other from the north pole, should they not respect each other like guests, treat each other with courtesy and politeness? With great formality, you respect me, and I respect you. This is what we call respecting and loving each other.

In so many modern couples, however, the man doesn't know how to act as husband and the woman how to act as wife, with the result that they argue all day long. While other couples respect each other in the way you respect a guest, this kind of couple respect each other like ice. When they are together, they are not happy, they are not warm towards each other and don't look at each other's strong points, but only know how to pick faults. And the more negative they are, the more their relationship turns into ice, until it is so cold that it becomes unbearable and one of them goes away to look for a different, warmer place.

In 2005, I met a lady from Jilin who was suffering from generalized flaccidity in her muscles. At that point, she was unable to even get out of bed or to open her eyes without pulling the eyelids up with her hand. As soon as she let go, the eyelid dropped back down. She had no strength at all in her limbs and couldn't even chew watermelon or rice gruel. To stay alive, she had to rely on drinking cow's milk. Her mother was an acquaintance of mine and therefore drove me to her daughter's house. When I took a look at this woman, I found her disease to be quite strange, it was my first time of seeing this kind of a condition. When the patient saw me, she asked me how she had contracted this disease. I told her: "You have produced pathogenic Qi through your resentment and blaming. These poisons are have lodged all over your body in the muscles and tendons. This is the reason why you have contracted your disease." Then I continued to ask her: "Who is the person who you hate most, who you disrespect most?" Without any hesitation answered, "My husband! I don't respect him at all." When I asked her why, she explained: "He does not come home. He has found another woman and has abandoned me." I asked her whether she shouldn't blame herself that her husband had run away. "Why would I blame myself," she responded. I then asked her whether he had acted like this in the past, to which she answered in the negative. So I told her: "You focused all your efforts on making money, and once you got enough money, you started treating him merely as a neighbor. You are afraid and you are angry, and that is why you have contracted this disease. Noticing that he doesn't come home sometimes, you started calling his cell phone to find him, but either his phone is turned off or he doesn't answer it." She agreed: "Yes, it is exactly like this. And because I cannot not find him, I spend night after night staying up in anger." I said: "Look at this situation: On the one side, here's your husband enjoying himself, and here you are on the other side, stewing with anger. You are a fool! Even if your anger would kill you, what good would that do? If you died from anger, wouldn't he only be even happier? From my perspective, you must continue living, and do it well. You must turn around to focus on yourself." She asked me how to do that. I told her: "Do not blame him. Blame yourself." "Blame myself," she asked, "why would I blame myself?" I responded: "Husband and wife must treat each other with respect like guests, and yet, when you found a problem with him, you changed and began treating him like ice. You have become like a large block of ice, with no warmth or affection at all for him. So of course he has gone looking elsewhere for a place of warmth. The wife should be like a warm coat for the man, giving warmth when he wears it. But you have taken all the padding out of the coat, turning it into a fake coat. When you wear a fake coat with no padding, you feel cold. So anybody would want to take such a fake coat off and replace it with a true padded coat. It is you who have given your husband ice and caused him to run away, and yet here you are, still blaming and hating your husband. Not only do you fail to admit your own wrongdoing, but you even say that he is the one who is wrong. And in the end, when you wanted him to come home, he wouldn't come. Tell me, is this how things happened or not?" And she admitted that I was right. So I told her: "Admit your fault. Don't blame the other person. It was, after all, you who have been unable to treat him well. If you had been able to treat him well, would he have been able to run away?" Hearing me speak these words, she began to cry.

I then spent another two hours with her while she cried and cried. And after she finished crying, she was able, just like this, to get out of bed. As soon as she got out of bed, she wanted to kneel down to express her gratitude to me, but I told her: "Don't kneel before me. I am not a living Buddha, and kneeling down before me does no good. Admitting your fault is what is useful." She kneeled down anyway and kowtowed twice, then stood up full of vigor and said delightedly: "How can it be that I can use my legs again like this? I am able to stand up, and I am able to keep my eyes open." Then she took an apple, tentatively took a bite, and chewed it slowly. "Look at this! I can even eat an apple!" In the following two years, whenever she experienced any discomfort, she would call me on the telephone, and we would chat for a while.

In 2007, she spent a few days in my home, during which she came to a full understanding of the reasons for her disease. As a result, she got rid of her illness once and for all. I told her: "This time, have you recovered completely? Previously, even though your condition improved a little, you still didn't fully grasp the Dao of human conduct." Therefore I say to the wives among us, you must fully grasp the Dao of being a wife. Let your husband constantly feel your warmth, and never play with him, manipulating him or deceiving him, or treat him with cold. If you are too cold to your husband, in the end you yourself will harvest the fruit (i.e. the karmic retribution) of this cold.

VI.6 DO NOT DIVORCE LIGHTLY

In our modern times, there are many couples who want to divorce just because of some minor disagreement about a few words. At the time of the divorce, the man might glare at the woman and simply declare: "I just don't want you." The woman might reply, not showing any weakness either: "Then I am kicking you right out the door." Some couples who are divorcing don't have such major issues of conflict after all: "Our living habits are different, our personalities are incompatible. So we cannot live together." And just like this, they divorce. Then why did you consider yourselves compatible in the first place? Let us think about this very carefully: The person we call our closest neighbor is precisely our husband or wife, so if you cannot live in harmony with the person closest to you, then who will you ever be able to get along with?

Our current divorce rate is too high. So many people reject the old and embrace the new; throwing out one thing, they look for something else. But if you have this attitude of throwing out this one thing now, you will certainly want to throw out the next thing tomorrow. Isn't this fickleness just like being blown around by the wind? And if you have this sort of a fickle attitude, you will have equally fickle children. Just wait until such children grow up, and they will follow in your footsteps. Each twist and turn in their marriage will cause you endless worries. Parents who don't understand this principle turn around and on the contrary blame their children for this situation. Parents who understand this, however, see right through this and recognize that it is the direct fruit of what they have sown. Everything happens according to cause and effect and is the result of our very own actions.

There are also some people who divorce to pursue their selfish happiness. As soon as something doesn't go according to their wishes, husband and wife have a disagreement and divorce. And after the divorce, the people who are most hurt are our relatives, our children. If they go with the mother, they don't have their father's love. If they go with the father, they don't have their mother's love. Parents who are able to give birth but not to nurture their children, or who are able to nurture but not to educate their children, these kinds of parents, aren't they criminals? We have a lot of divorcing couples nowadays who abandon their children to the care of society. This has not only caused a wound for the couple's respective families, but is also leaving behind a troublemaker for society and for the state to deal with. Children don't have a firm direction yet, and if they do not receive a good education and upbringing, they may act recklessly in defiance of the laws of society.

I have encountered a lot of children who are suffering from illness. How did they contract their illness? Either by hating their father or by hating their mother. When I ask them why they hate their parents, the child's answer is that they hate them because they divorced. There are also a great number of children, both male and female, who don't want to speak a word and who don't want to get married. When I ask them why they don't want to get married and create a family, they answer: "There is nothing to say. My mother and my father fought with each other forever, and then they split up. So much pain and suffering! I would much rather not create a family myself!" Aren't these children pitiable indeed? And who is it who caused such thinking? Their parents are the ones who caused this. And for this reason, husband and wife must never ever divorce lightly. There is only one result that can come from such a momentary impulse: And that is injury to others and injury to yourself.

Is it possible that divorce can offer release? Is it possible that divorce can lead to happiness? This is not certain either. Sometimes, even though there is a different environment after the divorce, because the person's personality hasn't changed, their life is the same as before, or might even be worse. I have encountered a great many divorced people who in the end regretted their actions. And where can you buy a medicine for regret? You can't. This is the only place, right here, where we can give you a medicine for regret: We make you repent your mistakes from the past, realize your own transgressions, and change your own personality. If the circumstances allow it, you might be able to reunite, which is the best option. But if the relationship is firmly beyond the possibility of turning back and reconciling, you may be able to establish a new family and with great effort walk this path to the end. It is only after you have plugged the leak, however, that you will be able to let go of your Yin nature.

VII. The Dao of the Elder

VII.1 A DISPOSITION LIKE ASHES

Some elderly people, when they hear me lecture on the Dao, exclaim with delight: "This is great! Liu Shanren is saying that children must all obey their parents with *xiao*." While children must certainly be obedient and practice *xiao*, nevertheless, you must also be able to act properly in your role as an elder. Each person has their own Dao, and elders also have the Dao of the Elder to follow. If you don't know how to act as an elder, it is difficult in turn for your children to practice *xiao* towards you.

When a person reaches the waning years of life, it is just like arriving in winter. "Winter is the time for storage." This is a season in nature, and old people must act in accordance with this natural season. How do you act in accordance with this season? It means to learn to be nourished and to store. The "Book of Changes (*Yi Jing*)" contains the following sentence: "With the heart cleansed, [the sage] retreats and withdraws into seclusion." When we are old, we retire from our positions at work. Whether we have made a living as workers or as cadres, it is called "retirement" for everyone alike.[7] This "retirement" is a name given to us by the state, and it is also the will of Heaven. What are we to do with this will of Heaven? We are to retire in order to cultivate. Cultivate what? Cultivate our Heavenly nature, cultivate our purpose in life, cultivate those areas where we are deficient, cultivate any problems we find in ourselves. When we were young and impetuous, busily involved in the professional affairs of our external lives, most of us didn't have time to take care of ourselves. But now that we have reached old age, we should rest and think about ourselves a little, we should "go into storage", when we must awaken to the Dao.

Old people have a disposition like ashes. They should carry their mistakes on their back, endure being wronged, and be able to suffer losses. In their heart, they should cherish the happiness of the entire family and ignore whether anybody is right or wrong. As they approach the season of winter in their old age, they should put family affairs aside. Smiling lightly with no worldly cares, they should cultivate their nature with eminence. Able to accept favors with kindness, they should be like stars of good fortune radiating forth in brilliance. This is what we as elders should be like. Distance yourself from all people, affairs, and things, and just allow them to take their natural course. Take responsibility for anything that goes wrong with any family member and whenever there is a family dispute, just say: "You young people, please don't quarrel! Just lay the blame on me!" If old people can be like this, the younger generations will stop arguing on their own.

So many old people are unable to act like this. The ashes in the stove still have fire in them, to the point where even dying embers may ignite again. There are some elderly women in particular who act like a little bit of ashes hiding in a blaze (instead of a little fire hiding in a pile of ashes). They preoccupy their mind, unable to let things go, and feel the need to demonstrate their power over all sorts of situations. They want to hold on to control over family matters, and over who is right or wrong. You tell me, when you meet this kind of

---

7   The Chinese text here includes a play on words that is impossible to translate into English. While the standard term for "retirement" is *tuixiu* 退休 (meaning literally "to withdraw and rest"), Liu Shanren substitutes a different character for the sound "*xiu*," namely 修, which means cultivation. As the result, the compound *tuixiu* 退修 then acquires the meaning "withdraw and cultivate."

an old person, how could her children possibly practice *xiao* to its fullest? No matter what happens, she wants to interfere recklessly. Muttering and mumbling, nagging on and on and on, look at the foam flying out of her mouth! Children most likely won't listen to her, because she's just an old lady. And if they do listen, she uses her old brain to judge new situations, without the ability to accept how times have changed. Young people may say: "You have grown old. You are unable to follow our modern circumstances. Please don't get involved." But she is unable to let it go and continues to insist on interfering. If the children don't listen to her, she flies into a rage, blowing up everywhere indiscriminately, firing off in all directions. She is like an airplane dropping bombs and firing artillery all over the place. Why do I say this? Visiting her daughter's family, she makes a scene, howling and crying. The people there won't listen to her, finding her unbearable, and she feels similarly angry at them. After she has blown up at her daughter's family, she runs out to visit her son's family. Again she howls and yells, and blows up, making everybody in her son's family angry. Isn't this like an airplane dropping bombs? This sort of behavior is wrong for an old person and can turn into bullying toward the children. And what children fear most is to be bullied by their elders. Whether your children act in *xiao* or not is none of your concern, this is their problem. Your role as elders consists of nothing but concerning yourself with your own Dao of kindness, nothing else should concern you the least bit. This is what is called bringing the Dao full circle in actions instead of in words.

In that case, what are the elderly to do? Stay out of the affairs of your family members, eat whatever food they have prepared for you, and wear whatever clothes they have bought for you. Spend your time in leisure with the grandchildren, guiding them in their play. Isn't this wonderful? Turn your gaze inward and observe without obstacles, observe in particular whether you are able to fulfill your role as an old man or woman. A true elder does not get involved in other people's affairs. Wang Shanren often told us how in his youth his old grandfather liked to interfere, getting up early and beating the bed with a stick, yelling at all the young people to get up. Whoever didn't get up he'd yell at. And what good did all this interference do? If you don't know how to stop, your children are unable to advance, so you must stop acting like that. If there is a mountain, people lean on the mountain. If there is no mountain, they stand on their own. If you constantly worry about them and exert yourself on their behalf, your children will not move forward on their own but instead acquire bad habits, never learning to manage on their own.

Nobody is able to live in this world forever, and when the old people pass away, the children still must go on living. There is a saying: "Children and grandchildren create their own happiness. Do not turn yourself into their workhorse." The person who spoke this sentence was Li Tieguai, one of the famous Eight Immortals. Li Tieguai was a man who had a lot of children but his household suffered from great poverty. Very often, they had to make do on one meal a day. What was he to do? He was forced to get by stealing. Isn't this what people in the past called "digging a hole"? So he went to the large home of a wealthy family to "go digging." And after he had successfully dug a hole through to the other side of the wall, he thought to himself: "First I will push a gourd through the hole, to see what kind of activity there might be inside. If nothing happens, I will squeeze through the hole myself without any further delay." Then he took a gourd and very carefully pushed it through the hole into the house. All of a sudden he heard loud a snapping sound from inside, which came from somebody having snapped off the tip of the gourd. Scared out of his wits, Li Tieguai flung the gourd aside and took to his heels as fast as he could. At this point, he did not return home but instead took off straight into the mountains and became a monk. Forty years later, when he had reached enlightenment, he returned home to his family, where he found that his family members had not starved to death but had all managed to survive quite well. Deeply stirred by this, he composed the following poem: "Forty years ago, I went out to steal something, but somebody broke off the tip of my gourd. Children and grandchildren create their own happiness. Do not turn yourself into their workhorse."

VII.2 DO NOT DICTATE YOUR CHILDREN'S MARRIAGES

A lot of old people place certain demands on their children, especially in regard to their marriage. Some parents do not give their consent to their children's choice for a partner, and the children consequently contract psychological disorders, depression, or in severe cases even schizophrenia. I have a great number of such children, and yet the parents still think that it is the children who fail to obey them, who are cruel-hearted. I tell them: "You are wrong! Do you really believe that your children are your immutable property? Wrong! They are the wealth of the entire country, the wealth of all the people who are only temporarily under your protection. They are just like money. Whose money is it? The money belongs to the universe, and is only temporarily kept by you. If you are able to use it (for the welfare of everybody), it will always remain yours. But if you don't know how to use it (only knowing how to use it for your personal enjoyment), Heaven will immediately collect it back from you. People are exactly the same. If you don't use them well, a single illness will take them from you. Then you can cry and yell all you want, raise a rock in your fist and throw it at the sky, all to no avail. So you must learn to accept things as they are."

There was a young woman like this, who had developed a mental illness. Sometimes she was confused, at other times she was very clear in her mind. Brought to see me by her mother, I asked this young woman: "How is it that a young lady like you of only twenty years has contracted this illness?" She answered that she didn't know either. I told her that she hated another person, and then asked her if she knew who it was. She said she did, and when I asked her to tell me, she pointed at her mother saying: "She is the person I hate." When I asked her why she hated her mother, she said: "How could I not hate her? She destroyed my relationship!" So you see here how this marriage business caused this young person to develop mental illness. Therefore I say that parents should not dictate their children's marriage. If parents look at a prospective partner and find him or her unsuitable for their child, they can make a suggestion and inform their child, but under no circumstances must they force them to separate.

I next asked this young lady how her mother had ruined her relationship, and she explained: "My partner and I had gotten engaged, and we both felt that we were the love of the other person's life and we were utterly committed to each other, when I left to go to the Da Xing An mountains. As soon as I got there, my mother told my fiancé that I had found another partner there and had gotten married. In a fit of rage, he found himself another partner, and when I returned home, they had already gotten married. I went to ask him and he told me that my mother had told him that I had gotten married, that I had cheated on him. And this is the reason why I now hate my mother!"

I told her: " Don't hate your mother! The salt your mother has had to eat is much more than the rice you have eaten, and the bridges she has had to cross are much further than the roads you have had to walk. Your experience is limited and your mother's experience much greater. Your mother has done what she has done for your sake. Don't hate your mother!" When she heard me say these things, this left her speechless for a long time. Then she agreed: "You are right. What you are saying makes sense. Which mother doesn't love her children dearly? They all just want to send their children off to a good place." I told her: "If you understand this, you shouldn't hate your mother any longer." And she admitted that she had done wrong by hating her mother. She turned to her mother, bowed to her, and said: "Mother! I was wrong. It is I have acted wrongly." After admitting her wrongdoing, she immediately vomited up a whole bowl of white foam, and after returning home, vomited up another bowl. And in this way, she began to gradually recover from her illness.

There are other situations, though, that are the exact opposite of this: Parents get angry because their children do not follow the arrangements they have made for their marriage, and the parents then fall ill. I met a man in Heilongjiang, 37 years of age, who had developed pancreatic cancer. In the beginning, I didn't know what illness he was suffering from, but after I had lectured him about illness and noticed that he showed no response at all, I thought to myself: "This must certainly be cancer, there is no way around it." So I asked him who the person was that he was so angry at. He replied that it was his daughter, and when I asked him he was so angry at her, he replied: "When my daughter found herself a partner, I did not approve of her choice. But she stubbornly insisted on marrying him and eloped with him. This made me absolutely furious, to the point where I have now developed this disease." And one month later, this father died. Look, everybody, what a great pity this is! Wang Shanren told us that we must never under any circumstances dictate our children's marriage. And even more importantly, we must never forcibly cause them to separate, otherwise no good will come from this, whether for the parents or the children.

LECTURE FIVE

Rebuilding The Root
Of Humanity

I. The Six Steps of Education in the Family

Wang Shanren proposed the following "six steps of education in the family":
education at the root, fetal education, education in newborn care, education
in breast-feeding, education in infant care, and educating the family. To rescue
the root of humankind and improve it, it is essential that we begin with young
girls, that we begin in childhood. This is what we mean by education at the
root, also called "Earlier Heaven (i.e., pre-natal, congenital constitution) education." It is only when the Earlier Heaven root is healthy that the Later Heaven
(i.e., post-natal, acquired constitution) seeds can grow and thrive in the field.
If the Earlier Heaven constitution is not good, the Later Heaven sprouts that
emerge after birth will certainly not be acceptable. Each of us bears individual
responsibility for creating a healthy human root. Whether we are able to live
up to this responsibility or not depends on whether we are able to address this
issue at its very source. If we as mothers and fathers are able to clearly understand this principle on a personal level, our children will surely be good, and
the family as a whole will surely be good as well.

I.1 STEP ONE: EDUCATION AT THE ROOT

I.1.a Education at the Root

The first of the six steps of education in the family consists of "education at
the root": "With a nature as pure and clear as Heaven and a heart as radiant

as earth, practice genuine loyalty toward superiors and *xiao* toward parents, and emphasize acting with virtue."

What is the goal of this education at the root? To first educate the parents. It is only when we have a good father and a good mother that there can be good children and grandchildren. The Dao of human relationships that we are discussing here must have a straight root and pure source. When the water in the spring is clear, the water coming out of it will be clear as well. When the water in the spring is murky, the water coming out will be murky as well. For this reason, education at the root places particular emphasis on educating the mother. To give birth to good children, young women must have a good character. According to my personal observations, a great number of illnesses in small children, but even conditions that arise in adults as old as twenty years, are related to the parents, and to the mother in particular.

What should the character of a young woman be like? It is of utmost importance that her Heavenly Nature is highly principled, in alignment with the Dao, and it absolutely has to be pure and clear. How is she to achieve this? In her nature, there must be no room for a bad temper. Otherwise her heart cannot be radiant as the earth. Her heart must be calm, conscientious, open and upright, with compassion and kindness towards everybody around her. She must be broad-minded and magnanimous. Only if she is magnanimous can she give birth to magnanimous children and grandchildren.

Furthermore, she must spare no efforts in the area of loyalty and *xiao*. "Practicing genuinely" means to truly practice what you preach, and "practicing genuine loyalty toward superiors and *xiao* toward parents" means to carry out loyalty and *xiao* to the fullest extent. "Emphasize acting with virtue" means that for every sentence you speak, for every action you carry out, you consider whether it is in alignment with the Great Dao of human relationships. If it is in alignment, you proceed; if it is not, you drop it. If a mother acts like this, she will foster virtue in her children. Even before children are born, future mothers must foster virtue like this. Only when they have fostered virtue can they put down a deep root. It is only when the root is deep and the base solid that the branches can be full of abundant foliage, flowers, and fruits. Wang Shanren also taught us: "Children do not need to be controlled. Everything can rely on their response to your virtuous conduct." If the virtue you have fostered is not deep, a gust of wind can blow you over, to the point where even your roots will be pulled out. The roots of virtue must be deep and strong so that no matter how strong the wind might be, it is unable to cause problems.

The ancients have taught us: "If you are hoping for a good son, you must practice loyalty and *xiao* to its fullest. If you are hoping for a good daughter, you must have a character rooted in great conscience. If you are hoping for riches, you must have a heart full of benevolence and justice. If you want good descendants, you must have goodness and virtue." In other words, to give birth to future loyal ministers and skillful generals, you must first devote yourself a 100 percent to practicing loyalty and *xiao*!

I once accepted Dr. Liu's invitation to give a lecture to some students at Tsinghua University. I told them: "We talk about the Dao every day, but what is this Dao? It is the Dao of being human. Being a good human is pretty difficult indeed! Why do I say that? When we look at the character for 'good' (*hao* 好), it is composed of the two characters for 'female' (*nu* 女) and 'child' (*zi* 子). This is to say, if you only have 'female' or if you only have 'child', this is not called 'good'. You must have a woman of outstanding conduct who is furthermore able to raise a child well, in order to call something 'good'. This 'goodness' is true 'goodness'." Look, everybody! Isn't this kind of goodness a bit difficult to realize? For this reason, we must strengthen our intention to improve the seed and rebuild the root of humanity. How do we give birth to good children? How do we leave behind good human roots for society, for our country? This depends entirely on us alone.

In our present times, however, so many parents do not understand this principle. They only know how to hope for their sons to turn into dragons and their daughters to turn into phoenixes. But where do such dragons and phoenixes come from? They can't just fall out of the sky but must come from the virtuous behavior of the father and mother. If parents don't cultivate their own virtuous behavior and perfect themselves, how can they possibly give birth to and nurture good children? Ultimately, they are only able to leave behind a blemish for humanity, to contribute a prodigal freeloading troublemaker to society. When I see children who haven't turned out well, who have become good-for-nothings, but their parents then turn around and blame the children, is this really the fault of the children? Blaming your children means blaming your ancestors, because the children are just a replacement, to continue the family line by taking the place of the ancestors. Even worse, when some mothers see that their children haven't turned out well, they directly blame the ancestors. They blame the grandparents for not having accumulated virtue, for not having accumulated enough merit for a good child. In reality, whose doing is this? Isn't it entirely the parents' own fault? A certain kind of mother will invariably produce the same kind of child. Stop blaming others and instead pay very close attention to yourself!

I.1.b The Problem of Infertility after Marriage

Nowadays there are a lot of women who are unable to get pregnant even after many years of marriage. What is the reason for this? There are many reasons, not just one.

Some women have had a number of abortions before they got married. Without a marriage certificate, without a formal ceremony, without being officially husband and wife, they get pregnant, a condition that people call "private pregnancy." Many wives have asked me: "Liu Shanren! Please tell me, we have been married for so many years now, but how come I haven't gotten pregnant?" When I then ask such women whether they have ever been pregnant before marriage, in most cases they confirm that. If that weren't the case, I wouldn't ask. When I then ask whether they have aborted the pregnancy, they confirm that as well. So I tell them: " 'Of the hundred forms of goodness, *xiao* is the greatest. Of the thousand forms of evil, lewdness is the worst.' You have already committed the worst of the thousand forms of evil, and yet a child came to you. You, however, considered this child an inconvenience and killed it through an abortion. Do you think the child would dare to come again? What if it came again and you killed it again?" Such women then end up crying and yelling in distress. But if they so desperately want a child, what business did they have to consider it an inconvenience earlier?

In 2006, at a time when I was right in the middle of tilling a field, a husband and wife came from DaQing to see me. Both of them were in great health, it was just that they were unable to get pregnant. It was not that the woman had not been pregnant before, she had indeed been pregnant several times, but every time they had aborted the pregnancy. When had she been pregnant? Before the two of them had gotten married, when they were still just dating, she had gotten pregnant. At that time, they both thought that it would not be appropriate, that they couldn't have this child, so she had gotten an abortion. And just a few months later, she got pregnant again, and yet again, they decided to have an abortion. In this way, she had aborted two children before they got married. And not long after they got married, she got pregnant yet again. Before the wedding, they had decided that they couldn't carry a pregnancy to terms because it would ruin their reputation. But what about now, after they had gotten married? Now they should have been able to give birth to this child! But this time, they were not happy with their current living situation and thought they would first earn money for a few years before having children, so they yet again aborted this child. And this was the beginning of their troubles. When they later wanted to have a child, the woman was unable to become pregnant again.

Now what was I to do about this? They had come to me, after all, and I had given them some sort of advice. So I had the woman watch a video recording of a lecture I had given at Peking University on "Transforming the Seed and Rebuilding the Root of Humanity." While she was watching it, she began vomiting and moreover experienced sudden pain in her lower abdomen. Observing this, I thought that maybe there was some hope here. Later on, she went with us on a trip to Zhaozhou. On the road, her belly ached so severely that she wanted to go to the hospital. In the end, the condition passed without her receiving medical care. In fact, when you encounter this kind of a situation, it is generally a sign of the poisonous Qi leaving the body, and if you don't handle it correctly, the poisonous Qi might get turned around instead and get pushed back into the body. Unfortunately, this lady did not keep in touch with us after she left us, so I don't know whether she ever became pregnant later on or not.

In another sort of situation, "there are no fish in water that is too clean," or in other words, if a woman's character is too eccentric, too rigid, and too fastidious about purity, this sort of woman also has difficulty getting pregnant. This is like water that is so clean that it contains no nutrients and therefore cannot nourish any fish. If on top of that the man or the woman's personality is too hard, too stubborn, especially if the woman has too fiery a temper, this means that there is poison in her blood, and again she is unable to become pregnant.

Furthermore, excessive greed can also lead to infertility. Because monetary wealth belongs to water and is something that should circulate throughout society, if you only circulate it in your own home, water becomes too big, and again it will be difficult to produce children. The Xuanjiang Shiyi ("Omissions from Preaching")[1] tells an evocative story of a very wealthy and powerful family who was unable to have children. Because of this lack of children, the master over time acquired three wives and four concubines, but still was unable to have children. Who would be there to inherit this great wealth?

Coincidentally, the wealthy man had a sworn blood brother. This blood brother was lucky enough to have four sons in his family. One day, the wealthy man and his wife decided to invite the blood brother over for dinner, and for this occasion they placed four gold ingots under the four legs of the dining table. The blood brother being a wretchedly poor fellow, how could he eat his meal in such a situation? So he only took a couple of bites here and there and went home shortly. At home, he told his wife what had happened at the dinner at his wealthy blood brother's home. Women being smarter than men, this wife thought up a plan: "Tomorrow, ask your brother to come to our home for dinner." Then she made her husband saw off the four legs of their dining table.

The next day, the poor man indeed invited his wealthy blood brother over for dinner. The wife prepared the food, carried it out to the table, and furthermore placed two stools on the *kang* for the men to sit on. Just sitting on the *kang* directly, the men had already been elevated too high, but now, sitting on the stools on top of the *kang*, how could they possible eat the food on the table? At this time, the wife addressed the wealthy man: "Older brother! Is this table maybe a little too low?" And the man agreed that indeed it was too low. She replied: "Well then, let's raise it up." And she yelled: "Somebody, come over here!" The four sons, who had been waiting for this sign, heard the shout and all came out together. The wife instructed them to each pick up one leg of the table to raise it a little higher. And in the end, they raised it too high. So

---

1   A book that contains many stories about *xiao* and was used extensively by Wang Shanren and Liu Shanren in their lectures.

she again addressed the wealthy man: "Older brother! Is this table maybe a little too high?" And again, the man agreed that it was indeed a little high. "Well," she said. "Let's drop it a little lower." Going back and forth like this several times, do you think the wealthy man was able to eat his dinner? After just two bites, he put down his chopsticks and went home, where he started to cry in front of his wife. The wife was bewildered: "Your poor blood brother has invited you for dinner. Why have you started to cry now?" He answered: "Don't say another word. You have caused me to fall into a trap." When the wife asked him what he was talking about, he responded: "When you asked my poor blood brother over for dinner, what business did you have raising the table by placing those gold ingots under the legs? Sure enough, he learned from you. His wife ordered her four sons to raise the table for me." The rich man's wife responded: "Isn't he telling us by this action that he has sons? All right! Ask your poor brother to come over once again tomorrow. I have something to talk about with him."

On the third day, the wealthy man once again invited his poor blood brother to come over. When he arrived, the wealthy man's wife said to him: "You have four sons, and we don't have even a single one. What can be done about that?" The poor blood brother answered: "Since you do not have any, I can give you one of my sons to adopt as your own." The rich man's wife, however, replied that was not an option. "In that case," the poor man asked, "if that doesn't work, what can we do?" Here the rich man interjected: "I have so many women here, three wives and four concubines. You can choose any of them, whoever you like among them, and you should certainly be able to help me get one of them pregnant, to bear me a child." The poor man thought to himself: "Why would my wealthy blood brother talk like this? Isn't it an old saying that you can wear your friends' clothes whenever you want to, but you must not get involved with their wives? If I do what my blood brother is asking of me, won't I lower myself to the level of immorality?" In this awkward situation, he suddenly had a stroke of insight, and so he proposed to his blood brother: "Yes, I can in fact help give birth to a child. But I must ask my older brother and sister-in-law to grant me three conditions." When the wealthy man asked what these were, the poor man explained: "First, take out 3000 tael of fine silver and allow me to spend it as I please. Second, for the next hundred days, you, my brother, and I shall remain together, inseparable like a body and its shadow. I shall not leave your side, and you shall not leave my side. Furthermore, we must be taken care of with good food. And third, the two of us must together read the book "Tai Shang Gan Ying Bian" (The Most Supreme Action And Reaction"). Within these hundred days, neither of us must go home to our families or touch a woman." When the wealthy man had heard his blood brother out, he found his conditions to be acceptable and thus agreed to follow every one of them.

During the next hundred days, the poor man used the 3,000 tael of silver to help the needy, relieve the distressed, aid the elderly, and support the poor. And at the end of the hundred-day period, he had spent the entire sum on alms. Then he told his blood brother that he had to visit his family. At home, the poor man told his wife that he needed to leave, and when his wife asked him where he was going, he told her that he was going far away to roam the world. Before leaving, though, he composed a song encouraging sexual abstinence, to warn all people of the dangers of lewdness.

After the poor man left like this, the rich man was furious, assuming that his blood brother would not come back. But who would have thought that half a year later both of the rich man's wives turned out to be pregnant! And just at this time, the blood brother returned. During the celebration that the wealthy man and his wives held to celebrate the children's completion of the first full month after birth, the blood brother stepped forward to congratulate them, but the wealthy man and his wives ignored him. After all the other guests had left, the blood brother exclaimed: "Older Brother! Older Sisters-in-Law! What a joyful occasion!" To this, the wealthy man replied: "What does this joyful occasion have to do with you?" The blood brother explained: "Had I not planted these roots of virtue on your behalf, would you have been able to have children now? With my first dose of medicine, I treated the fact that your ancestral line was not thriving. Even though your family had great wealth, it was all wrongfully gained. Treating the poor harshly, cheating by giving short weight, deceiving people out of their money, this kind of wealth you had a lot of, but it had cut off your lucky star for having children. For this reason, I gave 3,000 tael in alms away for you, to restore your virtuous behavior. In the past, you had been a sex addict, marrying three wives and four concubines, so you had exhausted your essence Qi. I made you stay away from women for a hundred days, thereby nourishing your essence Qi. This was your second dose of medicine. The third dose was to make you read the "Most Supreme Action and Reaction" to raise your conscience and expunge your sinful karma. After having taken all three of these medicines, you were able to have children!" Listening to these words, the wealthy man and his wives suddenly gained a deep understanding of what had happened and immediately kneeled down in front of the poor man to express their gratitude to him.

1.2 STEP TWO: FETAL EDUCATION

1.2.a Fetal Education

The second step of instruction in the family is "fetal education." During pregnancy, a mother must hold on to righteousness in her mind, eliminate all evil thoughts, moderate her food and drink, and take great care in her day-to-day activities.

The ancients have a saying: "Of the fruits from one tree, some are sour and some are sweet. Of the children from a single mother, some are fools and some are sages." If a mother bears nine children, none of them will be alike. In earlier times, women had many, many children, and their mental state was different during each of their pregnancies. The children grew up in accordance with the mother's mental state during her pregnancy, and the difference in the mother's mental state produced a difference in the children's personality.

"Holding on to righteousness" means that she must hold on to correct thoughts and ideas, which is also called "ensconcing an image." Whatever image you hold in your heart, this is the image you will ensconce in your child. Some mothers don't understand this principle and during pregnancy detest one thing and get annoyed at something else. Whenever they come into contact with somebody who does not please them, they get annoyed. In this way, these mothers guarantee that their child after birth will have a personality that is exactly like that of the person they disliked during pregnancy. What these mothers don't understand is that this is exactly the image that they have ensconced in the child. If you ensconce a singer, the child will take pleasure in singing; if you ensconce a paragon of virtue, the child will be a paragon of virtue.

"Ensconcing an image" is truly powerful indeed. It is also called "preserving the heart." We can look at the mothers of Confucius and Mencius. What were the thoughts they held in their mind during pregnancy? Confucius' mother followed her father's order and, practicing *xiao* to the fullest extent, married into the Kong family. Wanting to give birth to a sage for the Kong family, she indeed gave birth to a sage. Mencius' mother followed the behavior of Confucius' mother and thus gave birth to Mencius. We must have the same kind of heart that they have, and take a very close look at how the mothers of Confucius and Mencius succeeded. The women of today are also women, just like them, so why can't we leave behind this kind of human root for the sake of Heaven and Earth now? Some mothers not only fail to leave behind skilled and talented children to contribute to society, but they even produce disobedient or prodigal children. Why is that? For answers, they must look inside themselves.

When some people hear about this principle of "ensconcing an image," they think with great joy in their heart: "This time around, I can hold it in my heart that my child will become a sage." But I say to them: "If you don't have a sagely mother, it is sure to be difficult to think about giving birth to a sagely child." You must first succeed in your own cultivation, genuinely perfecting all the five points of being a young woman (the five special characteristics of cotton described above) as well as being able to uphold frugality in marriage, and then I guarantee that you will bear a good child. If you have not perfected these five points before getting married, and on top of that turn your wedding into a big flashy affair that reveals your hypocritical and superficial attitude, do you really think you can give birth to a good child? If you have a shallow heart, any child you bear will also be shallow. If you are hypocritical, any child you bear will also be hypocritical. After the child has grown up, he or she is bound to disobey you. Whatever thoughts the father and mother hold in their heart, the child will produce that same thought. The principle behind this is very deep and well worth studying very carefully. I have only scratched the surface of this topic here, and you have to comprehend it fully on your own. Confucius talked about the "investigation of things," and Wang Shanren did so as well. What is this "investigation of things"? Let us consider this carefully: Is every step that we ourselves have walked crooked or straight? Have we walked a righteous path or not?

"Eliminating all evil thoughts" means that we want to eliminate evil intentions and stop rash, reckless thinking. Your heart must not harbor evil thoughts, your feet must not step on evil ground, your ears must not hear evil sounds, your eyes must not see evil things. Just walking down the road, some young men or women allow lewd thoughts to arise in their heart when they see some-body good-looking on the other side. Such thinking creates boundless evils in the future. Terrible indeed! Everybody, think carefully, from the time we began to think on our own until the present, how many evil thoughts have we allowed to arise inside us? How many seeds have we planted? For every seed we have planted, we will harvest a fruit. Therefore I say, when a mother is pregnant, it is of utmost importance that she maintain purity in both her body and her heart and keep herself a fair distance away from people, actions, and things that can cause evil thoughts and evil intentions. Some couples understand this principle and therefore do not share the same room for the duration of a pregnancy. This sort of behavior has great benefits for the health and development of the fetus.

"Moderating food and drink" means that the mother must be careful to "guard life" in regards to her food and drink. "Guarding life" means that she must not eat meat or dirty food, because meat poisons the Qi and blood, and liquor wreaks havoc on the character. Her food and drink must not be overly extravagant; it is best if she eats pure and bland foods. So many newlyweds celebrate their wedding with a great banquet and indulge in great amounts of alcohol and meat. If the groom gets completely drunk and then a pregnancy results from the wedding night, such children's brain will be muddled and unclear, and when they grow up, they lack intelligence and fail to succeed in their studies. At that point, for the father and mother to turn around and then blame the child, putting great pressure on the child, is a huge mistake. You now want to sober up the child's brain, but it is already too late. What were you thinking when you acted like that in the past! Where did you plant the seed?

So many women ask me for advice because their children lack success in their studies and don't enjoy studying. In such situations, you must not blame the child but must search for the cause in yourself. If I had not lectured here on this topic of "fetal education," you wouldn't know what is going on. But now that I have told you this information, you should know that the cause lies within yourself.

When my youngest son's wife was pregnant with my two granddaughters, everything she ate was pure and vegetarian. As a result, the children she gave birth to turned out to be truly different from normal children, exceptionally bright in the head and with extraordinarily quick responses. From this situation, I have drawn the conclusion that a woman's food and drink are of the greatest significance during the time of her pregnancy. Nowadays, everybody speaks of "tonifying" this and "tonifying that." Tonifying what? In most cases, this means precisely eating meat and dirty foods, and in particular mutton and beef. At the time when animals are butchered, they are extremely terrified, to the point where after the animal is butchered and the meat cut off the carcass, the meat is still trembling. At the same time that the animal is terrified, it also experiences anger and hatred. When a person then consumes this kind of meat, it can have a negative effect. Because my youngest son's wife didn't eat any of these kinds of foods during her pregnancies, my two granddaughters are extraordinarily intelligent, especially the youngest one. When she attended the first grade in preschool, the first and second grades were combined in one room. While the teacher was instructing the older children in the second grade, my youngest granddaughter listened to their lessons while at the same time completing her own assignments. And after the teacher finished the lesson and asked the children in the higher grade some questions, she would call out from the other side of the room that she could answer, and would immediately give the correct answers. This shows us the health of her "earlier-heaven nature" (i.e., her congenital *xing*).

"Taking great care in day-to-day activities," lastly, means that the mother must maintain a certain composure whether moving or being still, sitting or sleeping, for the duration of her pregnancy. This is what the ancients called "sitting like a bell, standing like a pine tree, sleeping like a bow." Even though a pregnant woman is unable to move like the wind, she must still walk down the road with great straightness instead of veering now to the left, now to the right. Like Confucius' mother when she was pregnant with Confucius, sit upright with your clothes neatly arranged and always look straight ahead. During pregnancy, you must furthermore follow a consistent rhythm of work and rest, avoiding in particular to reverse day and night. To be active at night and to stay in bed during the day, this is harmful to the fetus' health and growth.

In addition, it is important during pregnancy that the mother performs some appropriate work. Some pregnant women are treated special and get pampered, as if they were carrying a dragon's fetus and all hell would break loose if they didn't nurture and protect it as best as they possibly could. So they themselves haven't lifted a finger from the very beginning of pregnancy, and the other family members haven't allowed them to work either. In my opinion, this is not necessarily the way to nurture and protect the fetus. When my wife was pregnant with our first child, she worked by my side day and night, without a single day's rest. And when she went into labor, she still helped me bring in the corn in the morning, climbing up and down the cart, and then just had the baby that very afternoon.

Wang Shanren explained this principle well: "Work for a living, work for a living! People can only live if they have used their life to work for a living. If you don't work, you die." The Chinese character for "live" (*huo* 活) contains the image of three drops of water, which signifies the concept that life has to flow like water. There is a saying: "As long as movement doesn't stop, life doesn't cease." People nowadays don't want to be active. As soon as the woman gets pregnant, the couple hires a housekeeper or has her mother or mother-in-law come to wait on her. Who among us doesn't know that the good fortune in each of our lives has a limit, and that if we use up all our good fortune like that, afterwards we will meet with hardship? For this reason, the ancients reminded us over and over to cherish our good fortune and to use it sparingly, to allow it to grow.

I.2.b The Importance of the "Precious Record of Physiology"

Some children suffer from serious brain damage from the moment they are born. What is the reason for this? It can come from many different areas. First, a lack of *xiao*. As soon as the couple gets married, if they don't get along with the older generation, and on top of that, when the woman then gets pregnant, if she constantly gets angry with her elders, a child born under these circumstances can very easily suffer from paralysis in the brain. Second, if the timing when the husband and wife have sexual intercourse is not right, this can also lead to a great number of physiological problems. What do I mean by "right timing" here? It means to avoid having intercourse on specific inappropriate days or at inappropriate times. For example, on the first and fifteenth days of the lunar month, on the day before and on the first day of each of the four seasons, on the day before and on the day of the four solstices and equinoxes, in rough wind and torrential rain storms, during thunder and lightning, on your parents' birthday, and on the Buddha's birthday, at those times you must not have intercourse. If you break this rule, the child born from this intercourse will either suffer from paralysis or from being feebleminded. This is called a "great change in physiology," and you can consult the appendix of the "Precious Record of Physiology" (*Sheng Li Bao Lu* 生理寶錄) on this subject. What I am explaining here is by necessity incomplete and lacking in many details, so please look at this appendix. In addition, you must also pay attention to the time of day, to each of the 24 hours in each day. At the three hours of 11-1 around noon and midnight, and from 5-7 in the morning and evening, you must not have sexual intercourse either, because these are the times when Yin and Yang switch. In the ancient saying that "Heaven and humanity are one," Heaven refers to the time, and if you have sexual intercourse at a time when you shouldn't, this might bring you a child who is not normal, because of this correspondence between Heaven and humanity.

One time, when I was in Changchun, a lady came to see me, carrying a small child. She overheard me saying, "On the first and fifteenth days of the lunar month, husband and wife must not have sexual intercourse. If they do have intercourse, a child born from this situation will either be feeble-minded or paralyzed." The lady responded to my lecture, exclaiming: "Then I am done for! This child of mine will not be able to recover." When I asked her to explain, she said: "What my son is suffering from is precisely paralysis. And it is true, I conceived him on the first day of the first month." So you see, everybody, how important this "Precious Record of Physiology" is! It is a treasure transmitted to us from our ancient ancestors, which we all must study with great diligence. We may not have another opportunity to apply this wisdom ourselves, but we still have descendants. We must help them understand these rules and principles, that we must not seek gratification of only a single moment, thereby causing boundless retributions for our children and grandchildren.

I.2.c The State of Mind During Pregnancy

There are a lot of children nowadays who suffer from hyperactivity disorder or twitching. These are physiological disorders that were planted when the mother was pregnant. Physiological disorders are very difficult to treat. Autism, for example, which I have seen many cases of, is generally speaking very difficult to change, but there have certainly been cases that have improved.

In 1994, I met a 9-year-old boy in Fangzheng County in Heilongjiang, who was brought to me by his mother. This boy suffered from autism, had never spoken a word in his life, and in addition suffered from hyperactivity. I asked the mother what the circumstances had been like during her pregnancy and where she had been during that time. She answered that she and her husband had gone to Japan after getting married in order to find low-wage work there, and that this was where she had the child. As soon as I heard that, I knew the reason for the boy's condition, so I said to her: "You planted the cause for your child's disorder over there. When you arrived in Japan, you didn't understand the language and you are already quiet to begin with. On top of that, you worked in a menial job for others who ordered you around, yelled at you, and treated you harshly. Did you dare to make a sound? No, you didn't. Not daring to complain, you suppressed your emotions inside. Because your child was born into this kind of an environment, he contracted autism." My words made the boy's mother cry. Everybody, look at this situation. The wife and her husband toiled so hard that in five years they earned 1.5 million RMB, and yet they returned home with this kind of a child, suffering from a disease that even twice that amount could never cure.

The boy's mother cried for a long time with the boy sitting by her side, just sitting there, until he eventually also began to cry. His crying made the mother in turn cry even harder. Under tears, she said: "This child of mine has never cried before. How come he is crying today?" I explained, "Because you have spoken about these suppressed feelings today. If you are able to release what you have been suppressing, there may still be hope for your child." She sat there and cried for more than half an hour, when all of a sudden this boy opened his mouth and said: "Grandpa! Thank you!" As soon as the child uttered these words, his mother exclaimed in happy astonishment: "Our child has never spoken a word before! Hearing him say this sentence today brings me the greatest joy."

What does this story show us? It shows us that as soon as the mother's inner world was turned around, the child was able to change.

When the mother and child were just about to leave, the boy suddenly spoke in front of a large crowd: "Thank you, everybody! We are going home now." So you see how important the mother's state of mind is. Therefore I say to those of you who are mothers: During pregnancy you must control your state of mind with utmost care, and you must pay attention to this subject of "fetal education."

1.3 STEP THREE: EDUCATION IN NEWBORN CARE

Education in newborn care follows right after fetal education: "For childbirth, follow the course of nature. Regulate the temperature and put hygiene first."

When mothers deliver babies, it is best to practice natural childbirth, to follow the course of nature. Nowadays so many births are caesarean births, so many children are delivered by artificial methods. This is not natural. Some mothers who give birth by C-section even choose the day and time. Tell me, isn't this ridiculous? If the child is not born in a natural way, what use is there in choosing a good time or auspicious day?

"To regulate the temperature" means that parents must adjust the temperature just right for the sake of the baby, to make it perfectly comfortable and balanced. Male babies fear heat most, because if it is too hot, they can easily contract pneumonia and their windpipes can be damaged. Female babies fear cold most, because if it is too cold, the kidney channel can contract disease.

"Put hygiene first." Hygiene is extremely important. In your role as mother, you must pay close attention to the baby's hygiene. Do not allow the baby to get too dirty, and be especially careful during the breast-feeding stage.

There is one other area of concern: In the past, people in Northern China had the habit of wrapping and tying their babies up as soon as they were born. Nevertheless, swaddling babies too severely is not beneficial but may influence the baby's healthy development. Otherwise, why is it that the brains of babies from the North of China are not as nimble as the brains of babies from the South? They tie them up so tightly that nothing can move, and then insert a board in the back, which the back of the baby's head is pressed against until it is flattened. Because the baby's cerebrum is irritated and constrained, the brain is not nimble as a result. Why is it that Southerners are so good with their brains? Just look at the skulls of people from the South: they protrude in the front and in the back, with the cerebrum and ventricles being particularly well developed. I have visited numerous places in the South, in Guangdong, Guangxi, Fujian, Hunan, and Hubei. I have noticed that Southerners are not very tall but have very large skulls. If you want to engage in business, Northerners are not nearly as witty. So, in conclusion, we should give birth naturally, and after childbirth, allow the baby to grow as naturally as possible.

1.4 STEP FOUR: EDUCATION IN BREAST-FEEDING

Education in breast-feeding concerns important things that the mother should pay attention to at the times when she is breast-feeding: "When your disposition is stirred or your body fatigued, never nurse a baby. When the heart is balanced and the Qi harmonious, this is best. If babies are crying, make them cheer up first. Feed four times during the day and three times at night, no more and no less."

"When your disposition is stirred or your body fatigued, never nurse a baby." This means that a mother, when she is agitated or exhausted, must not feed that milk to the baby. The reason for this rule is that when you are agitated or get angry, your milk contains poison. And when your body is exhausted, your milk contains fire. When the mother's disposition is stirred, the milk that she nurses her baby with is "Qi milk," and any baby that drinks "Qi milk" develops diarrhea. When the mother has fire rising inside her, the milk that she nurses her baby with is "fire milk," and any baby that drinks "fire milk" develops a high fever. When small children develop a cold and a fever or fall ill with diarrhea during the breastfeeding stage, what is the reason? It is precisely that the baby consumed "resentment Qi milk" or "fire milk." If the mother were not resentful towards others, how could the child fall ill with diarrhea? If the mother did not have fire rising inside her, how could the child develop a fever?

We actually experienced this very issue in my own family. When my eldest son was born, my wife had a lot of fire in her disposition, and our child was constantly sick. I asked my wife: "All these illnesses that our son is suffering from, aren't they your responsibility?" She replied: "All you do is blame me! How come you don't speak of your own role in this?" I explained to her: "What he is drinking is your milk; what is sustaining him is your blood.[2] How could I not blame you?" In fact, though, blaming my wife was wrong. It was that I as the man in the family had failed to act as a leader. At that time, I had not yet grasped that principle, so whenever I got upset, I just wanted to discipline my wife. The more I disciplined her, the more the fire in her flared up, and the more our son fell ill. How awful indeed! Because I had this direct personal experience, I take what I learned from my own situation and teach that to everybody else. This is what Wang Shanren was referring to when he said: "Do not leave the anvil when you forge iron; do not leave your own experience when you teach the Dao." To be able to explain something and to allow everybody to grasp what you are trying to say and receive benefit from hearing it, you truly must have experienced it, you must have walked down that road yourself and know what you are talking about.

"When the heart is balanced and the Qi harmonious, this is best." This phrase explains that it is best when the mother waits until her heart has calmed down and her Qi smoothed out before she lets the baby breastfeed. The reason is that harmonious Qi results in harmonious milk, and harmonious milk in turn makes the baby's body harmonious and balanced, and so the baby will not fall ill.

These days, so many mothers lack common knowledge when it comes to "education in breast-feeding." Unknowingly, they plant the cause of illness in their children when they nurse them. When the mother is angry, the milk will have a Yin quality to it and can even turn sour. This kind of breast milk is poisonous milk, and children who have consumed this milk easily develop liver disease. When the mother has too much fire in her, too much hatred, the milk will be poisoned by fire. And children who consume this kind of milk easily develop heart disease. Why is it that these days we see so many small children

---

2   In Chinese medicine, breast milk is seen as a transformation of the mother's blood.

with liver disease? That so many small children suffer from heart disease? All of these are related to the fact that they consumed their mother's "Qi milk" or "fire milk". I have seen, discussed, and explained a great number of these cases. If the children are still small (under the age of 12) and the mother is able to turn her conscience around, recovery may be possible.

In 2004, I met a young man from QiQihar in Heilongjiang Province who was suffering from uremia. His relatives came knocking at my door at 2 in the morning, telling me that this fellow had faith in me and had asked for a face-to-face meeting with me, for which he would happily give his life. I had no choice but to go, since they were so determined to force me to go with them. As soon as I got to the hospital, I saw with my own eyes that the young man was indeed in very serious condition. At the moment he had received the diagnosis of uremia, he had fallen to the ground paralyzed, unable to move at all. In my mind, I thought that he first needed a bit of psychological support, so I addressed him: "Young man, is it true that you wanted to see me?" He opened his eyes, so I next asked him how he was doing. He replied: "Uremia! When you contract this disease, there is no cure." I countered by telling him that he was not suffering from uremia. Surprised, he asked me again, and again I told him so. So he asked, "Then why is it that I am in this condition?" I explained: "You have been frightened. This is the psychological effect." He confirmed that he had indeed been utterly frightened, and I agreed: "You are correct. You have surely been frightened very badly." At this point, all of a sudden he sat up and explained: "With this sentence of yours, you have brought sudden clarity to my mind. I have my strength back!"

Just look, everybody, how great the effect of the mind can be! A physician once told me that of all the cancer patients, not everyone dies from the cancer. When I asked him to explain, he said that 60 percent of them do die from the cancer, but the other 40 percent die from fear. The young man with uremia had simply been frightened deeply. After he opened up his heart, he got his spirit back, and he happily stated that he was ready to leave the hospital right then and there. I advised, though, that he not leave right away but stay for 2 or 3 days longer, until he had fully recovered. He said that he trusted me and would follow my advice. I then turned around and called the young man's mother out into the hallway where I asked her: "Please try and remember closely: When you were feeding your son, were you ever experiencing great anger?" She replied: "Yes. In the second year of his life, I once felt deep rage towards his father. I laid in bed for three whole days without moving at all, and my son climbed up onto my body to breast-feed." So I explained to her: "Your son's illness was planted by you at that very moment. How big do you think that rage was if it caused you to lie in bed for three days without moving? And however big that rage was, this is how big the poison was. And this poison entered your blood and eventually transformed into your breast milk. Feeding on this poisonous milk for three days, this is how the roots of his disease were implanted firmly. But why is it that this disease has only surfaced thirty years later? Because before your son started working in a job, while he was in school and studying, there was nothing that troubled him too badly. It is only after he started working that he encountered situations that didn't go his way, so he constantly got angry and flared up with rage. This caused that old root to get pulled to the surface." When she asked me what to do about this now, I advised: "Wait until your son is out of the hospital, and then you come to my place together. I will explain the reason behind this whole situation to both of you. If you are able to turn your conscience around and fundamentally transform yourself, it may be possible to save him still."

Three days later, the young man left the hospital, looking like a completely healthy person. After leaving the hospital, he now wanted to come to my place with his mother, but his older brother and brother-in-law told him: "Don't go! We don't know what sort of a person he is. At the hospital, he told you that you didn't have any illness, that it was all just caused by your mind. And sure enough, you look like you really don't have any serious illness, so don't go!" The fellow was unable to counter their opposition and turned around to go home instead of coming to see me. After a month, his illness struck again and shortly afterwards he died. So you can see, everybody, how essential it is that the mother maintains a good disposition while she is breast-feeding.

"If babies are crying, make them cheer up first." Do not breast-feed babies when they are crying but make them cheer up first before you feed them. When you are nursing, listen closely to the sound of the baby's crying, whether the sound comes from the throat, the tongue, the lips, the teeth, or the nose. By examining the sound of children's crying, you can know their inner nature (*xing*). And at the time when you breast-feed, you can "call their inner nature" (*jiao xing*).[3] For example, if the child has a fire nature, while you nurse him or her, you chant "*Wo er ming li, wo er ming li*" ("my child is *ming li*, my child is *ming li*"), and then you chant "*Wo er rou he, wo er rou he*" ("my child is *rou he*, my child is *rou he*"). In this way you pour Yang Qi into your child. This advice is a precious gift that Wang Shanren realized after he comprehended the connection between Heaven and *xing*. We must sincerely utilize this gift and sincerely cultivate the next generation. "Feed four times during the day and three times at night, no more and no less." It is essential that you manage the number of feedings properly. It is best to feed four times during the day, and you must not exceed three feedings at night, so even if you deviate from this norm a little bit, you cannot deviate too much. If you can follow this rule, the child will have a healthy appetite, and a healthy spleen and stomach. This is what is called "able to breast-feed."

Those of us who are mothers and want to give birth a healthy child must comprehend the principles outlined above. In the context of "education in newborn care," I lectured on the importance of paying attention to neonatal hygiene, but what is the most important aspect of hygiene, of guarding life?[4] It is precisely this: that mothers must never ever get angry or allow the fire of rage to flare up during the stage in their lives when they are raising children. If you get angry and allow the fire of rage to flare up, this is not "guarding life."

1.5 STEP FIVE: EDUCATION IN INFANT CARE

To continue, let us now discuss education in infant care: "In the heart of newborn babes, in the eyes of infants, Heaven's truth is reflected. Teach *xiao*, teach *ti*, and their inner nature will return to the root."

"In the heart of newborn babes, in the eyes of infants, Heaven's truth is reflected." Right after children are born, their hearts are particularly pure. The reason for this is that their true heavenly nature is apparent. At this time,

---

3   See appendix, "Heavenly Nature Affirmations" on page 276.

4   There is a little play with meaning going on here since the Chinese word for the modern concept of hygiene, in the sense of sanitation, literally means "safe-guarding life" *wei sheng* 衛生.

children are just like blank sheets of paper. Whatever we draw on them they will manifest. Whatever we teach them they will learn.

"Teach *xiao*, teach *ti*." Children must grasp *xiao* and respect for the older generation and unity and love for friends from an early age on. This is the most fundamental aspect of education, which they must begin to learn from infancy on. Mom and dad are the child's first teachers and when the child's intellect is just beginning to develop, every word or deed of yours, every act and move, will leave a profound mark in the child's brain. For

small children, teaching with your words is not as good as teaching with your actions, and the parents' behavior is therefore particularly important. If we want to educate our children well, we must first set a good example in our actions.

"Their inner nature will return to the root." Whether a child's body and heart are healthy or not depends directly on the parents, because the parents are the root of the child. Modern people are for the most part not aware of this point, and as soon as their child develops any kind of health problem, they run straight to the hospital. We don't act like this in my family. I have one grandson and three granddaughters, and in the past, when both of our daughters-in-law were away on business in Changchun, my wife and I entertained the children in our home. Whenever any of the children fell ill, I first called up the child's mother and informed her: "Your child has caught a cold and is running a fever. What shall we do?" And we would not say anything more. As grandpa and grandma, you don't want to tell your daughters-in-law too much, just get to the point and say no more. If you say too much, they might resent you for nagging, so just alerting them briefly is all you need to do. This technique works exceptionally well: My daughters-in-law would receive our phone call and respond: "Don't you worry. I know what's going on." After she said that she knew, the child would invariably just recover quickly. This is called the "heart connection between mother and child," referring to the fact that they are connected with each other. Even though the children were no longer drinking the mothers' milk, these seedlings had been planted and cultivated together by the mother and father. If you consistently sprinkle sweet dew on them, they will surely grow well. But if you consistently roast them in the fire, they will most certainly fail to grow.

There was a young boy in Yi'an County, Heilongjiang Province, who was barely three years old. As soon as he entered a room, no matter how many people were present, he would go and grope every one of them. And then he would break any and all nice things that you might have in that room. When his mother took him to the market, he would go into every single stall and pick up everything, but if you stopped him from doing so he started yelling. And if he still didn't get his way, he started to hit, and then, if he was unable to win the fight, he opened his mouth to bite. This was the kind of child he was.

This boy's maternal grandfather had suffered from liver cirrhosis with hematemesis and I had gone to explain to him about his illness and suggested that he also have surgery, as a result of which he had regained his health. The boy's maternal grandmother had had a uterine tumor, which she had also recovered from. Therefore, as soon as the old couple saw what was going on with their daughter's son, they had their daughter bring him to my home. This was in 2006. At that time, I said: "This boy's illness is his mother's problem. It is only because your disposition is not good that the child is acting like this." But the mother initially refused to admit her fault. It was only after her own mother admonished her over and over that she finally came back with her head bowed low and admitted her wrongdoing. After she had broken down and cried deeply three times in front of me, I felt that this was good enough and told her that she could take her son home.

Upon returning home, even though they went to the market as before, the boy looked at all the things in the stalls but did not touch anything. Everybody was quite surprised by this and asked him: "How did you change like this? Why are you not taking things?" He simply answered that he didn't take things. When they asked him why he didn't yell at people, he answered that he didn't yell. And when they asked him why, he replied: "My mother has learned to be good, and I have also learned to be good." So you see, a three-year-old child is able to achieve such a degree of change! Wang Shanren lectured: "When the parents' nature is good, the children will also be good. When the parents' nature is bad, the children will also be bad." This sentence could not be any clearer. Word for word, it states the truth. When your child does not listen, do not hold the child responsible, because the root for the behavior is still inside your own person.

To give you another example, I met an 18-year-old boy once who had suddenly become shortsighted. His myopia was quite severe, with a score of 750. Since this young man had previously enjoyed perfectly normal vision, why had he suddenly become so shortsighted? When his mother asked him why his eyes had so suddenly changed like this and whether he had developed a negative attitude towards a schoolmate or teacher, he said that nothing had happened. I understood this child and knew he truly had not done anything. Since the child did not have a problem, I turned around and asked the mother: "This shortsightedness in your child here, where did this come from? In your role as a mother, you must reflect and look inside yourself very carefully." Just a moment later, she told me that she understood what was going on and that this issue was indeed her own problem. What kind of a problem? Previously, she had gotten into an argument with her brother-in-law, during the course of which he had slapped her in the face twice. This situation had made her furious and caused her to cry again and again. Whenever she saw her brother-in-law, she just couldn't let it go, and had thereby planted disease in her son's body. Later, when she examined herself, she realized that she herself was too small-minded in her heart. Why wasn't she able to be like Wang Fengyi and genuinely practice *bu yuan ren* ("do not blame others")? After truly experiencing regret and confessing in earnest, breaking down twice in tears, though, her son was able to get rid of his glasses. So you see, everybody, it is true that mother and child are connected in the heart, and the role of the mother is therefore of utmost significance!

1.6 STEP SIX: EDUCATING THE FAMILY

The final step is educating the family. "First there are the father and mother, and then afterwards children and grandchildren. To know what they will be like in the future, look at the cause in the past. If you want to make your sons have *xiao*, you yourself must serve as their good example." The meaning of this quotation is quite obvious: Whatever the parents are like, the children will invariably turn out likewise. We all want our children to have a heart full of *xiao*, but the good example must come from us ourselves. If you treat your relatives with *xiao*, your child will most certainly treat you with *xiao* in turn. If you go against your relatives, your child will most certainly go against you. This is the order of nature and Heaven's cycle of rewards and punishments.

Whether your child is good or bad, do not blame the child. In our role as parents, we must carefully consider the following questions: What kind of a son or daughter have I been in the past? What kind of a mother or father am I right now? Has my behavior been up to standard or not? The parents plant the seeds and the children harvest the fruits. Every intention and thought of the parents, every word and deed, every act and move, are all causes, and the ways in which the children later live their lives are the fruits. When you plant melons, you get melons; when you plant beans, you get beans. When you plant a Bodhi tree, auspicious flowers are bound to bloom. If you have not planted anything in the spring, what will you harvest in the fall? We all desire to have a good harvest, and we all desire to have children with a heart of *xiao*, but if you haven't planted good causes, how can you harvest good fruits?

I once read the following story about a virtuous grandson acting in *xiao* towards his ancestors in a book on the Dao of *xiao*: There once was a couple who did not have a lot of *xiao*. They had two children. The parents of this couple were getting old and they were quite garrulous, chattering on and on all day long, which the couple did not like to listen to. So they put their heads together and hatched out a plan. At this time, it happened to be summer. The couple built a thatched hut in the mountains and made the parents leave to live in the mountains, so that they didn't have to hear their nagging. But they told the old people: "We have prepared a place for you in the mountains where you can get away from the heat of the summer. You can rest there and cultivate yourselves in tranquility, with no need to worry about our family affairs. And when the weather turns cool in the fall, we will bring you back home." As soon as the old parents heard this, they thought that the children truly had a heart of *xiao*, and so they happily agreed to this plan.

Summer passed quickly and fall arrived, but the husband and wife failed to keep their previous promise to bring their old parents home. Because the grandson and granddaughter, who were already more than ten years of age, were missing their grandpa and grandma, they often went up in the mountain to go visit them. One day, the old grandparents asked when the children's father and mother were coming to bring them back home. The grandchildren had not heard either of their parents talk about wanting to bring the old grandparents back home but, not wanting to hurt their grandparents' feelings, responded casually: "Our father and mother have said that they will soon come to fetch you."

When the children returned home and their parents still did not mention anything about bringing the grandparents home, what were they to do? A little older than the boy, the girl pondered this situation for a while, until she at last came up with a solution. She told her brother: "Quickly go and bring me the cart that we used to take our grandparents up to the mountain." Her younger brother responded: "Why should I look for that cart? It broke a long time ago." The sister told him not to worry about that and to just find it so she could repair it. The brother had no choice but to obey his older sister, found the old cart, brought it back, and they started hammering away at it. Seeing her children act like this, the mother thought this strange and thus asked them what they were doing, hammering away at this old broken cart. The older sister answered: "In the future, when you and father are old, what else should we use to push you both up the mountain? So we are now repairing the cart for the future." These words struck the parents like a crack of thunder striking on a sunny day and made them break out in sweat from the top of their heads and center of the back. The parents said to each other: "This is not good! The children have learned from what we did. Let us go right away and bring our old parents back home." You see, whether a person's root is good or bad relies entirely on the influence of the parents. "If you want to make your sons have *xiao*, you yourself must serve as their good example."

II. Exalting Frugality In Marriage

As we have discussed before, if we want to give birth to good children, to leave behind good human roots for our descendants, we must first focus on education of the root. Before a man and a woman get married, the two parties must both purify their heart and mind and regulate their own words and deeds. In addition, at the time of the wedding and after, it is best if they can implement a "marriage that exalts frugality."

II.1 THE FOUR PURPOSES OF MARRIAGE

First, to better look after the elders in both parties' families, to set their minds at rest, to give them joy and happiness. Second, for the husband and wife to care for and love each other, to guide and support each other, to allow each other to succeed. Third, to bring up sons and daughters, to raise children with *xiao* and virtuous grandchildren for the family line, to raise raw material for future ridge poles of society. Fourth, to become a model husband and wife, to establish a model family, to provide leadership for the improvement of public morals. Husband and wife are the beginning of human relationships and the foundation of creation. It is for the sake of the rest of the world, and it is likewise for the sake of the rest of the world that we raise sons and daughters.

II.2 A REASONABLE BETROTHAL

When getting engaged, pay attention to three key points: First, the father and mother must approve. If father and mother are steadfastly opposed, from beginning to end, and refuse to agree, you must not go against your parents' wishes and act in willful disobedience. This would be in violation of *xiao* towards your parents and not being in alignment with their heart. Second, accept fate. "All the myriad things are determined by fate, not even the tiniest point is determined by people." People nowadays all fight against fate. And while fate is limited by one's lot, it is only when you carry out acts of goodness, merit, and virtue that your lot is drawn at all. Third, and this is the most important one, the couple must be harmonious in heart and mind. Only if this is the case can we call it a "union of Yin and Yang." It is only when Yin and Yang are united in harmony that they can produce a virtuous wife. And only when there is a virtuous wife can you have a good mother, can you have children with *xiao*. It is only a family like this that can be harmonious and happy, with a good relationship between mother-in-law and daughter-in-law.

11.3 A MARRIAGE THAT EXALTS FRUGALITY

The sages and worthies of the ancient past admonished us: "Relationships for the sake of power break apart as soon as the power ends. Relationships for the sake of profit become distant as soon as the profit ends. In relationships for the sake of sex, love changes as soon as the flower drops. Relationships for the sake of the Dao, though, are like the vastness of Heaven and the old age of Earth." Marriages that are formed for the sake of power and influence, material wealth, or outward appearance all fall into the category of worldly marriage and lack a solid foundation. Eventually, when these external premises disappear, the feelings of the husband and wife immediately lose their safeguard.

For this reason, the bride's family should not demand betrothal gifts at the time of the wedding. Regardless of how many cars, how many multistory buildings, how much wealth they get, all of these are just external things. If you only focus on these, what do you make yourself look like? Don't you make yourself look like nothing but a commodity? Hasn't that turned the marriage into a business transaction? Therefore I say, we must value ourselves, respect ourselves for our own sake. Why do we marry? We marry to fulfill the Dao of husband and wife, to complete this mission, and not for the sake of material desires. This is the most basic attitude that women should have towards marriage, and when their attitude is straight, everything else is straight as well. But when their attitude is crooked, everything else is crooked as well.

In addition, when you arrange the wedding ceremony, avoid ostentation, extravagance, waste, and squandering of wealth. Because if you squander wealth conspicuously, anybody who got harmed will later seek retribution from both parties. Why is it that some people fail to find happiness after they get married? Because the graft has not successfully joined together with the rootstock. And if the graft and stock are not joined together well, there is even less of a chance of improving the "Later-Heaven (i.e. post-natal) root."

I don't know about young people in the city, but in the countryside they place great emphasis on betrothal gifts. These days, these can amount to more than 100,000 Yuan. For rural families to acquire a daughter-in-law, they need 160,000 to 170,000 Yuan, in high cases even 180,000 Yuan. And when the wedding is completed, the young couple has turned into wealthy moguls while the old parents have become paupers who are forced to beg for food. Why do I say that children are here to collect the debt from our past? Think carefully! Isn't this what happens: Even though they have caused this great hardship (the debt the parents owe because of the costs of the marriage), the young people don't care. And the old people, advanced in age already, how are they going to repay it? Only able to cultivate a small piece of land, they are worried and gloomy all day long, while the young couple, on the other hand, is happy and joyous all day long. Where is their conscience? Do they have no humanity left in them?

I once met an old couple in this kind of a situation who had sold their house, their land, and even their car to get together the dowry for their son's wife. After the son got married, the parents moved into a rented house. One day, they came to me, crying bitterly. I told these two old people: "Don't cry, and don't have any resentment either. This is a debt, a bill. Just accept that it is time to pay it. If you try, bit by bit, you may yet manage to repay it." And after I exhorted them like this two or three times, they indeed came to let go of their resentment.

Later, I ran into them again. This time, they were no longer upset but told me happily: "We have really been able to let go of our resentment. All the things you told us, we were able to remember. This situation is truly a debt, and if we don't repay it, then who will? So we have no choice but to gladly repay it." I replied: "You are right! If you gladly repay it like this, won't the debt eventually be paid off and disappear?" In fact, in my opinion there is yet one more reason for this kind of result: Do you know where this debt-collection came from? To discuss this from the perspective of the Dao, in reality this money should have been spent on supporting the elders. If the money that we give to our children exceeds the money we spend on supporting our elders and it thus appears that we only attend to our children but not to our elders, this is called attending to our Yin fate, and losing our Heavenly fate (*tianming* 天命). Because we have forgotten the root, the children that we give birth to will not be *xiao*.

11.4 IN THE CHOICE OF A SPOUSE, DO NOT SEEK TOO HIGH

Wang Shanren told us: "The higher we are, the higher we set our sight. The higher we are, the more dismal the situation." If you only know how to seek what is high, once you reach it, it is truly dismal. In terms of their material desires, women should therefore not reach too high. If a man is inferior to you in all areas, then just tell yourself: "Since no other girl will marry you, I will help you be successful." Someone who does not understand the Dao might tell you: "How can you be such a fool! You may want money but he has none; you may want power but he has none. And on top of that he is quite a simpleton." But a person who understands the Dao will say: "This girl has a true grasp of the Dao. She is able to provide support to a simpleton. One who gives support to a simpleton is a sage." What is the true significance of all teachings, ancient or modern, and of all sages and saints? Isn't it precisely to provide support for simpletons? In such an important matter as marriage, if you take a person who is inferior to you and give him support, accepting him joyfully instead of rejecting him, aren't you making great strides towards sagehood? If you are able to act like this, in the future you are bound to give birth to good children. If, however, you regard yourself as clever but always look down on your husband as a simpleton and think he can't accomplish anything, he will in fact fail at everything. This is called "cleverness being misled by its own cleverness" or "quick-wittedness falling victim to its own quick wit." If you have ten parts intelligence, you can use eight parts but must leave two parts to give to your children and grandchildren, because you cannot overuse intelligence.

There was a female college student once in Zhaoguang County in Heilongjiang Province who went to work in a sugar factory close to her home after she graduated. Both she herself and her mother heard me lecture about the Dao. When she subsequently looked for a partner, she chose a young man who had also gone to college but who had a little deformity: He was a hunchback, with a bulge in his spine. After her mother met him, she did not quite agree with her daughter's choice. So the daughter told her: "Mother! What happened to the Dao that you heard Master Liu lecture us about? Didn't he tell us that if there is nobody else who wants to marry somebody, we can help make them successful? Now there is nobody else who will marry him, so I will. In addition, I do not want a single betrothal gift." As soon as the girl's mother heard these words, she knew that she had been mistaken and so she approved of this marriage. So as soon as the girl had obtained her father's and mother's permission, she indeed went and married this boy. They registered their marriage certificate and were thus formally married, without even the neighbors noticing anything. This event took place in 1999.

After the couple got married, they bought train tickets and got ready to go to Shanghai. I was just coming back from Changchun and happened to run into them. The girl told me: "At the moment I only have 30 Yuan in my pocket, which is just enough for the two of us to live on for a single day. But you wait and see, grandpa Liu, how I put this money to good use!"

She then went to Shanghai with her husband for work, and in a single month, they were able to earn more than 3,000 Yuan. One day, her husband's older brother called them up and told them that his son wanted to get married but they were short a lot of money. This lady immediately took all their money and borrowed some from others, so that they were able to send 15,000 Yuan to the husband's older brother. And after she mailed the money off, she even told her brother-in-law that the money was a gift for his son and that he didn't need to pay them back. Not long after this, she brought her mother-in-law to Shanghai, where she cared for her with great devotion. She subsequently gave birth to a child who was not only intelligent but also had a straight back.

This lady once told me: "I don't act for the sake of money or material things. I just want to set an example for society, to cause others to not just care about wanting money. The current situation is so bad." So everybody, look at this story and the integrity that this lady has! What a shame that there are so few people these days who promote public morality like this. If there are only one or two like this, the effect is so limited! To promote public morality, we need everybody to strive together, to practice what we teach, to quietly go ahead and act on our conscience, to quietly change ourselves.

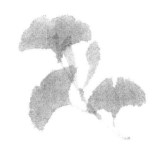

LECTURE SIX

Daily Life and Cultivation

I. Cultivating Both Our *Xing* (Inner Nature) and Our *Ming* (Heavenly Mandate)

Somebody once asked me: "Cultivation! What is it that we cultivate? And how do we cultivate?" Generally speaking, the sages of the five great world religions all taught the dual cultivation of both *xing* (性, "inner nature") and *ming* (命, "heavenly mandate or destiny"). If you cultivate *xing* without also cultivating *ming*, your divine radiance has no application. If you cultivate *ming* without also cultivating *xing*, it will be difficult to become a sage even in countless lifetimes. We must cultivate both *xing* and *ming*. This is the only way if we want to reach a state of utmost goodness and obtain karmic fruits of utmost goodness.

What does it mean to "cultivate *xing*"? To cultivate *xing* means to get rid of our bad habits, to transform and dispel our acquired nature (*bingxing*) and to round out and perfect our heavenly nature (*tianxing*). "At the beginning of human life, the *xing* is rooted in goodness." Our original nature is always good. Then why is it that this heavenly nature of fundamental goodness does not reveal itself? Because it is concealed by material desires, covered up tightly by "later-heaven" bad habits and our acquired nature (*bingxing*). Due to later-heaven contamination, under the influence of weather, landscape, geography, and the ancestral lineages of our parents, our acquired nature (*bingxing*) and habits have taken shape. And the roots of this acquired nature are very deep indeed! If that were not the case, why would we have the saying, "Rivers and mountains are easy to change but the *bingxing* is difficult to shift"?

If we are thinking about transforming and dispelling our *bing xing*, we must start with our bad habits, because bad habits are the root of the *bing xing*. Killing, stealing, lechery, recklessness, and alcoholism, extravagant diet and clothing, smoking and drinking and gambling away large sums of money, all of these are bad habits. It is only after shaking off such bad habits that we are able to transform and dispel our acquired nature and perfect our heavenly nature. If we do not shake off these bad habits, it will be very difficult to transform our acquired nature. Wang Shanren told us: "Those who live for the sake of fame die on account of fame. Those who live for the sake of profit die on account of profit. Those who live for the sake of riches die on account of riches. Those who live for the sake of sex die on account of sex." If you say that you want to cultivate yourself but as soon as you encounter liquor, sex, or riches your heart starts itching intensely, what can you possibly cultivate like that? Of course you must get rid of all your bad habits, but in addition you must also preserve your good habits, rather than cutting yourself off from everything in one fell swoop. If you throw off all your habits, including your good ones, then there will be nobody left to perform good deeds.

What does it mean to "cultivate *ming*" ("heavenly mandate")? To cultivate *ming* means that we clearly understand our central role in life. To give everything in the service of this central role in our life, this is to cultivate *ming*. Whatever your title is in this life, this is precisely your *ming*.[1] In relationship to your parents, if you are a "son," you correspondingly have the mandate of "son." If you are a "daughter," you have the mandate of being a daughter. If you fail to act as a proper daughter, you have lost your *ming*, and losing your *ming* means violating Heaven's mandate. The reason for this is that this name was given to you by all of humanity, and all of humanity simply means Heaven.

---

1   The Chinese here uses a play with words, since the Chinese term for "title" (名) has a similar pronunciation to the term *ming* ("mandate").

Let me use myself as an example. Everybody addresses me as "*shanren*" ("Virtuous Person"). In the beginning, I did not like being called "virtuous person" by everybody, and whenever somebody addressed me as such, I turned away. I was not pleased because this title was too great and I feared that I was unable to live up to it. Later on, I pondered this and examined myself. Why was everybody calling me "virtuous person"? Because I had already been lecturing about illness for a full thirty years. The sick people who came to my home, they came from all over and were all sorts of people. When you come to my place, I give you food to eat, I give you a place to stay, and I also give you explanations about your illness. And when your illness is cured, you go off to wherever you want to go. I do not accept money for food or for lodging, or even for explaining your illness. For this reason, everybody has given me this title of "*shànrén*." And when I thought about it like this, I came to accept it calmly in my heart. In return, I must be a "virtuous person" who truly lives up to this name, otherwise I have violated Heaven's mandate and Heaven will punish me. Lecturing about the Dao, I have also said in the past: "I do not live for the sake of fame nor for the sake of profit, neither for the sake of myself nor for the sake of my family." Then what is it that I want to be doing? I want to make the whole world my family, roam the Four Seas and help all living beings, until everyone among us is healthy in body and mind and enjoys a long life. I want to allow every family among us to be harmonious and happy.

II. The Dao of Being Human

II.I BEING ABLE TO BE HUMAN MEANS TO BE A LIVING BUDDHA

Wang Shanren once said: "Do not chat about mysteries or discuss miracles. Just explain the Dao of being human." When we discuss the Dao, we discuss this topic or that topic, but we never depart from this one word: human. This is because the Dao comes out of our cultivating our human-ness. If we leave the Dao of being human as we chat about cultivation, then we have strayed from what is near to pursue what is distant, strayed from the root to pursue a branch, which means we have deviated from cultivation altogether. Study the

Dao of being human, don't study what deviates from this. A deviated Dao will not be able to help you become a Buddha or a sage. Nowadays, however, quite a few people pray to the Buddha or chant scriptures, praying to the point where they scatter their family. How do they scatter the family? An older couple separated. Just past forty years of age, they lived separately. Worshipping the Buddha like that, can your partner be happy? The founders of the five great religions all wished for harmony and happiness in our families. Who among them would cause us to split our family apart?

Here is another perspective: We cannot wait until we die before we become Buddhas, but we must be living Buddhas. How do we become Buddhas while we are alive? By keeping a Buddha's heart, speaking a Buddha's speech, managing a Buddha's tasks, we become perfect in this body and turn into a Buddha right here in this lifetime. If you are able to be human, you can be a living Buddha. If you are unable to be human and wait until after you have died to become a Buddha, it is doubtful that you will succeed. Because Buddhahood is accomplished by being human. If you have not fulfilled your role as a human, how can you become a Buddha?

Now when we lecture on the Dao, our goal is to let you know in what position you stand in life, how you should act to fulfill your Dao. This is very important. If you are able to live correctly in the role of the young woman, then you are a young woman Buddha. If you are able to live correctly in the role of the old lady, then you are an old lady Buddha. It is only when the human Dao is accomplished perfectly that the heavenly Dao can return. What we practice is the human Dao, what we obtain is the heavenly Dao, and what we become is the Buddha Dao.

Students of Buddhism understand that every single human is caught in the wheel of transmigration. What is this thing called "transmigration"? Transmigration is in fact not something that awaits us after we die, a process by which we turn into a cat today and into a dog tomorrow. That is talking about something too far away. What happens before birth and after death is something that none of us can see or touch. In fact, though, transmigration is relevant right here and now: The family is one cycle in the wheel of transmigration. Every one of our family members is caught in this wheel of transmigration. To live is to transmigrate. Yesterday you were the young girl, today you are the daughter-in-law, tomorrow you will be the mother, and the day after tomorrow, you will be the mother-in-law, and the day after you will be the grandmother. Isn't this a continuous turning of the wheel of transmigration? Each of these roles we must play, and we must play them well. And whichever turn you have not played well, that is a turn that you have transgressed in. And since you were unable to pass that bar, you are unable to exit the cycle of transmigration but must continue on from one turn to the next.

A man once told me that he was afraid of ghosts. I told him he was talking nonsense and asked him where these ghosts were. So he asked back, "how could there be no ghosts?" I answered: "Humans are ghosts, and ghosts are humans. If you act like a ghost, you are a ghost. If you act like a human, you are a human. If you act like a saint, you are a saint. If you act like a Buddha, you are a Buddha. It all depends on how you act in every-day life." If you are pure in your heart and keep silent, not saying anything good and not saying anything vile, then you are a Buddha. If you are satisfied and constantly joyful and find joy in helping others, you are a saint, a living immortal. If you are selfish and self-centered, find happiness in taking advantage of others but get angry when you suffer a loss, doesn't this make you a ghost? If you allow your *bing xing* (acquired nature) to take over, act like a contentious and greedy rabble-rouser, yelling and cursing, hitting and fighting, then you are living in hell at that moment. When I was young, I had a terrible temper and was not afraid of anybody. If you wanted a fight, we'd fight. I'd risk my life to fight with you. Otherwise could I have gotten so sick that I was at the edge of death? Isn't this state something that I myself created, so that I harvested the result of my actions?

Human, ghost, saint, and Buddha, what condition are they all created from? They are all created from the human condition. If you employ a ghost's heart, you are a ghost. If you employ a human heart, you are a human. If you employ a saint's heart, that are a saint. If you employ a Buddha's heart, you are a Buddha. Wang Shanren once said: "Even if you have worn out your mouth praying and broken your legs kneeling, if your inner nature is not transformed, you are still a ghost living in hell." It is of no use at all to go on and on all day about how you are studying Buddhism. What matters is what you do. If you preserve a

Buddha heart, speak Buddha words, and carry out Buddha actions, then that simply shows that you are a Buddha. What business do you have to talk about it!

It is too bad that people nowadays all are willing to be ghosts but are not willing to be Buddhas. Why do I say this? Because as soon as they open their eyes, they look at other people's faults, and as soon as they close their eyes, they think of other people's faults. This person is wrong, that person is wrong, everything is wrong. And when other people are wrong, you just get angry, and when you get angry, you get sick. There is an old saying that refers exactly to these kinds of people: "If your Qi is like a ghost, you will fall ill like a ghost." Therefore I say, just let it go! Stop taking on other people's shortcomings and mistakes and thereby punishing yourself.

II.2 FULLY LIVING UP TO OUR RESPONSIBILITY

The Five Elements (*wuxing* 五行, "five dynamic movements": earth, metal, water, wood, fire) operate on the level of the human body, and they also operate on the level of the family and on the level of the country. In the family, each of us has our very own title, our very own Dao. In society, because of our different professions we are responsible for different tasks. To scrupulously and fully carry out our duties is also a way to fulfill our *ming* (destiny or mandate). As for the Five Elements at the level of the country, they are: scholar, farmer, worker, merchant, and official. Each of these professions has its own use, each has its own strongpoints, and none of them are dispensable.

The scholars are there to teach from the books, they are the teachers. They allow people to have knowledge, culture, competence, to understand science and promote development. These are the responsibilities of the scholar. Confucius taught people and became a sage. Why was he able to become a sage? Because he taught everybody, regardless of whether they were wise or foolish, poor or rich. The poorer or more foolish his students were, the more he taught them, and to support and lift up fools is what a paragon of virtue does. We have all read in the "Record of Words and Actions" (*Yan Xing Lu*, the title of a book by Wang Fengyi) how muddle-headed Li Yongcheng was, which is why everybody called him "Idiot Monk." Wang Fengyi, however, did not despise him for his lack of intelligence but kept him close by his side until eventually Li

Yongcheng became a Buddha. Therefore, we must also learn to support and lift up fools, to cause them to transform into paragons of virtue.

Farmers are there to cultivate the land. Regardless of blowing wind or pouring rain, farmers must tend to the land so that they can harvest grain to provide food for all the people on earth, to lay the foundation for the country. This is the proper task and duty of farmers. Nowadays, farmers use scientific methods to grow crops. In northeastern China, harvesting, threshing, planting, and tilling have all been mechanized. And the national government has opened up new opportunities for us. Not only have they stopped collecting taxes for the land but they even hand out subsidies for fertilizer and for diesel fuel, so that we can earn more than 20 Yuan per *mu* of land. In this way, they have raised farmers' enthusiasm for working the land, and farmers now all want to cultivate more land and are able to do so well. One *shang* of land (equal to 15 *mu*) is now able to produce more than 20,000 *jin* of corn.

Workers also carry the responsibilities of workers. They must not steal, trick, cut corners, or act like crooks in their own self-interest. Whatever they construct must be sturdy and solid and they must constantly improve their skills. This is what it means to fully live up to their Dao. In addition, if they are unable to be utterly diligent and sincere and to do their job by laboring hard and enduring criticism, they are disloyal. Being disloyal to their boss, disloyal to their country, disloyal to the people means that they are failing in their job.

What is the obligation of merchants? Merchants are associated with water among the Five Elements. Water flows and transports, and likewise they circulate commodities between north and south. They transport things from the south to the north, so that people in the north can enjoy the goods from the south, and they transport things from the north to the south, so that southerners can also enjoy the goods from the north. This is the Dao of merchants. And while they are buying and selling, they must not deal in stolen or counterfeit goods or play dirty tricks to deceive customers. They must not alter weights to cheat consumers, but their scales must be fair. Because the human heart is not fair, scales were created, and the three good luck stars of happiness, good fortune, and long life are embossed on the scale. If you do something unconscionable and give short weight, you directly harm your three stars of happiness, good fortune, and long life. You may think that when you deceive people nobody will know. But in reality you yourself know so in your heart, and hence everybody else knows so as well, because the human heart is directly connected to Heaven's heart.

In the "Record of Words and Actions," Zhao Pinsan asks Wang Fengyi whether merchants have a Dao, and Wang Fengyi replies: "Yes, they do have a Dao. They have the merchant's Dao." While they were talking like this, they saw a farmer push his cart up to an oil mill to sell his soybeans. The farmer asked what the going price for beans was, and the proprietor of the mill who was receiving beans answered, 1.15 Yuan per *jin*. The farmer rejected this price as too low and pushed his cart to a different mill to sell his beans there. As soon as the farmer had left, the proprietor of the first oil mill called up the boss at the second oil mill to inform him: "A farmer just came to sell beans and I told him I'd buy them for 1.15 Yuan, but he didn't sell and is going over to see you now." When the farmer got to the second mill and asked what the going price for soybeans was there, the proprietor there offered him 1.1 Yuan. The farmer told the proprietor: "I didn't' sell my beans for 1.15 Yuan, so I most certainly will not sell them for 1.1 Yuan." And with that said, he left to go to yet another oil mill. When he got there and again asked for the price, the proprietor there quoted him a price of 1.05 Yuan. The farmer responded: "If I didn't sell my beans for 1.15 Yuan, how could I sell them to you for 1.05 Yuan?" The farmer then returned to the first place, which had offered him 1.15 Yuan and wanted to sell his soybeans there, but the proprietor told him: "That is no longer possible. I just got a phone call from Harbin and the price of soybeans has fallen to 1 Yuan per *jin*. Will you sell them to me or not?" The farmer had no choice but to sell his beans off at 1 Yuan per *jin*. According to Wang Shanren, this kind of a person is a deceitful merchant, and his behavior is harming the Dao of merchants! Because of this, the boss of this oil mill was robbed three times in thirty years, or on average once every ten years. As a result, after thirty years had passed he had no wealth accumulated and had only the building left to his name. According to an old saying, wealth that is amassed by wrongdoing will scatter sooner or later. This is absolutely true.

Furthermore, merchants must not seek exorbitant profits. An ordinary profit should fall in the range of 25-30 percent. "Profit that is more than half is not good profit," or in other words, if your profit exceeds half of what you paid for something, you must give it up, because this is not your money. It is everybody's, it is Heaven's. It just happened to fall into your hands for a while and that is all.

I mentioned a lady before who had given birth to three children, all of whom had died in infancy. In the end, she changed herself on such a deep level that she was able to give birth to a daughter who not only survived but in addition was also very intelligent. Nevertheless, this girl had a small medical problem: Her skin was scaly like the skin of a snake. Her mother came and asked me why her daughter was always suffering from this skin problem, so I told her: "Do you still remember your old father-in-law and this usury business of yours, lending out money at exorbitant interest rates? When a family fell on hard times, they went to your home to borrow money and you charged them interest rates not of 10 or 20 percent, but of 30 up to 50 percent! How can you call that lending money? That is called stripping off people's skin! And since you stripped off poor people's skin, Heaven is now stripping off your skin." When she heard me speak like this, the child's mother broke down in tears and asked me what she could do about it now. I answered: "Since it has already come to this, there is no easy solution. If you are able to carry out lots of good deeds, with merit for others and virtue for the world, the condition may not develop further to worsen in the future." Eventually, this child's condition did in fact stop to develop further.

Why did I say that this child's illness came from their wealth? Because the mother also had a younger sister-in-law who was only 16 years old and suffered from a skin condition as well. She had white scabs on her skin, layer upon layer all over her body. Because of the terrible itching, she scratched and scratched continuously until she ripped the scabs off, leaving her whole body looking like a bloody gourd. I told her: "Seeing how you are just a young girl, how can you have contracted this kind of a disease? Maybe it was passed down to you from your elders? It must be a problem rooted in your father's relationship to money." When the girl went back to her family and told her father this, he answered: "If this disease truly comes from this issue, then I don't want any of the interest for all the money I have lent out to people. With the poor, I will even give them any money they borrowed, to help them out in difficult times."

As soon as the girl's father made this vow, within the space of three days, all the scaly skin on the young girl's body completely fell off. Taking the kind of shovel that people in the countryside use for burning coal, in a single night she lost a whole shovel full of this snake skin in a single night, collecting three shovels full in three nights. This is how serious her skin disease was, and how quickly she recovered from it.

The official, lastly, is the leader. The official is in charge of uprightness: upright above, loyal below. When the people at the top are upright, the people below are loyal. If the leaders are not upright, the followers will not be loyal. Therefore I say to those of us who are leaders: Do not look at whether those below are loyal or not, but first look at whether you yourself are upright or not. If you are not upright, take bribes and pervert the law, act foolishly and commit crimes, you are violating and turning your back to the Dao of the official. In that case, how can you expect those below you to carry loyalty to its fullest?

These are the Daos of the scholar, farmer, worker, merchant, and official. Every profession has its own Dao and its own responsibilities. If they are all able to be upright in their proper position, each carrying out their responsibility to the best of their ability, wind and rain will naturally be gentle and auspicious, and the country prosperous and the people at peace.

II.3 ALCOHOL, SEX, MONEY, AND QI ARE THE SEA OF SUFFERING

These days, a lot of people live in a Sea of Suffering. What is this "Sea of Suffering" (kǔ hǎi 苦海)? Conflict and greed are the Sea of Suffering. Conflict over what? Greed for what? For alcohol, sex, money, and Qi. Alcohol is a poison that pierces the intestines; sex is a steel knife that cuts up bones; Qi is a rabid tiger coming off the mountain; and money is the source of all disaster. Alcohol, sex, money, and Qi, these are four turning points that the people of this world are all hung up on. Men and women with a strong will are able to see through these, break free of them, and jump up into the ninth level of Heaven. Alcohol, sex, money, and Qi. These are four walls that the people of this world get buried inside. Alcohol, sex, money, and Qi are what everybody loves, so everybody keeps walls around them, in the front and back and to the left and right, which cages us in tightly. We only have to push these four walls over, and we can escape from the suffering of impermanence. How do we topple these four walls? It is not that we must completely eliminate alcohol, sex, money, and Qi from our life, but we must know how to handle them in our heart, we must exercise restraint and discipline, in order to keep them in their proper place.

Alcohol. Without alcohol, it is not a feast. But when you drink, don't drink to the point of intoxication. Our ancestors have given us a piece of advice in this saying: "In terms of alcohol, drink just a little. In terms of your actions, think them over three times. In this way, you avoid regret later on." It is not that you cannot drink any alcohol, drinking an appropriately small amount is actually beneficial for your health. But at the time of drinking, you must have fortitude and not exceed your limit. To drink alcohol without getting drunk is the sign of a true gentleman. If you can hold yourself to the proper limit, this shows that you are a true gentleman.

Nevertheless, ordinary people are not able to control themselves when they are drinking alcohol, and for this reason, the prohibition against alcohol is one of the Five Prohibitions in Buddhism. In addition, when many people raise their cup, they immediately think of getting the other person drunk, with the final result that they hurt others and themselves, which is disastrous for both sides. They have taken a substance that is able to promote health and turned it into something that is ruinous for the body.

I personally do not drink alcohol, but I do offer it in my home. When I have guests who want a drink, I bring out the wine and invite the guests to drink on their own. Someone might say: "You don't drink and you don't gamble. You don't join me in drinking, so how do you let me drink like this?" To this I respond: "You don't need another person's company to drink. You yourself must reflect on what your proper limit is. When you feel like you have had enough, you just put your cup down." Before I studied the Dao, I did not drink any alcohol either but I constantly saw other people drinking to the point of being tipsy or falling over. Having had too much to drink, they spoke without thinking, saying anything that came to their mind, such as: "Drinking without getting drunk? That is not enough loyalty! That is not enough friendship!"

Is getting drunk together really a sign of true loyalty? Isn't it rather a way to entrap your friend?

There is a common saying: "After drinking, there is no virtue. After drinking, careful speech is lost. After drinking, bad deeds are committed." After people have had too much to drink, their courage gets too large, and they rely on their alcohol-related courage to commit evil acts. Doesn't this mean that they have drunk themselves into disaster? I once saw a man, after drinking too much and overcome by the force of the alcohol, grab a woman. The woman accused him of rape and caused him to sit in jail for fifteen days. Think carefully, everybody: If this man hadn't been drunk, could he have grabbed somebody like this? Moreover, many people get sulky when they drink alcohol, and this kind of drinking can easily lead to liver cirrhosis or in serious cases to liver cancer, to the point of costing a person's life.

Sex. If there were no sex in the world, wouldn't this mean the end of the human race? Sex is certainly necessary, but it must be controlled. "To drink alcohol without getting drunk is the sign of a true gentleman. To see something sexually arousing without being thrown into turmoil is the sign of a hero." If somebody is not your own husband or your own wife, regardless of their beauty, you must not lust after them. You cannot even have dirty thoughts. Lusting after them is already a transgression, is already a crime. As the sages say: "Of the hundred virtues, xiao ("reverence for one's elders") comes first. Of the myriad evils, lewdness is foremost." Wanton lewdness is the greatest of all evils. If we have never transgressed in this area, we must be extra careful to guard against it. If we have transgressed in the past, we must quickly turn around to head towards what is right.

Money. "Without money, we cannot nurture the Dao," if we don't go out and earn a living, it won't do. Nevertheless, the gentleman loves money but follows the Dao in obtaining it. You cannot covet money of injustice, and you cannot consume food of injustice. As Wang Fengyi said, "These days, the Dao has become waterlogged. The Dao has disappeared under water." This sentence speaks the absolute truth, the Dao has truly become waterlogged. Nowadays, too many people only care about money and do not talk about the Dao. To get their hands on money, by hook or by crook, they use tricks or force. Hasn't this caused the Dao to become waterlogged?

In December of 1998, I met a patient in Yi'an County in Heilongjiang Province who was suffering from aplastic anemia. Only in his forties, he had a ghastly pale complexion, with no color in his face at all, and was barely able to walk, having to stop and pant every eight to ten steps. The weather in the Northeast is very cold and he would wear a fur-lined heavy jacket and hat and a big muffler, but still, no matter how warmly he dressed, he was still shivering with cold. After falling ill, he had gone to the hospital and had been treated there with everything they had to offer until he had spent every last penny, but his disease had not been cured, and over time even gotten more serious. In the end, the hospital had informed him that his condition had deteriorated to such a degree that it would be too difficult to cure, so they had sent him home.

Since the hospital wouldn't allow him to stay there, he had no choice but to go home and wait for death. At this point, he happened to be present just in time to hear me lecture about illness to other people, so he sat down on the side to listen. On that occasion, I spoke at length about the Dao of merchants, about the need to offer genuine goods at a fair price when engaging in any sort of business transaction, about how we must not sell stolen or counterfeit goods, or alter weights to shortchange customers, or take life or murder for the sake of money. This man was deeply moved and, knowing where he himself was at fault, stood up to speak: "I know how I have contracted this disease of mine. I engaged in trade, and in that role always used an altered scale to cheat my customers. When I sold vegetables, if a customer did not want them, I used the original scale to measure them, but if a customer wanted to buy them, I gave them 8 tael at most out of a full *jin*. In addition, when I was buying grain, I'd alter the scale so that I would bring it in at a high weight but take it out at a low weight, and I even adulterated the product within the scale." When I asked him how he adulterated his products, he explained: "I mixed dirt or sand into my soybeans. Since the sand sank to the bottom, the boss would stand by as I was filling the sacks but not notice anything." I responded: "Just look how much harm you have done with this trick! In order to make money, for the sake of exorbitant profit, you have hurt so many people! Some of them you may have even cost their lives. There was a shopkeeper like that who was dealing in soybeans and once sent a shipment of soybeans to the seaport in Dalian to prepare for shipping abroad. Because there was too much dirt mixed into the soybeans, the port inspectors did not let it pass inspection, and so the beans could not be exported. This made it difficult to sell them, and so they were stored somewhere for an extended period of time. Because of all the dirt mixed into this batch and some moisture they were exposed to, the beans started sprouting until the sprouts bore their way through the sacks to the outside. When the proprietor who was trying to sell the beans saw this scene, he could not bear the sight so he jumped into the sea and drowned himself. If these beans were bought from your store, aren't you responsible for taking this man's life? Or in other words, wealth is associated with water, and blood is also associated with water. Things with identical Qi are attracted to each other, and for this reason you have now contracted such a serious problem with your blood." He continued to speak: "One more point: I also engage in butchering cows, horses, and sheep. I have killed all the sheep for three communes. Because I have a good eye, when a flock of sheep is walked past me, I am able to predict how much meat I get from each animal, guessing within half a *jin* in each case. So before the meat is sold, I already know how much money the animal will bring me." I responded: "Look at this! You have killed such a large number of creatures and spilled their blood! No wonder that now your blood is also all exhausted." So he asked me what he should do, and I told him: "Put down your butcher knife and become a Buddha right away."

When our conversation had reached this point, he knew that he had wronged and he resolved from now on to be a very honest and straight person and in addition to perform a lot of virtuous acts to extinguish his sinful karma. I said to him: "To confess your wrongs just with your lips does not work, but it must come from your heart. If you want to save your life, you must completely change who you are, you must strip yourself down to the bones and begin from zero." Afterwards, this patient stayed with us for 200 days and truly went through a complete transformation, which did in the end save his life.

He did manage to save his life, but his blood and Qi were still not abundant, and he would still get out of breath just from walking. I asked him again whether he knew why his blood count continued to be so low. He responded that he knew, and when I inquired after the reason, he responded: "My virtuous

acts are not enough. I do not have the ability to practice virtue." I told him:
"You are right. As Wang Fengyi has said, wealth is associated with water, and
blood is also associated with water. You have killed life in the past for the sake
of money, so now you must rescue life. Frequently buy a few fish or birds and
'release them into life,'[2] and maybe this will cause your blood count to go up.
But remember, I am telling you to release them into life, so you must make
sure that they do not release them into death!" He asked me to clarify what
I meant by "release them into death." So I explained: "At the time that you
release them, you must not shout out loudly, 'I am releasing these animals!'
Otherwise you let other people know, and they may just come to scoop them
up. Doesn't that mean that you are 'releasing them into death'? Furthermore,
some people who engage in the practice of 'releasing into life' will place an order
for a certain weight with the fishmonger who they are buying the fish from.
This fisherman may risk his life to scoop up such a large number of fish. And
the fish, originally happy creatures frolicking in the water, receive a great fright
when they are scooped up and thrown in a huge pile, some getting squished
to death, others suffocated. Doesn't this also then become a case of "releasing
into death"? If you want to practice releasing into life, you must keep it secret
in your own heart. Just look around for any creatures that are lively and lov-
able, and buy them whenever and wherever the opportunity arises, and then
stealthily set them free. When doing good deeds, do not let other people know.
This is what is called 'hidden merit' or 'hidden virtue,' and the power of this
practice is enormous!" After this patient heard my words, he indeed went to
release animals to the best of his ability, and subsequently his blood count did
in fact rise little by little. At present, this person is still alive and moreover able
to earn a living. He is able to drive a truck on his own, cultivate land on his
own, as much as 70-80 *mu* of land, all of this he manages to do.

I often get asked whether money is ultimately a bad or a good thing, and I
reply: "It is both good and bad. It can be good or it can be bad. The key is
whether we are able to use it or not." If we are able to use it, we can transcend
the Three Realms[3] If we are unable to use it, it is difficult to escape sinning.

---

2   This is a technical term referring to the Buddhist practice of saving lives by releasing
captive animals, for the sake of collecting good karma.

3   A reference to the lower three of the four realms of existence, namely *shen* (realm of the
body, physical addiction), *xin* (realm of the selfish heart, emotional suffering), *yi* (realm

What counts as being unable to use money? Pure selfishness, eating and drinking, whoring and gambling, to act in service of one's desires, this counts as being unable to use it. The Record of Words and Actions by Wang Fengyi tells of such a person who said: "Ever since I came into money, I used my money to help my relatives and friends, allowing all of them to have money as well. Previously I thought I was doing the right thing, but after hearing Wang Fengyi speak, I know now that my actions were wrong. Because after my friends and relatives had money, they all acquired many women, they went whoring and gambling, smoked opium and created the seeds for limitless sins. And who was it who created these bitter sins for them? All of this was created by me." So you see, everybody, this was a man who did not use his money well. Today there are also some parents who give their children a whole lot of money and allow them to cultivate so many bad habits, squandering and wasting their wealth and reveling in wanton pursuit of luxury. Is this what it means to love your children? Or is it to push your children down into hell?

What counts as being able to use money? Rescuing people in trouble, supporting the sick, cherishing our elders and having compassion for the poor, repairing bridges and mending roads, renouncing ones bodily needs to spread the Dao, and building schools, all of these count as being able to use money. There are many people nowadays who live a frugal and simple life but use all their remaining wealth to assist the poor, to establish projects of hope, and to support homes for the elderly. To use money like this means to reach a higher level and gain merit.

Now that we have concluded our discussion of money, let us talk about "Qi." If we do not have strength of Qi, we have no capability and we cannot accomplish anything. But when our temper flares up, we must endure it, we must let things go. Enduring when necessary and letting go when necessary. The top of the Chinese character for "to endure" (rěn 忍) consists of a knife, because whoever fails to endure suffers the consequences of a knife. Isn't it true that nowadays so many people commit violent and evil acts because they are unable to control their temper for a moment, to endure their Qi, which turns into a grave wrongdoing that they will suffer from for the rest of their lives?

of consciousness), with the fourth and highest level beings that of zhi (realm of "will," Buddha-level, enlightenment)

There is an old saying, "Not allowing your Qi to rise is the medicine for longevity; not letting your five fires flare up is the magical anti-aging elixir; not retaliating for an injustice is true cultivation." What is this Qi? Qi is the helper who steals your life. Letting your Qi rise by getting angry is just like taking poison; it can drive you to your death. What are the five fires? The five fires are five demons, namely hatred, resentment, irritation, anger, and annoyance. They are killing, stealing, lewdness, recklessness, and alcoholism. If you want to get rid of these five fires, you must use the virtues explained by the sages, namely compassion, righteousness, ritual and politeness, wisdom, and trustworthiness. "Compassion is able to nurture the liver and guards against anger and killing. Lack of righteousness damages the lungs, as do the offenses of stealing and irritation. With principles bright and a straight heart, lewdness and hatred are rare. Wisdom eliminates the water of annoyance and causes the kidney to bloom. With the trustworthiness of earth, no recklessness and no worries The five Qi gather to provide the source for a family of Dao and De."

"Compassion is able to nurture the liver and guards against rage and killing." Killing, stealing, lewdness, recklessness, and alcoholism constitute the Five Prohibitions of Buddhism. Hatred, resentment, irritation, anger, and annoyance constitute the five poisons mentioned by Wang Fengyi. Compassion, righteousness, ritual and politeness, wisdom, and trustworthiness constitute the Five Constants of Confucianism. While these Five Prohibitions, Five Poisons, and Five Constants are all different from each other, they all fall under the command of the five elements. Among these, killing, anger, and compassion all belong to wood; lewdness, hatred, and ritual and politeness all belong to fire; recklessness, resentment, and trustworthiness all belong to earth; stealing, irritation, and righteousness all belong to metal; and alcohol, annoyance, and wisdom all belong to water. On the basis of the five-element connections, we can see that killing and anger are of the same nature. When we lecture on the Dao, we consider anger therefore as identical with killing. Compassion being able to nurture the liver points to the fact that if we are able to keep the virtue of compassion in our heart, hold on to great kindness and mercy, grieve for Heaven and take pity on humanity, we are able to nurture and hold our liver. If people have a heart of compassion and virtue, they also will not produce any thoughts of killing or generate anger.

Some people who are suffering from liver disease have come to me asking: "I have been a vegetarian for many years now and I have been abstaining from killing and freeing captive animals. Why have I still contracted liver disease in spite of this?" I respond to them: "Is that true? Even though you have been a vegetarian and have been releasing captive animals, it is not necessarily the case that you have abstained from killing, because you have not yet dropped your anger. It is only once you manage to stop generating any Qi of anger that you can truly say that you abstain from killing. You see, those people who kill do so with a thought of killing that was stirred up by a single instant of anger. If they had no anger, would they be able to stir up the thought of killing in their minds? Therefore, as long as anger is not eliminated, killing thoughts are not eliminated either, and you can therefore easily harm your liver." When they hear me say this, they all respond with great shock because they all like to generate a sense of frustration, of suppressed anger, which is most likely to damage the liver.

"Lack of righteousness damages the lungs, as do the offenses of stealing and irritation." Righteousness is able to nurture the lungs, and if people disregard their sense of right and wrong, they are most likely to injure lung metal. Similarly, if they commit the offense of stealing or constantly feel irritated by others, this can also easily damage the lung.

"With principles bright and a straight heart, lewdness and hatred are rare." Ritual and politeness are able to nurture the heart, but what do I mean by "ritual and politeness"? It refers to social etiquettes. To maintain etiquettes, you must possess the skill of overcoming the self. Confucius also said, "Overcome the self and return to ritual and politeness." Now how do we overcome the self? First of all, we must understand the principle of the Dao. Only if people can understand principles can their heart be straight, can lewd desires be dropped. Furthermore, it is crucial to be able to understand the Dao of the other person. If you are able to understand the other person, to reach through to the other side, then you are able to treat them with consideration. Consequently, the hatred in your heart will simply lessen on its own.

"Wisdom eliminates the water of annoyance and causes the kidney to bloom." Most people these days have some sort of problem with their kidneys, and even though it may just be a common issue, if it worsens just a bit, they may develop what is called kidney disease in Western medicine. Why are there so many people these days who suffer from kidney disease? The reason is that they lack wisdom, that they are unable to let things go. People who are generally dissatisfied start brooding as soon as they encounter anything, which causes fire to flare up in their heart. And as this fire rises inside them, their predisposition for annoyance manifests itself. Annoyance can damage the kidney, and when this persists for a long time, kidney disease will affect the body. But if we have wisdom, annoyance and irritation disappear, and we are able to generate healthy kidney water. If we think about wanting to cultivate ourselves, we must begin with the kidney. The kidney is the root of the five internal organs, and this root has to be solid and firm for cultivation to be successful.

"With the trustworthiness of earth, no recklessness and no worries." Trustworthiness is the direct opposite of recklessness. If you are trustworthy, you will not be reckless. And if you are reckless, you will not be trustworthy. In the context of the Five Prohibitions in Buddhism, the most important aspect of recklessness is reckless speech, which refers to double-tongue, to a foul mouth, and to lewd speech. And what is the greatest recklessness of all? It is when words are inconsistent with deeds, when you say one thing and do something else. Wang Shanren said: "To talk about the Dao but not to practice the Dao is evil of the first degree." If we are able to make our deeds and our words one and the same, to talk about the Dao and to practice the Dao, if we truly implement this trustworthiness of the earth element we will be free of all worries.

"The five Qi gather to provide the source for a family of Dao and De." If we are able to integrate and implement as one the three teachings of Buddhism, Confucianism, and Wang Fengyi, if we can truly put them into practice, we are able to manifest a household of Dao and De on the basis of the gathering of the five Qi. And having a family of Dao and De is necessary in order to produce children and grandchildren who have Dao and De.

11.4 THE CONSISTENT JOY OF CONTENTMENT

The human realm resembles a deep abyss, with humanity mired in greed inside it. Workers are greedy for skills, farmers are greedy for harvest, merchants are greedy for wealth, and even those who practice good deeds are greedy for merit. People don't know contentment, all are greedy, it is just that their greed is expressed in different ways.

Let me tell you a story from ancient times about a beggar. It was deep winter, on a day full of ice and snow, and this beggar was sitting by a fire he had built under a bridge. Holding half a broken bowl, he was eating plain rice cooked in water until he began to sweat. In between bites, he proclaimed: "Today is an excellent day, to be able to eat until I am truly full!" Just at this moment, a high-ranking official passed by on the bridge above and overheard this sentence. He thought to himself: "On such a cold day, how can there be a person under this bridge stating that he is eating so well? What is he eating?" Leaning over the bridge, he looked down and saw the beggar holding his broken half of a bowl and eating watery rice. The official thought to himself: "This man eats this kind of a simple meal and is content, but I feast on delicacies all day long, from morning to evening. How can it be that I know no contentment?" Subsequently, the official ordered his chamberlain to bring the beggar to his home and put him in charge of his accounts. Everybody there started calling him "Mister Contentment."

A few years passed, and during this length of time Mister Contentment's living conditions were nice and stable, but he gradually forgot how to be content. What happened? He started teasing the official's servant girls and was eventually observed doing so by the official. The official was upset that the man was no longer content, but still felt like he couldn't just kick him out. So what was he to do? He pondered this problem for a while and finally came up with a plan. So he told the man: "Mister Contentment! You have spent such a long time at my place, the time has come for you to advance in public. Let's do this: I will send you away so that you can find a small official post somewhere else." As soon as Mister Contentment heard this, he felt that this was a great opportunity for him and quickly replied: "Old Master, I depend entirely on your patronage." The official said: "I will equip you with a horse and a saddle, a traveling stipend, and a hand-written letter, make haste and set out on your trip. But remember carefully: Unless you run into hard times, do not open this letter!" Mister Contentment then asked where he should go, and the official replied: "Go to Nanjing. There is a prime minister there with the last name Jia. Go find him and you will be alright." Believing all this to be true, Mister Contentment happily set out on his journey. But where was he to find this prime minister named Jia in Nanjing? He looked all over without success, and after a while used up all his money and had to sell his horse. When he had reached the end of his rope, he opened this life-saving letter and found the following message inside: "Mister Contentment teased the servant girl Lamei and forgot how he had once warmed himself by a fire under a bridge. Where to find Prime Minister Jia in Nanjing? It was a way to make you leave so you would never return." So you see, everybody, wasn't this a complete waste?

Let us think this over carefully. Thirty or fifty years ago what kind of a life would we have lived? And what kind of a life is it that we are living today? Isn't it like a life in paradise? If you are still not able to find contentment, it is because in the middle of misfortune you still don't know how fortunate you are. If you have good fortune, you must be able to enjoy, and when you don't have good fortune, you must know how to find it. Just look, this beggar was happy eating half a bowl of watery rice, because he knew how to be content, which shows us that even a beggar can enjoy happiness. But those big fish in fancy restaurants who eat to stuff their faces until they are dripping oil, they still complain that the food wasn't good or didn't have enough fragrance. This is an example of not knowing good fortune in the midst of good fortune. If they are not content in that kind of a situation, how can they ever enjoy happiness? Of course they experience only suffering.

I once met a lady in Beijing whose family was extremely well off and yet her face was full of sorrow. Nothing could make her happy. For half a day she told me of her sorrows, without me saying a word. In the end, I asked her one sentence: "Knowing contentment brings constant joy. Since you don't know contentment, are you able to find joy?" Hearing me say this, she started roaring with laughter and explained: "I am so overjoyed! I have never been this happy before in my entire life. This one sentence of yours has woken me up, I am simply too discontent." I replied: "That is right. If you own hundreds and thousands of riches and yet you are discontent, you will be nothing but a pauper."

If you look closely, in most cases people with a lot of money tend to be very tired. What is the reason for this? They are allowing money to pressure them. These kinds of people are most often extremely wealthy in material possessions, but suffer greatly in their spirit. Didn't Wang Shanren tell us, ""Those who live for the sake of fame die on account of fame. Those who live for the sake of profit die on account of profit. Those who live for the sake of riches die on account of riches. Those who live for the sake of sex die on account of sex." Money and material possessions are external things, and if you put too much emphasis on them, you will get exhausted by them until you might die on top of them. For this reason, I say: Having money is not necessarily a good thing, because it may not be that you are holding on to money but that you are letting money hold on to you.

III. Deeply Trust in Karma

III.I UNDERSTANDING KARMA IN HUMAN INTERACTIONS

A sage once said: "Karma is not an empty theory, it is never wrong by the tiniest amount. Retribution is unmistakably evident, like a shadow following a shape." Indeed, the doctrine of cause and effect is not empty and void, and never fails even the least bit! When you plant beans, you get beans, and when you plant melons, you get melons. When you plant a Bodhi tree, it will invariably rain down flowers of good fortune on you. If you haven't planted in the spring, what are you going to harvest in the fall? I am a farmer and I understand this principle. To use farming as an example, whatever seeds you planted in the spring, these are the fruits you will harvest in the fall. If you haven't planted seeds of goodness, how can you harvest fruit of goodness later?

The famous Daoist text *"Writings From the Supreme High on Stimulus and Response" Tai Shang Gan Ying Pian* (太上感應篇) explains: "Good fortune or bad fortune are unpredictable. It is only humans who summon them themselves." Fortune or misfortune are all something that we ourselves create and harvest. All of us standing right here have come together here on the basis of karma. The kind of people we are comes from the kind of karma we have, and the kind of karma we have comes from the kind of people we are. For this reason, when we encounter a person or an event that we do not like, it is of no use to blame the outside, but we must first seek very thoroughly where we ourselves have wronged. If you are unable to recognize and penetrate the cause and effect, this means that you don't know how to examine yourself but just want to develop an attitude of resentment and hatred. And as soon as you become resentful and hateful, your karma will double. And when hatred, resentment, irritation, anger, and annoyance all start up, how can you possibly keep the internal organs from developing illness?

Some people talk about past lives and future lives, but I only discuss cause and effect in the here and now, instead of the intangible aspects of karma. If we cannot grasp the relation of causes and effects in our current human interactions, grasping the invisible aspects of karma is even less possible. But if we are able to resolve the kindnesses and resentments in our present human interactions, intangible causes and effects will resolve themselves on their own.

What do we come into this present lifetime for? We come to repay debts of the human realm. Whose debts are we here to repay? The debts that we owe to our children. In the present age, children who want to collect debts are numerous like the hair on a cow, but children who want to repay debts are rare like a unicorn's horn. If you grasp this principle, you give your children whatever they want, without a single word of resentment or blame. This is the only way to repay your debts. After children become adults, some of them know to give back to their parents, some of them give back very little, and some of them give back absolutely nothing. In rural families, you see this situation quite often, that children after they have grown up live only for their nuclear family, for themselves and their child. For their wife and children, they shell out great sums of money without any hesitation, but when they have to pay out even a tiny amount for the old people, they want to haggle over the price. There are also some children who feel resentment after they grow up and complain that their parents let them down because they didn't accumulate wealth to pass on to them. If we encounter such children, we elders must not hold resentment against them but still first ask ourselves how we previously have treated our own elders, how much we have supported our own elders in the past. If you have treated your parents with *xiao*, your children will treat you with *xiao*. If you have gone against your parents, your children will certainly go against you. This is Heaven's principle. If you do not practice *xiao* towards your elders, I can guarantee that your children will not practice *xiao* towards you. And if your children do not practice *xiao* towards you, this simply means that you have not practiced *xiao* towards your elders. Cause and effect work in karmic retribution; you reap what you sow, with not the slightest exception.

Just after the Spring Festival in 2010, a father and son from Henan came to see me. The son was 18 years old and was suffering from depression. He had not finished middle school but had dropped out. His father had taken him everywhere in search of medical treatment, and he had been treated for a long time but without any positive results. They had watched a video of me lecturing about illness, inquired everywhere about me, and finally come to visit me at my home.

When they entered the room, I was just in the middle of lecturing a group about disease. Not long after they sat down, the young man all of a sudden cheered up, but as he became more cheerful, he also started slapping his father on the mouth. He was hitting his father with such force that the sound of the slapping carried throughout the room. His father neither resisted nor uttered a word, he just sat there and suffered his son beating him. The people in the room could not bear the sight of this scene and wanted to defend the father. Seeing this situation, I immediately knew that there was more going on here, so I asked the father when the son had begun hitting him. The father responded that the son had started acting strangely and hitting his father from the moment they left their home and got on the train. So I explained: "Without pre-existing cause, there can be no effect later. It is impossible that this child would be hitting you without any reason, so you must carefully reflect on this and examine yourself. How did you treat your own parents? Were there any areas where you let them down? When he heard me ask this question, his eyes became teary and he responded: "My child hitting me like this is indeed my own wrongdoing, the fruit of what I have sowed. I have done my father wrong. When I was young, he was sent to prison, and my classmates teased and made fun of me, causing me to completely lose face. So I carried extreme resentment and anger in me against him, hatred so deep that it went into my bones. Later, after he returned from prison, I intentionally got mad at him, scorned him, yelled at him, even hit him. Not much later, he died from a broken heart, killed by my anger." I explained: "When your father had to go to prison, he already suffered enough emotional pain from that. And when he got out, not only did you fail to understand him and help him, but you even resented him, hitting and yelling at him. How could you as his son act like that towards him? Were you really not able to relate to his state of mind?" As soon as I uttered these questions, he flung himself on the ground and kowtowed, crying out loudly: "Father! All of this is my fault for not practicing *xiao*! I have failed to think of your difficulties. I beg you to forgive your son!"

On the morning of the next day, his son's thinking had cleared up considerably. Why was that? Because as soon as the father had admitted his fault, his conscience had been turned around. Therefore we say that between the older generation and the younger generation, the elders are like the roots of the tree and the children are like the branches at the top. As soon as the tree roots move, the tip of the tree naturally moves as well. Father and son stayed at my home until the third day, and by then the son had more or less recovered from his illness.

Four months later, when the son encountered some difficulties, he was unable to take them lightly and suffered a relapse. His father again came looking for me, and I told him: "The heart of the parent is the body of the child, and the body of the child is the heart of the parent. If your child is not well, it simply means that you are still not well. If your child is not straight, it means that you are not straight yet. You must still spend more time and carefully seek for the root of this problem within yourself."

The father and son stayed at my home for three days. The child had almost recovered from his disease. Four months later, the child reacted very strongly to something and the disease reoccurred. His father came to my place again. I told him, "The parent's heart is the child's body. The child's body is the parent's heart. The child did not get well because you have not yet become good. The child has not really recovered because you haven't really changed. You have to find your own problem." Hearing this, the father cried once more for a good while, and not long after he stopped crying, his son called him on the telephone from Henan to tell him that he had recovered and wanted his father to come home. So the father went home.

I had another experience with a similar kind of person, a man who greatly loved cleanliness by his nature but had all of a sudden developed a dirty illness. What do I mean by dirty here? He normally did not have a runny nose, but as soon as he started eating a meal his nose started running and dripping continuously. For a person who so loved cleanliness to be affected by this kind of a dirty illness was truly loathsome to him personally, and he therefore asked me why his nose always started running as soon as he picked up a bowl of rice. After he asked me this question twice, I in turn asked him whether he knew why he had contracted this illness. When he couldn't answer me, I explained that it was because he disliked old people for being so dirty. He had a sudden insight and exclaimed: "You are correct! My father fell ill with cerebral embolism and started always drooling, so I despised him for being so dirty. And from this point on, my nose has started running as soon as I pick up a bowl of rice. Even dirtier than my father!" Saying this, his eyes filled with tears and he could not stop them from falling. Stirred with emotion, he said: "Have I not studied this Dao in vein? How could I continue to disdain my elders?" After his thinking had become enlightened like this, he no longer got a runny nose when he picked up a bowl of rice. So you see everybody, karmic retribution, it truly never fails by the least bit. When you despise old people for being dirty, you will end up eventually being even dirtier than them.

III.2 ACKNOWLEDGE YOUR DEBTS AND ACCEPT THEM

When faced with a disagreeable situation, some people force themselves to endure it stubbornly and stiffly suppress it in their mind, but this does not work. Whatever we are able to eat, we still have to be able to keep it down, and whatever we are able to keep down, we still have to be able to transform it. If we are able to endure it but are unable to transform it, it is bound to explode violently sooner or later.

How are we to transform things? By trusting in cause and effect, by honestly acknowledging our debts and honestly accepting them. Didn't Wang Fengyi say: "Smoothly accept any adversity you encounter, and heaven will add to your good fortune. When things come flying at you, compare them with former causes." Whatever comes to you has a previous cause, so see if you cannot acknowledge your debt. If you are able to come to accept certain people or events, this is called acknowledging your debts and accepting them. Accept them, accept them, for as soon as you accept them, they are settled. Otherwise if you do not settle your karma, if you do not extinguish your debts, you will have to come back for another round. If you didn't owe other people, they wouldn't be able to come into your life. Those who come to you do own a share, so do not dislike and reject them, but give with happiness and a smile. And once you have returned enough to them, they will no longer demand things from you. Therefore Wang Shanren told us: "Accept them, accept them, for as soon as you accept them, they are settled." You can settle your debts only if you can accept them, but if you cannot accept them, you cannot settle them.

When I first started lecturing on the Dao, I met a lady from Baiquan County in Heilongjiang Province. Because of the constant beating and yelling that her husband abused her with, she was so upset that she had become extremely emaciated and haggard, to the point where she couldn't even pick up a basket of firewood and would stumble over a mere willow branch. I asked her to explain what the matter was. She responded: "I am so upset that I just can't take it any more. Every night around nine, my husband comes home drunk and starts yelling as soon as he enters the yard. No matter whether I am right or wrong, I get yelled at. And of course when he yells at me I get angry, and as soon as I get angry he yells at me even more viciously. If I handle the situation wrongly, he then starts beating me. In this way, he tortures me every night until about midnight before we go to sleep. I cannot bear this situation any longer. Please, Liu Shanren, can you save me?" I told her that I was able to save her if she could trust me, but had no way of helping her if she couldn't trust me. She responded that all she wanted was not to get yelled at any more and she would be believe in anything. So I told her: "After you get home today, when your husband comes back, don't wait for him to enter the house but go to greet him at the entrance to the yard." She responded: "Go to meet him? If I don't go to greet him, he yells, and if I go to greet him, won't he yell even more?" I said: "Even when he yells at you, you must bear it. You must not only keep your calm and not get angry or talk back, you must even be joyful." She said, "What, I must be joyful?" I said: "Yes, you must be joyful. And if you only have a joyful face, this doesn't count. You must have true joy in your heart. What purpose has he come into your life for? To help you extinguish your past sins, to help you settle your debts. If you are able to do as I told you, your past sins will be extinguished, and your debt will be settled. And after today, he will no longer yell at you. Do you think you can follow my advice?" She thought about it for a long time and finally responded, "This will surely be very difficult…" I reminded her: ""Accept it, accept it, for as soon as you accept it, it will be settled." "Truly?" she asked. "Yes, truly," I replied. "I absolutely guarantee and stand by everything I have said." "Then I will listen to your advice," she said.

That evening shortly before nine o'clock, she did indeed go to the front entrance to wait for her husband. And as soon as he came in, she ran up to him and took a hold of his hand saying, "You have come home!" The husband hadn't changed and started yelling at her as usual. In her heart, though, she thought: "You just yell. This time I must not yell back at you. In a previous lifetime, I yelled at you, and in this lifetime you yell at me. Yelling at me is correct. Yelling at me is good. But Liu Shanren not only prohibited me from yelling back but even told me to be happy. How can I make myself be happy in this situation? Letting somebody yell at me and on top of that having to respond with joy, this plan is just too difficult!" As she was having these thoughts, though, she let out a chuckle and started laughing, and the more she thought about the situation, the happier she became.

Leading her husband by the hand, she walked towards the house and as soon as they were inside, sat down on the bed. Regardless of how much the husband yelled at her. She did not utter a word, but simply sat there, holding her husband's arm and smiling. Smiling, she said: "You go ahead and yell. You go ahead and yell. I am not allowed to yell!" After he had yelled for a while, the husband asked whether she really was not going to yell back, and she told him that she was indeed not going to yell. To this, he replied: "If you are not yelling back, let's drop it and go to bed." Hearing this, she felt even greater joy. Lying down on her blanket and covering he head, she felt persistent joy. Why was she so full of joy? Because in the past the yelling had gone on for three hours every single day, but today it had only been one hour, so her husband had yelled at her for two hours less! This was wonderful!

Early the next morning, she came to see me again, so I asked her how it had gone the previous evening. She told me: "Liu Shanren! The advice you gave me was extremely effective. Last night he only yelled at me for one hour, so I was able to go to sleep at ten o'clock. But I am really worried, if he comes back tonight and yells at me again and I still don't utter a word, what shall I do if he starts beating me? How shall I make through this beating?" I replied: "If he starts beating you, here is the advice for beating: When you go home, get a broom ready, like what you use to sweep the *kang*. If he wants to beat you, push the broom into his hand, but in such a way that he will use the twigs on the top to beat you, instead of beating you with the handle end of the broom. If you whip people with the top of the broom, it doesn't hurt. But when he wants to beat you, you must still not have any emotional response in your heart." She said that she could follow my advice since she had already weathered his yelling, so she would now let him beat her. I told her: "Yes, this is what is called to accept your debt. If you can act like this, you will see how he changes afterwards."

On the third day, she came to report again: "Following your instructions, I once again went out last night to greet my husband at the gate. He didn't say two words but again just started yelling at me. Entering the house, he sat down on the *kang* and before he had yelled for even ten minutes, he asked: "I am continuously yelling at you, and yet you are not yelling back. Why is that?" I answered that I could not yell back. He responded by threatening to beat me: "If you don't respond, your old man will beat you!" Raising his hand, he came over to hit me. I immediately grabbed the broom and pushed it into his hand, saying: "Use this to beat me. If you use your hand, the clapping will cause you pain." I turned around, with my back towards him and my head covered, and let him beat me. After he hit me about a dozen times and saw that I didn't try to strike back, he tossed the broom to the side and said: "I yell at you, and you don't yell back. I hit you, and you don't hit back. You had better remember: From this moment on, I will not yell at you again and I will not hit you again." And from then on, she indeed never again had to endure yelling or beating.

There is another lady with a similar story, from my home area in Keshan County. She came to see me because she had contracted rheumatism. This

lady had a son who demanded money from her whenever his ferocious nature
erupted and would not take no for an answer. He always took the money, went
out to eat and drink extravagantly until it was all gone, and then came home
to demand even more. Over time, he had wasted all the money in this family,
leaving them penniless. After this lady had stayed at my home for some time
and her arthritis had begun to improve slowly, she asked me: "Liu Shanren,
next time my son asks me for money again, how shall I handle it?" I responded
that if he asked, she had to give him money, if he came to her wanting to collect
his debts, she had to repay him. She told me that she didn't have anything left
to give him and asked how she could possibly give him more money. I said:
"If you don't have anything else left, he will most likely ask you for the title
of your house." She confirmed that: "You are right. He has already demanded
the title from me. Shall I give it to him or not?" I told her to give it to him. So
she asked what would happen after I gave him the title. I said: "Once you have
repaid him enough, he will leave it at that. Once he has demanded enough,
he will have to leave." She responded: "If he should really leave, I would be
overjoyed. I will no longer have to live with him." Just see how badly this son
had scared his own mother! Subsequently, this lady indeed gave the title of
her house to her son. As soon as he received the title, he sold the house, and
within a single month, he spent all the money from the sale of the house. And
just a day later, he was run over and killed in a car accident.

We have discussed so many clear-cut examples here, so everybody, think them
over very carefully. What is this human life after all? The ancients say that life
is like a dream. And indeed, life is a dream, an opera, for which the family is
the stage. Once we have entered the stage, what song shall we perform? And
when we all leave the stage, don't we just scatter in the four directions? And
since we are all just performing in this play, what need is there to hold on to
past feelings of kindness or blame? The fact that we have come together here
is a predestined bond, which we should cherish deeply. If you blame me and
I blame you, this predestined bond has transformed into blame. This Qi of
blame will spread through Heaven and earth and plant the seeds of illness, and
once we die, we don't even know why we died. Isn't this a great pity?

IV. Accumulating Merit By Doing Good Deeds

IV.1 GOODNESS IS REWARDED WITH GOODNESS

Someone might say: "I see other people running wild and wreaking havoc but with no consequence whatsoever. I on the other hand have performed quite a few good deeds and have not received any good retribution either. Why should I care so much? From now on, I will just live happily for the moment." If they really think like that, they are wrong. The ancient sages have told us: "If somebody commits evil and we do not see evil results, that is because they had left-over merit from a previous lifetime. As soon as that merit is exhausted, we will invariably see evil consequences." In actuality there are indeed lots of people who indulge in reckless debauchery and drinking on a regular basis, who commit all kinds of outrageous wrongs, and yet we don't see them suffer any consequences. But, my esteemed audience, don't be in a hurry here. Just take your time and watch them patiently, wait until their left-over merit has fluttered away, and you will see evil consequences. In the end, the settling of accounts will take place after the autumn harvest. Some will be struck by a sudden calamity that will break up the family and scatter the people, and some will contract serious illness, use up all their money, and perish in the end. Everybody, observe very carefully, there are truly too many examples to demonstrate this fact. Why don't you see good deeds rewarded with goodness? Because of some kind of deficit in a previous lifetime, because there is a hole in your *ming* (destiny) that you have not yet filled in. Continuously accumulate merit by doing good deeds, and slowly, slowly you will fill up this hole, this deficit. Don't lose heart, don't retreat in your will, but always act by going straight ahead, and I guarantee that you will be able to see good results.

IV.2 DO NOT ARGUE, DO NOT BE GREEDY

The founders of all the great religions in the world were highly cultivated people. Why were they so successful in their cultivation? Because they were able to forget themselves. Forgetting themselves, they only acted for the benefit of all sentient beings, which is the only way to succeed in cultivation. The ages that the sages lived in, the people they faced, and the methods they employed to educate and transform people were all different, but they all shared a single goal: To stop people from doing evil and make them cultivate goodness. If people can stop doing evil and cultivate goodness instead, they will naturally incline towards good fortune and avoid bad fortune. For this reason Wang Fengyi was happy to support any kind of religion even if he was not religious himself. I endorse the same perspective: Even though I have not converted to Buddhism or do not believe in god, I have great respect and admiration for all religions.

We have met a few religious people, however, who are not like this and who insist on arguing that they are good and other people are bad. They ask me: "Tell me: Which religion is the right one?" I tell them: "They are all good. If they were not good, they would not have been able to create sages and saints." They respond by insisting that the religion they believe in is still better than the others. I tell them: "You are wrong. You may think that this sort of attitude is supporting the founder of your religion, but in reality you are injuring him. He did not think like this, he wanted us humans to come together as one. Only if humanity is united can we achieve great harmony in the whole world." Didn't the ancients say: "If all the people are of one heart, the earth under our feet will turn into gold"? If we bring all our hearts together as one, we will surely be able to make society harmonious. If, however, in our cultivation, we still have high and low, if we still have arguments and greed, then this is simply wrong. Arguing is a sin, greed is a transgression, agitation is evil. Arguing, being greedy, and agitating, these are not minor sins. Abstain from arguing and greed, and your happiness and good fortune will be limitless.

Nevertheless, I do not mean to say that engaging in conflict is always a sin, because it does depend on who you are in conflict with, what you are arguing for. If you are arguing for the benefit of society at large, this is an act of merit, but if you are arguing for your own sake, this is a sin and transgression. Take our scientists: If they do not argue for the sake of progress, our civilization will not advance and society will not be able to evolve. For the benefit of who are they arguing? They are arguing for everybody's benefit, to allow the whole society to enjoy happiness. Being single-mindedly devoted to the benefit of society, this is benevolence, this is wisdom.

IV.3 DO NOT SEEK ANYTHING IN RETURN FOR YOUR GOOD DEEDS

With anything that people do in the world, everybody hopes that good will come out of it. In fact though, goodness is not something that you have to think about. Even if you think about goodness, you may still not be able to make it good. You merely must try as hard as you can and do things to the best of your ability, and you might achieve good results naturally. It is just like the ancients said: "Merely carry out good deeds but never ask what the future may bring. Broadly accumulate hidden merit but do not seek retribution."

There once was a geomancer, a man who specialized in the auspicious siting of tombs. One day, he was going somewhere in a great hurry and therefore had broken out into sweat on his head and become very thirsty. Passing by the home of a very wealthy family by the side of the road, he saw some workers mixing mortar for a wall and the owner watching from the side. The geomancer bowed to salute the owner and asked politely for a drink of water. The wealthy man ordered a worker to ladle out a dipper full of water and then quickly took it upon himself to toss in a bit of crushed wheat, before he walked over and handed the water to the man. This geomancer was displeased by this, thinking to himself: "I only wanted a drink of water, and now you are playing this bad trick on me. I shouldn't drink the water, but you brought it all the way over here. Or maybe I should drink it, but somebody tossed some left-over crushed wheat into it." In the end, he had no choice but to take a deep breath, blow the bits of crushed wheat aside, and then reluctantly drink the water. After he had finished the water, he sat down for a chat and intentionally revealed his special skill in siting tombs. As soon as the wealthy man heard this, he said joyously: "How fortunate that my family is just in the process of choosing a tomb site, so may I ask you, sir, to please come with me to have a look?" The geomancer, however, was still holding a grudge in his heart because of the situation with the water and now saw an opportunity to get even, so he chose a location for this family that had five tigers and a flock of sheep gathered. If anybody was to be buried in this piece of land, after three years the inevitable result would be that the family would break apart and its members perish.

Three years later, the geomancer passed by the rich person's home again and wanted to see the results of this trick that he had played years before on the wealthy man. When he saw the outcome, though, it took him by great surprise: "Oh-oh! How can this family on the contrary have become even more prosperous? With armed guards standing watch at the gates, they must have produced a high official. I wonder what happened?" He had the gatekeeper go inside and report his arrival to the owner. Not a moment later, the owner himself rushed out to welcome the geomancer and asked him to come in. He instructed the servants: "Our benefactor has come! Quickly arrange a feast to entertain our visitor!" The astonished geomancer asked: "How did I become your benefactor? I should be seen as your enemy!" Equally puzzled, the wealthy man asked him why he would say that, so the geomancer asked him: "Do you still remember how I asked you for water a few years ago?" And when the wealthy man said yes, the geomancer again asked: "Do you still remember how you once tossed me some left-over cracked wheat?" And when the wealthy man again said yes, he asked again: "What was the significance of that?" The rich man explained: "I saw you hurrying down the road in such a rush that your head was full of sweat, so you must have had great heat in your lungs. Had you suddenly drunk cold water, this cold Qi would have surely damaged your lungs. So I tossed some leftover wheat in your water. By first having to blow this cracked wheat off, you not only had to take a deep breath, but you also blew away the hot Qi in your lungs, and afterwards you could drink without doing any harm to yourself." When the geomancer heard, he let out a deep sigh of regret, saying: "Originally, you had kind intentions, but I did not read them as good intentions. Let me go take another look at your grave site tomorrow." The following day, when he went to look at the grave site, he realized that the direction that the entrance of the mound faced had been changed and that the site of five tigers and a flock of sheep had been transformed into a site where five dragons gathered. Does everybody here understand what I am trying to say here? Regardless of what we do, the key is always where our heart is at. If your heart is good, Heaven can see that. And if you are wronged by 80%, you will eventually receive 100% retribution.

When some people carry out good deeds, they think in their heart: Since I paid out such-and-such an amount, I must receive such-and-such an amount in return. What is this called? It is called "seeking something in return." And seeking something in return is selfish, it is presumptuous. At the time when we pay out something, we do not seek whatever retribution. What is this called? This is called "hidden work," it is also called "hidden virtue." In addition, when we are accumulating virtue and doing good deeds, it is best not to let people know, not to brag and show off. If you do brag about your good deeds, that is called "selling virtue" and it may lead to gossip or attract hardships and tribulations.

IV.4 TRANSCENDING THE WORLD AND TRANSFORMING OTHERS

The length of a human lifespan is numbered, and our allotment of good fortune is also numbered. What we eat, what we drink, what we wear, all of these things are available in a fixed quantity. But we cannot allow those numbers to restrain us, we must overcome the numbers, leave the numbers behind, shift the numbers. How do we shift these numbers? You must hold the three words Virtue, Service, and Merit in your heart and you must accomplish extraordinary good deeds. Mr. Yan Liaofan was able to truly accomplish this, and therefore he was able to "shift his numbers." If we are truly able to accomplish our goals, we can also follow his example and shift our numbers.

How do we do that? There are a great many ways in which we can practice goodness. You may say that you don't have any money, but you don't have to spend money to practice goodness. Goodness in your body, goodness in your heart, goodness in your *xing* (inner nature), these are also aspects of goodness, and moreover, these are signs of great goodness. Giving away money does not measure up to giving away your life;[4] giving away your life does not measure up to giving away your heart; and giving away your heart does not measure up to giving away your *xing* (inner nature). After we have accomplished good deeds and have accumulated good merit, in the end we must also attain goodness in our *xing*, because only the *xing* will last forever without fading away. If we save somebody's life, we save them from a single instance of suffering, but if we save somebody's *xing*, we save them for eternity. Didn't Wang Fengyi tell us: "Even if you have worn out your mouth praying and broken your legs kneeling, if your *xing* is not transformed, you are still a ghost living in hell"? Some people have performed a great number of good deeds and have spent a

---

4 舍身 has two meanings, both of which may be intended in this context. It can mean sacrificing your life or renouncing the world to join a religious order.

large amount of money and riches, and they are even able to lecture with great clarity about the principles of the Dao, but their *xing* has not transformed into goodness yet, so they are unable to succeed. Isn't this a great shame indeed?

One more thing: If we want to "shift the numbers," the best approach is to make a firm commitment in our heart to promote the teachings of Goodness, to promote the straight Dao. Why is that? Because "at the beginning of human life, the inner nature is rooted in goodness." The original nature in every one of us is good. The reason why evil people commit evil acts is that they do not understand the principles of the Dao, because nobody has explained them to them. Once they have heard the teachings of Goodness and grasped the Dao of being a good human, even great fools can transform into great sages, great evildoers can transform into great philanthropists. I am an excellent example to demonstrate this point. Throughout all my time of lecturing on the Dao, there have truly been so many, so very many people who have utterly transformed themselves down to the very marrow of their being because they heard me and understood the Dao. For this reason, I say that the merit of promoting the teachings of Goodness is particularly great!

Some people might question how they could be qualified to go out there and promote the teachings of Goodness after all the bad things they have done in the past. But the sages have taught us that the Dao does not belong to just one or two people, but that it belongs to everybody. Everybody possesses the Dao; whoever practices it possesses the Dao.

If you act as a bad person, then you have a bad Dao. If you act as a good person, then you have a good Dao. When we discuss the Dao, we do not talk about others, we talk specifically about ourselves. How do we talk about ourselves? This simply means that you talk about your own personal experiences. Before you studied the Dao, what was your physical health like? What was your emotional state like? What was your family like? And after you started studying the Dao, how did all this change? Study yourself very, very closely. If you have been able to make yourself transparent through self-study and have made yourself act genuinely, then you have attained the Dao. Only this is the genuine Dao of true action and true practice. And if you now take this Dao and lecture about it to everybody else so that everybody can benefit from it, this then is called having virtue (De 德). Daode, Daode, the virtue of the Dao, to turn it around to talk about ourselves, this is the meaning of Virtue.

In the past, people considered it the greatest expression of *xiao* to observe a mourning period for one's deceased parents. During the time when Wang Fengyi was lecturing on the Dao, there was a son famous for his *xiao* in Fuyu County with the last name Wang. He mourned his parents' death for three years, and not only that, the way he mourned them was by observing the so-called "Elixir of Frost." This "elixir of frost" meant that even in the dead of winter he would not allow himself to warm up or put on a hat, and he only wore a single layer of clothing and walked around in bare feet. Nevertheless, this practice did not cause him to freeze to death. Later on, he lived in a mountain cave for three years and did not eat anything for half a month, but again he did not starve to death. After Wang Fengyi heard about this man, he went to the cave to invite him out, saying: "Come on out! Do not stay sitting there! Even though you didn't wear enough clothes, you didn't freeze to death, and even though you didn't eat, you didn't starve to death. Do you really think that you have attained enlightenment like this? Not enlightened yet! You are still lacking one aspect of the Dao, namely to transcend the world and transform others." What this means is that people must have a consciousness of forgetting themselves, of sacrificing themselves for the sake of others. To explain the Dao and discuss virtue, to transform other people's hearts, this helps all humans to correct their bad habits and to establish a view of life that raises Daode.

After this conversation, this paragon of *xiao* named Wang did in fact emerge from his cave. At that time, there were educational societies and lecture halls everywhere, and he went wherever his fate took him to give lectures, until he eventually ended up in Harbin where he became a monk under the saint Xuanhua at Sanyuan Temple. When he died, a large number of sacred relics were found among his ashes, which proves that he had in fact attained enlightenment. Therefore let me ask you, what accomplishment and merit is the greatest? It is precisely this merit of transcending the world and transforming others.

In 2007, I encountered a woman from Changchun who was suffering from such an advanced stage of pancreatic cancer that she was close to death. She had a lot of sisters who all visited me to ask me to see her. I declined, telling them that I would not be able to cure this illness with my talking and that I would only get disheartened if I went because I would try exert great efforts with no chance of success. She later underwent surgery at the hospital where the head of her pancreas was removed, as well as a part of her stomach and a section of her intestines, and the entire gallbladder. After being operated on in these four places, she just laid in bed, unable to get up. In the end, the hospital staff told her: "Consider whether you can afford to stay in the hospital. If you can afford to stay, you will die in the hospital. If you cannot afford to stay, just go home to die there. She pondered her options and then decided to return home and die there. So she went home. Her sisters again came to see me and implored me with great persistence. I told them: "The disease has reached such an advanced stage that anything I can do will only be like treating a dead horse as if it were alive.[5] If she recovers, don't be too delighted with me, and if she dies, don't be irritated with me either." They promised to obey.

So I went to the woman's home to take a look, thinking to myself that the situation was truly hopeless and that she truly would not be able to recover. The incisions from her surgery had not closed, and pus was draining from inside her abdomen and trickling out from her surgical wounds. She could not even breathe without difficulty. When I asked her whether she really thought I'd be able to save her even though she was in such a bad condition, she responded that I was her last glimmer of hope. I said: "Fine then. Take a look around you, who is at your bedside serving you?" She responded, "my mother-in-law." And when I asked her who else was there, she acknowledged the presence of her husband and her younger sister. When I heard her answers, it struck me that there might still be some hope because the first person she mentioned was her mother-in-law. I replied: "That is correct. Originally, it should be you who is serving your mother-in-law, but now you are lying here, letting your mother-in-law serve you. Think closely: Do you feel like you have a clean conscience?" As soon as she heard this, she began to cry. I continued: "When your mother-in-law brings you some water to drink, do you feel gratitude towards her? Up this point, you haven't thought about being grateful, have you?" She admitted that she had not. I said: "Think again! Should you feel gratitude or not? As your mother-in-law has been wiping the spittle from your mouth, she

---

5   This is an old Chinese expression to refer to a totally futile effort, since you cannot bring a dead horse back to life.

hasn't despised you for being dirty, and still you don't feel grateful. Do you still have a clean conscience?" At this point, she cried even more severely. I informed her: "This disease of yours, it is caused by your resentment towards your mother-in-law. You have become angry with your mother-in-law, as well as with your husband, and even with your sisters. Now all these people are surrounding you as you are lying in your bed. Don't you feel grateful?" The more she cried, the more heart-broken she became. In the middle of crying, she began vomiting up water, until she had omitted up a small bowl full in about an hour. Seeing that she had finished vomiting, I told her that I was leaving. When she asked me not to go, I promised her: "I shall come back to see you again tomorrow morning. For the rest of the day, contemplate step by step what resentment you have felt towards your mother-in-law, your husband, and your sisters. Recollect these occasions one by one, and admit your wrongdoing, one incident at a time. Heaven does not kill people who repent, so if you are able to confess your wrongs, you will be alright. Our human legal code has a rule: Leniency if you confess; harsh punishment if you refuse. So everything depends on whether you are able to confess." She promised me that she'd be able to confess, so I said: "Good! In that case, you must tell them to their face how you have wronged them and how you have resented them."

The next morning, I went back to see her. Her spirit had returned and she had strength in her voice. As soon as she saw me, her tears started rolling again. In my mind, I thought that it was good that she was crying, because she would only be able to recover if she was able to cry. Why did she have to cry in order to recover from her illness? Because people can only truly cry from the bottom of their heart if their confessions are made in utter sincerity. This is what I call turning over the conscience. I spent two nights at this lady's home and went to see her twice. Before I left, I asked her what her plans were for the future if she recovered. She replied: "If I recover, I also want to lecture everybody on the Dao, like you. I want to lecture on what kind of an illness I contracted and how I was able to cure it. This is what I plan to do from now on." I said: "This sounds good. The Sea of Suffering[6] has no limits ahead, but turn your head and there is the shore. Once you see through the human world of suffering, the sooner you cultivate yourself the better. Do not waste your time swimming in

---

6 A Buddhist expression referring to the endless suffering that is the reality of human existence as the result of desire for permanence in an impermanent world.

the waves of this sea of human suffering, because no matter how far you swim, where is the harbor? There is no harbor. But there is one more point that I need to tell you: Once you have recovered, for the first three years do not even think about earning money. Wait until you have firmly consolidated your health at its root before you think of making money." She promised to do so, and I left.

After only one month, she was able to get out of bed and take care of herself. After two months, was able to come downstairs. After five months, she was able to climb up five sets of stairs to cook for her entire family. And after seven or eight months, when I went to see her, hadn't she recovered completely? She certainly had, but she had broken her original promise and was only concerned for her own family instead of thinking about lecturing on the Dao. Our family, what is our family? The family is a locked cage. People all allow their families to lock them up, allow their wives and children to lock them up, so they have no place at all to turn.

A good while later, when I again went to see this lady, what was she doing? She was selling shoes in the market. Originally she had been a teacher but through some personal connections had managed to retire on account of her illness. But after retiring, she had taken her government retirement pension to start her own business. What is this called? Taking a salary from the state but not working for the state. She was only working in service to herself, not in service to the people. For this reason, I told her as I was leaving: "Regarding your medical expenses, you must absolutely not submit them to the government for reimbursement. You already owe our country a huge debt, and you must absolutely not request reimbursement of your medical expenses." She responded: "If I recover completely, I will not seek compensation."

Later on, she in fact recovered completely from her illness. But in the blink of an eye, she wondered what she'd do if she didn't have enough money to do business. So she asked somebody to help her request reimbursement of 15,000 Yuan of medical expenses. At that time, all of her family members were opposed to her seeking reimbursement, but she told them that once she received the reimbursement she would donate it to charity." Did she really give the money to charity? No, she didn't. She spent 10,000 Yuan to lease a market stall for her daughter and gave another 5,000 Yuan to her son-in-law to lease a car. In the end, though, he had an accident 15 days later and lost those 5,000 Yuan to pay for it, and her daughter also lost the entire 10,000 Yuan within just a month. And because things had turned out bad, as soon as her smoldering anger, she suffered a relapse of her disease.

At this time, I just happened to be in Changchun, so she again came to see me. I said: "You made a promise but you have not acted in accordance with this promise. This time around, I can no longer save you." She responded by wailing and kowtowing at the same time, but I told her: "This time you can smash your head to pieces kowtowing and it still won't work. I truly cannot rescue you!" You see, humans are really difficult! Wasn't it extraordinarily lucky that she had been able to survive when her illness had progressed to such a critical stage? But to not know how to treasure such extraordinary good fortune, this is truly impossible!

What does this example tell us? There are two things in the world that we must not wait with: To practice *xiao* to its fullest, and to do good deeds. If we fail to establish merit and to practice virtue when we are in the prime of our lives but wait until we are old to do these things, it is simply too late. In any spare time we may find, we must urgently practice *xiao* and do good deeds. Then one morning, when we find a disaster hanging over us, the Buddha's light will be able to shine on everything. But if you have whiled away your days enjoying your leisure and have not fulfilled your *xiao* or performed good deeds, one morning when disaster strikes, you will become very anxious. You will burn incense and make vows and kowtow until the cows come home, but it will be too late! At that point you may even blame Heaven or blame Earth, blame God or blame the Buddha: "I have complete faith in you, so why don't you reveal your power?" Why don't they reveal their power? Because you are one of those people who do good in words only, those people who are good only on the surface, but you have not put your words into practice.

Wang Fengyi once said: "There are three categories of bad people in the world. Those who speak of the Dao but do not practice the Dao are the first category. Those who have heard the Dao but fail to act on it are the second category. Those who find joy in taking advantage of others and get angry when they suffer losses are the third category." If you lecture others on the Dao but do not personally put it into practice, you are the worst kind of criminal. This applies to those religious masters, including also people like me, if we don't fully practice what we preach, we belong to this first category of bad people. Why is that? Because if you have grasped the principles of the Dao but still fail to act in accordance with the Dao, this is like knowing the law but violating it. Given that this causes others to lose faith in the teachings of goodness, isn't this adding another crime to the original one? People who have heard the Dao but fail to act on it fall into the second category of badness. Heaven does not fault those who are blind, but you are not a blind person. According to the common expression "Ignorance makes you innocent," if you do not know, it is not easy to settle an account with you, but now you already know. If you still refuse to act, doesn't that put you in the second category of bad people? Lastly, "those who find joy in taking advantage of others and get angry when they suffer losses," these make up the third category of bad people. But people who have grasped the Dao turn this exact sentence around and find no joy in taking advantage of others, but suffer losses and still find joy. Why is that? Because these people understand that to suffer losses is to earn merit but to take advantage of others is to leave behind a debt for the future.

IV.5 HELPING OTHERS WITHOUT SELFISHNESS

There are many who hear the Dao but few who practice it. There are many who practice Buddhist cultivation but few who reach enlightenment. This is truly a case of not a single grain of gold in ten thousand grains of sand! How did the Buddha reach enlightenment? By overcoming the self, by abandoning the ego, enlightenment leaked out from the midst of contention and greed. If we want to reach enlightenment, we must cast off our selfish heart, we must cast off our heart of greed and contention. We can only reach enlightenment if we don't act for the sake of fame, profit, ourselves, or our family.

In Chairman Mao's words, "With all your heart and soul, act in service to the people!" The people are Heaven, the public is Heaven. To act in service to the public means to act in service to Heaven. When we act in service to the public, we must not have regrets, feel wronged, or expect compensation, but must only quietly go and take action. Whether we do good or do bad, Heaven will remember. Wang Fengyi also told us: "Act for the sake of others and not for your own sake, this is the root of Buddhahood." To act for the sake of others is to serve the public, and to serve the public is goodness. To act for our own sake is selfishness, and selfishness is evil. Me, me, me, if you don't go beyond me whether your mouth is open or closed, this is selfishness, this is evil.

To tell the truth, where is enlightenment? Enlightenment is not on the outside, but only inside the heart. If you can keep a Buddha heart, no matter how much strength you have, you use all that strength to help other people, to benefit society. And while you are alive, everybody will speak of you as a living Buddha, you will in fact be a living Buddha. Why should you have to wait until after death to become a Buddha?

V. Establishing a Commitment

V.1 IF YOU DO NOT ACCEPT POLISHING, YOU CANNOT REACH ENLIGHTENMENT

Each and every one of us has a Buddha nature and is able to reach enlightenment. Why haven't we turned into Buddhas yet? Because chanting alone cannot make you reach enlightenment, enlightenment is something that is accomplished through action. When we look at the story about the monk from the Tang dynasty who went to India in search of Buddhist sutras, wasn't Sun Wukong[7] originally called Sun Xingzhe.[8] We likewise are just walking on the road and may also encounter a lot of tribulations to polish us. Nine times nine makes eighty-one tribulations, of which not even a single one could be avoided. What are these "polishing tribulations"? They are negative things that help us in the long run, with a great power to help us. Without having endured such polishing tribulations, we cannot succeed. So if we want to be successful, we must first overcome these polishing tribulations. And every tribulation that we overcome is one juncture that we pass.

7   Literally translated, the name means "Realizer-of-Emptiness Sun." This is the name of the famous monkey king who accompanied the Chinese monk Xuanzang in the "Journey to the West" (Xi You Ji 西遊記), encountering 81 tribulations in their travels.
8   Lit. "Walker Sun"

There are people who make up their mind and say that they are going to reach enlightenment. But enlightenment is not that easy to reach, enlightenment is something that must get polished out of us. To become enlightened, you have to get polished, it just depends on whether you can endure the polishing or not. If you are unable to tolerate the polishing, you cannot reach enlightenment. Why do I use language like this? Because our acquired nature (*bing xing*) has been formed over many eons and has become like an old chunk of pig iron that is covered by a very thick layer of rust. If you want to become enlightened, you need to have grinding stones to polish you with. And the coarser the grinding stone, the more vigorous the polishing will be, and the more quickly the rust will come off. If the polishing is too light, it just won't work. You may get rid of a bit of rust, but more rust is bound to form. You must polish your *xing* until it is gleaming, with not a spot of dirt or dust on it, and only then can you make the original Buddha nature come out.

A lot of people simply give up when they encounter a difficult situation, thinking "I didn't do that person any wrong. Why does he or she have to give me such a hard time?" So they want to retreat, in the belief that Heaven is not fair. But Heaven is in fact fair. Heaven's justice is circular. Because the intention that you set for yourself is so big, Heaven wants to test you. And to test you, Heaven makes other people polish you, makes your friends and family around you polish you. Without polishing, there is no shine. The more you get polished the greater you shine, and the greater you shine, the more you get polished, straight to the point where you have truly been polished to perfection. Without demons, you cannot see through the world of mortals; without tribulations, where would you find unmatched commitment and true cultivation? So we must really feel gratitude towards those people who polish and grind us down.

Mr. Yi Zhi, the author of a book called "Brief Description of Wang Fengyi's Philosophy of *Xing* and *Ming*" (Wang Fengyi Xing Ming Zhexue Qianshu 王鳳儀性命哲學淺述), followed Zhu Xuntian personally for close to forty years but not even once witnessed Mr. Zhu get angry. This kind of a person is truly extraordinary! Not once getting angry in forty years! Do you think that is easy? Otherwise why would Wang Fengyi have called him Zhu Zhuangyuan?[9] When

---

9 This translates as "Zhu The Very Best".

Zhu's wife wanted to divorce her husband, she moved permanently back to her parents' home, refusing to come back to him. Wang Fengyi told Mr. Zhu to go there and try to bring her back three times, that this would be considered being in accord with the Dao. So Mr. Zhu went to her parents' and tried to take her back six times, and every time his wife only yelled at him and even set a dog loose to bite him. Not once did Zhu Xuntian get angry! After the sixth time, Zhu Xuntian finally said: "I will go over there one last time, and if still insists on a divorce, I will grant it to her and sign the divorce decree." When he arrived, she once again let the dog loose on him to bite him, so Zhu Xuntian told her: "Please don't make the dog bite me. I will go through the divorce formalities with you." Instantly, his wife became very happy and cooked him a meal and served him wine. When she had finished entertaining him as an honored guest, she accompanied him outside to send him off. This is the kind of man Zhu Xuntian was, able to endure such a trial.

A long time ago, there was a highly cultivated Buddhist monk who was known as somebody who had not emitted any smoke for thirty years, or in other word, for not getting angry in thirty years.[10] He had built himself a very nice temple in the mountains, so nice that the walls were covered with fancy glazed tiles. When he had finished building this temple, he hung a sign on the gate on which was written: "No smoke emitted in thirty years."

Of course, if you hang up such a sign, somebody is bound to come and test you, the Buddha is bound to want to polish you. On this occasion, an old Daoist priest came along, holding an iron club in his hand. Arriving in front of the temple, he said: "No smoke emitted in thirty years? Let's see if you will emit smoke or not." And with that, the old Daoist used his iron club to strike the tiles on the wall, striking them neither too slowly nor too quickly. Bang!, he smashed a tile. And bang!, he smashed another tile. After he had broken three tiles, a young monk came from inside the temple to see what was going on and exclaimed: "Hey there, old master! Stop striking the tiles! Stop striking the tiles!" Maybe it would have been better for him not to say anything, because the more he said, the more the old Daoist struck the tiles. Taking one look at this bad situation, the young monk dropped his head and ran to find

10   "Emitting smoke" 冒烟 is a euphemism for getting angry, allowing one's temper to flare up, since anger is associated with fire in Chinese culture.

his master. The wise master then emerged, his palms brought together in a gesture of respectful greeting, and said: "Merciful Buddha! Old priest, stop striking the tiles!" And he asked him to stop nine times, and each time he asked, the Daoist priest smashed yet another tile. Seeing this, and wondering how this fellow could go on smashing his tiles, the Buddhist master began getting angry. So he said: "I have asked you to stop for half a day already! How can you continue smashing tiles like this?" The old Daoist turned around, took a long look at the wise master, and said: "For thirty years, no smoke emitted! But today, smoke has been emitted." So you see, everything we experience is a test, to see how you will handle a situation. Since the Buddhist master's practice turned out to be imperfect in the face of difficulty, he had to start again from scratch. If we personally feel that we have accomplished a whole lot, that we are quite satisfied with our actions, this is bad. In other areas, we must know how to be satisfied. But when it comes to practicing the Dao, we must never know satisfaction. If you look at yourself and are satisfied with your conduct, this means that you will no longer be able to progress.

V.2 ESTABLISHING A SINGLE-MINDED COMMITMENT

So many people repeat the same small mistake in their cultivation practice: The commitment they establish for themselves is quite big, but as soon as they encounter an adverse situation, they immediately retreat. In addition, there are quite a few people who know that they have done wrong and yet, when they encounter a certain situation, they repeat exactly the same mistake, again and again offending and reforming and offending and reforming. What is the reason for this? Their determination is not firm enough. If the commitment is not firm, the intention not solid, you will not be able to obtain the true, genuine Dao.

In Wang Fengyi's time, somebody asked him: "When I was three years old, my dad left the family. I am now 18 years old and I have not seen my father in fifteen years. I want to go looking for my father. Will I be able to find him?" At that time, Wang Fengyi gave him the short answer that it depended only on his commitment. "Great!" the young fellow answered. Then he wrote his father's name and his own name on his back, and also wrote that he was a son looking for his father, and left his family to go searching for him. After looking for three years, he indeed found his father in Heihe City. There you can see how important a firm commitment is!

A young man from Qitaihe in Heilongjiang Province came to see me, looking for me on three different occasions. Why did he come looking for me? In order to formally apprentice with me as his master. I told him: "I don't accept any disciples and I don't serve as anybody's master, but I only explain the Dao of human life. Whatever it is, just come right out and ask me directly." It was only on his third visit that he finally spoke up: "I have a younger sister. My aunt once took her out to play and my sister got lost and disappeared." Answering my questions, he told me that she had been twelve years old when she had gotten lost and would now be twenty-four, so twelve years had passed since then. Then he asked me whether I thought that he would be able to find her. In response I recounted for him the above story about the son finding his long-lost father and then told him that it all depended on his commitment. He replied: "Very well. In that case, I will certainly be able to find her. Being of the same flesh and blood, we will get reunited!" Not much more than a month later, he gave me a phone call and told me that he had found his sister in Sichuan. Take a look at this situation: He had no idea where to even look for her in the whole wide world, so how was it possible that he succeeded in finding his sister? These two examples show us that "where there's a will, there's a way." It all depends on whether you have a single-minded commitment or not. Why do we call this a directed commitment? Because you need commitment, but you also need direction, to lead you to the place where you want to go.

Establish a single-minded commitment can of course involve great hardships, like in the case of the young man above who spent three long years looking for his father for three long years, day and night. What hardship! And then there was the other person who went looking for his sister. In one month on the road, he went through all his money until he had no more traveling funds. On his way home, he had to borrow a hundred Yuan from a friend in Changchun just to get back home. If you all want to study the Dao, you must first ask yourself whether you have a single-minded commitment or not.

VI. Humbleness and Strenuous Effort

VI.1 STRENUOUS EFFORT

There is a saying in Buddhism: "After studying the Dao for one year, Buddha is in front of your eyes. After studying the Dao for three years, Buddha is on the horizon. After studying the Dao for ten years, Buddha is in the Western Paradise." Why is it that the more we study the more distant Buddha becomes? Because we only pray to Buddha but are unable to act as Buddha. Only praying and not acting, how can Buddha not get ever more distant the more we pray?

Some people go to the temple to worship Buddha, and they burn incense and pray to Buddha: "Bless me, oh Buddha, please bless me!" Surely Buddha wants to bless you. But after you have been loafing around in idleness, committing all sorts of outrages, and carrying out a great many actions that go against the principles of humanity, how can Buddha bless you? Buddha wants to bless us all but is unable to do so. If you yourself don't go and put your cultivation into practice, if you don't make any sacrifices, but only want to enjoy an easy life and ask everybody else to help you, how could it be this easy and convenient! Moving the mouth is not as good as moving the heart, and moving the heart is not as good as moving in action. If you yourself have accomplished things and have been genuine, there is no need to go out of your way to pray to Buddha, Buddha will come and bless you on his own accord. Why do we speak of cultivation through suffering? Our bodies are made to suffer hardships, you must pay out merit by doing hard work. If your body has had to work a few hard jobs for a living, whoever received your assistance has been made happy by that. By earnestly performing meritorious service with our body, we are able to tie extensive bonds of friendship with humanity. By having a good heart, we are able to tie a bond with Heaven. By having a good *xing* (inner nature), we are able to tie a bond with Buddha.

There are other students of Buddhism who spare no effort at reading the sutras out loud when they are in the Buddhist halls of prayer. But when they leave the place of worship and come home, they look at the shortcomings of their family members, picking on them and making them angry. Doesn't that mean that they have read the sutras wrongly? What are the sutras after all? They are precisely an expression of the experiences of the Buddha, of the actions that he carried out. And as we read each sentence, we must then go out and put that sentence into practice. Practice is the only way to be genuine! If you can act in accordance with the Buddha's words, you simply become the Buddha, and subsequent generations will read about you, about your experiences. But if you only read without acting on it, indulge in empty chatter about deep mysteries, regardless of whether you produce lotus flowers from your mouth, you will have difficulty reaching the Buddhist paradise.

A child prodigy named Jiang Xizhang once asked Wang Fengyi to address the following question: "Between a commentator on the Diamond Sutra and a lecturer on the sutra, which of them would be able to become a Buddha himself?" Wang Fengyi responded: "Neither the commentator nor the lecturer is necessarily able to attain Buddhahood. Only the person who practices the Diamond Sutra is able to attain Buddhahood." Hearing this sentence, the child prodigy gave him the thumbs-up and said: "You are indeed worthy of being called a sage by everybody. You truly do possess the qualifications of a sage. I have travelled all over, to the East and to the West, and nobody has been able to respond to my question until you, Master Wang Fengyi, were able to do so."

When I was lecturing in Changchun in 2002, I had a discussion with a professor and four physicians after a class. Sighing deeply, the professor exclaimed: "At present there are so many academics who do know a lot but for the most part lack insight, unlike you who not only has knowledge but also has insight." What is this insight he was talking about? Insight is the understanding that is gained from experience. As Confucius said, "To learn and then at times to practice it, is this not joyful indeed?" Once we have studied something, we still must apply it in practice, go out and act on it. The Dao is there to be acted out. De (virtue) is there to be put into practice. Without action, there is no Dao. Without practice, there is no De. What are books but medicinal prescriptions. If you only look at them, only look at the medicinal prescription, but don't take the medicine, how can your illness get cured? Merely looking without acting means that you have misread the book.

Regardless of whether we are talking about the ancients or about modern people, whenever we find somebody to be a good person, we take them as our model and act in accordance with their example. If we are truly able to act accordingly, the radiance of their spirit will illuminate us as well. And if we act in accordance with Shakyamuni Buddha's words, Shakyamuni Buddha will come and bless us. Every single one of us has a Dao. Your Dao and my Dao and everybody's Dao are interlinked. Act on it without making a big deal about it, and success awaits you.

VI.2 ASSUMING A HUMBLE STATUS IN LIFE

When a person once told me that he had studied the Dao for many years and had studied Buddhism for many years, I warned him not to talk like that or others might laugh at him. What would they have to laugh at, he asked. I answered: "Those people who have not studied the Dao might look at you and tell themselves that even though you have studied the Dao they are still better than you. Since you haven't done any good but are only full of big talk, how can you not make others laugh at you?" For this reason, regardless of where I go, I never dare to state that I myself am a person who lectures on the Dao. Because humans are never perfect, with every single word and act, move and turn, it is difficult to avoid a leak. And once there is a leak, it will leak Qi, just like a hole in the inner tube of a tire will leak air. And the leak doesn't have to be big. Even a hole as tiny as a pinprick disables the tire. For this reason we had better conduct ourselves with humbleness.

Wang Fengyi also taught us: "Be low! Be humble! Humbleness means being a Buddha." Where does Buddha reside? Buddha does not reside in high places, but in low ones. Buddhahood is formed in low places. The masses of humanity are Heaven, and if you are able to humble yourself so you are lower than the masses, you can prop them up from below, and thereby you have supported Heaven. Be just like water, which flows towards wherever there is a hollow, wherever there is a low spot. Isn't there a saying: "Those who live in confusion are the masses. Those who are enlightened are Buddhas." Once you are able to wake up and become enlightened, you are able to lower and humble yourself, you are able to prop up the masses, you have become a Buddha. If we look at all those who have attained enlightenment from ancient times to the present, how is it that they all achieved success? Shakyamuni was a prince who abandoned his fame, fortune, and position of power and instead turned his heart single-mindedly towards the Dao. To eat a meal, he made his rounds holding out his begging bowl, begging for alms. He truly was somebody who truly humbled himself, and hence he became a Buddha. Now let us look at the Bodhisattva Guanyin: She toiled and labored alongside the palace maids and servant girls, enduring exhaustion and blame. This is also a case of truly humbling herself. And again, look at the Bodhisattva Dizang, who is famous for having said "If I don't descend to hell, who will?" He went even lower yet!

Nevertheless, humans do not want to be low, they all want to be high up, they want be famous and appear in the limelight, rolling in fame and fortune. Take a careful look around you! All those people who consider themselves of great importance and power, who are very high up there in society, they have such a difficult time achieving success. Why is that? Because they crave height and love only the best. No matter what, they always want the highest and the best. But to be in high places, they have to struggle with others, and if they do not succeed in your struggle, their heart is stirred and they get angry. Therefore I say that this is terrible indeed. They higher you are, the more terrible it is. The higher you rise, the more painful the fall will be.

High places involve danger, while low places are peaceful. The Dao is found in low places. If you do not climb upwards but turn around to go downward, you cannot fall and you cannot get knocked over. We must go lower and lower still, until we are three feet under ground, so that even somebody with a 2-feet long hook is unable to hook you. And then do you think you will succeed or not? Of course you will! Therefore we must not look at ourselves as so high up but must always walk towards a lower place. We must not look at ourselves as so big but must always shrink ourselves to make us small. The smaller we can shrink ourselves, the more generous we will be, and the more generous we are, the more virtue we have.

What do we learn when we learn the Dao? We learn how to be humble, how to be short, how to be foolish, how to suffer losses, how to retreat, how to yield. As I have told you above, you must endure your burden, you must give others a break. The Chinese character for "to endure" (rěn 忍) contains the character for "knife" (dāo 刀) on the top, because if you are unable to endure, you will come under the knife. Enduring for a while calms the wind and makes the waves subside; retreating a step opens up a space as boundless as the sea or the sky. If we intend to transform our inner nature and to walk the Dao of a good person, we must learn how to be able to endure and yield, we must learn how to retreat. When other people engage in conflict with you, you simply retreat, and by retreating, you advance. Retreat means advance. When others move up high, you lower yourself, and by lowering yourself, you become high. Being low means being high.

Wang Fengyi has taught us a brief sentence: "When meeting a person of high status, don't lower yourself. When meeting a person of low status, don't elevate yourself." Why did he say this? If you have a person of low social status and you look down upon them even further, they will have a very difficult time pulling themselves up. One who supports and lifts up fools is a saint. The more foolishness you see, the more you should prop them up. Whenever we therefore encounter people of a low social status, we must absolutely not elevate ourselves above them. And in addition, whenever you encounter a person of high status, do not lower yourself either. If you do lower yourself, the people around you will call it "smoothing his beard and patting his horse's hindquarters." He has power and might, fame and wealth, and if you fawn on him and flatter him, in other people's eyes it looks like you are patting his horse's hindquarters. Therefore it doesn't matter whether you interact with a person of lower or higher social status, you must always maintain a level heart.

During Wang Fengyi's lifetime, there was a person with the name Li Yongcheng who everybody referred to as the "idiot monk." Why did they refer to him as the "idiot monk"? Because he lived in a temple for seven years and each winter went through seven pairs of padded trousers because of his incontinence. The other monks in the temple all said that he was crazy and dim-witted and ultimately did not allow him to stay in the temple any longer. Wang Fengyi said: "If you don't want him, I want him. If nobody else wants him, I will pick him up." Thereupon, he took him in and arranged for him to stay at his free school. He had him go shopping for the students, and Li Yongcheng was so dim-witted that he could only remember a single item to buy each time. From the perspective of the rest of us ordinary people, this man was mentally retarded, but in Wang Fengyi's eyes, he was a venerable Buddha, and therefore he arranged for him to be by his side.

Shortly before his death, Wang Fengyi said: "I am going to go to Heihe one last time, to offer the world a treasure." Everybody asked what kind of a treasure he was talking about. Wang Fengyi answered: "I am bringing along Li Yongcheng." Everybody laughed at these words. One old lady who was present at that time is still alive today, being more than ninety years old now. She told me: " At this point, we almost died we were laughing so hard. Taking along this idiot, what kind of a treasure was he offering up?" Li Yongcheng simply asked our Good Man Wang: "Since you are taking me with you, what shall I say when I get there?" Wang Fengyi said: "You don't need to say anything. If there are people who speak to you, just tell them, 'You are Buddha.' Saying that will be enough." Li Yongcheng agreed to follow this advice. Later on, Wang Fengyi did in fact bring him to Heihe and whenever Li encountered people he greeted them with the words: "You are Buddha." And to this, the opposite side would respond with the same words: "You are Buddha too." Since everybody in the crowd told him that he was Buddha, he in fact simply became Buddha. In the beginning, all of us fools failed to understand: Why on earth did Wang Fengyi bring him along? Good Man Wang had everybody confer Buddhahood on him.

To tell you the truth, all people are good people, all people have their strong points. All you have to do is not look at another person's weaknesses but instead praise his or her strengths and he or she will gradually transform and improve. In our family, you can never say under any circumstances what a loser your son is or how your daughter is not worth anything. If you plant that kind of a seed in them, they will indeed be worthless losers. But if you steadfastly keep that thought in your heart that your child can do no wrong, I guarantee you that he or she will be capable of being like that.

Nevertheless, there are some people who say that when other people surpass them it fills them with jealousy. But this is clearly wrong. I have the following standpoint: To praise others is to dignify oneself, to help others is to help oneself, to make others succeed is to make oneself succeed. I hope that everybody excels, that everybody surpasses me. Only then do I feel happy. Please think carefully for a moment. If others are all able to surpass us, doesn't that mean that we are living in paradise? But if others constantly struggle and contend with us, arguing and yelling, wrestling and fighting, doesn't that mean that we are living in hell? Do you still have to wait until after death to descend to hell? No, you are already living in hell right here!

VII. Gratitude Towards Your Country

King Wen of the Zhou dynasty ruled a hundred officials by means of *xiao*, and the hundred officials ruled myriads of people by means of *xiao*. And as a result of this, the Zhou dynasty was able to have a history of more than 800 years. At present, the leaders of our country also genuinely express the sentiment of loving the population like your children in their actions. I am a farmer, and farmers are the most likely of all professions to learn through practical experience. From the ancient past until today, which dynasty has not exploited the farmers with ruthless levies and exorbitant taxes? But our current government is not only not demanding money from us but even gives us money, in the form of grain subsidies, fuel subsidies, and even reduced insurance in old age. When I talk about this subject, I cannot help getting moved to tears. Moreover, our government is currently investing great efforts into promoting traditional culture, to teach our children and grandchildren about ethics and morality from childhood on and guide them to become a good human being. The government is taking such loving care of us, even more so than parents take care of their children. Are we able to experience our government's earnest efforts and laborious expenditures or not? How can we not respond to this only with gratitude in our feelings and actions?

Given that our country takes such loving care of us, how can we as the population reciprocate and repay our country? First, we must cultivate and rectify our bodies and minds and establish harmony in our own families. It is only when we have a concordant body and mind that we can have a concordant family. And it is only when we have a concordant family that we can have a concordant country. And it is only when we have a concordant country that we can have a concordant society. This is precisely the principle that the old sage Confucius taught us about "investigate things, acquire knowledge, make the intention sincere, rectify the heart, cultivate the body, align the family, govern the country, and create peace Under Heaven."

What does this concept of *ge wu* 格物[11] ("investigate things") mean? "Investigating things" means that you must intimately review the road that your own life has taken, down to the smallest detail. From the very beginning of your memory, in what roles have you served, how did you walk that path step by step, how did you act at every individual step, where did you not act to your satisfaction? Let us say you are a woman. In your natal family, did you love and obey your parents with *xiao*? And after marriage, have you respected and loved your parents-in-law with *xiao*? Have you been a virtuous wife and good mother and are you on good terms with your sisters-in-law? And eventually, when you have reached the high status of an old lady and mother-in-law yourself, how have you acted in that role? Let us all sum up our lives with the greatest care possible. It is only after you have "investigated things" that you are able to "acquire knowledge," and only then are you able to know where you personally have gone wrong.

Once you know where you gone wrong, you must repent with sincerity. To pull the truth out from within the truth, this is the meaning of "make the intention sincere." If you know where you personally have done wrong but act with pretense and hypocrisy rather than correcting your behavior, this is not right. Genuine people carry out genuine actions, while fake people carry out fake actions. Genuine people are genuine towards themselves, while fake people are fake towards themselves.

What is the meaning of "rectify the heart"? Rectifying the heart means that in our heart there is no selfishness or evil thought, but that we treat all people exactly the same. It is only after we have set our heart straight and pledge to keep our body healthy that we are able to "cultivate the body." To cultivate the body means to get rid of all of our bad physical habits and maintain and develop the good habits. Haven't you heard the following saying: "It is only with joy and laughter every day that we can chant the Buddha's name correctly." If you are plagued by chronic diseases all day long and do not have a healthy body, it is also difficult to practice good self-cultivation. It is only when

---

11   *ge wu* 格物 This is a central concept in Chinese philosophy that became particularly important for the revival of Confucianism during the Song and Ming dynasty (so--called Neo--Confucianism). It refers to the rational investigation of natural phenomena in order to detect the underlying principle with the ultimate purpose of self-cultivation.

your diseases are cured and your body is healthy that the family can be well, that the family can be in alignment. These days, there are a lot of people who study Buddhism, but from dawn to dusk their spirit is at a complete loss and they suffer from distraction. Why is that? Because your body is not healthy, because you are unable to keep guard over your monkey-heart or tether down your galloping horse-mind.

Once we have cultivated our own body and mind, the next step consists in "aligning the family." Aligning the family does not mean that you make your family members fulfill your wishes, that you control your family members. We must go and control other people but we must first learn to control ourselves well. When you have first transformed yourself, your family members will follow you and transform on their own. Once a single person has changed him- or herself, the entire family has changed. And when a single family has changed, all the relatives and friends around them are changed, so that you can say that a considerable part has changed. The people who have been influenced by you furthermore go out into different environments where they again influence a large sum of people. Therefore we can say that when a single person has turned bad, it turns bad a much larger part of society, and when a single person has turned good, it also turns good a much larger part.

Appendix

Precious Record of Physiology

The thirty-six days after both the summer solstice and the winter solstice are a time for preserving your essence. Sexual intercourse is prohibited during this time.

The first and fifteenth day of each lunar month are days when humanity and Heaven and Yin and Yang meet. Sexual intercourse is prohibited during these days.

Among the twelve two-hour periods of each day, the times when the Yuan Qi (source Qi) in the body compounds are *zi* (11 pm to 1 am), *wu* (11 am to 1 pm), *mao* (5 am to 7 am), and *you* (5 pm to 7 pm). Sexual intercourse is prohibited during these times.

Sexual intercourse is prohibited on overcast and rainy days; otherwise any children conceived then will be stupid, muddleheaded, otherwise mentally disabled, or unconscious.

Sexual intercourse is prohibited during times of thunder and lightning; otherwise any children conceived then will be malicious, involved in shady business as adults, have a violent temper, or be physically disabled.

During the execution of sexual intercourse, the woman must lie on her back; otherwise any children conceived then will either be mute or suffer a congenital disease. The key lies in mutual harmony between husband and wife.

Sexual intercourse is prohibited on all the following occasions: during the mother or father's birthday, in the light of a lamp or under the moon, in violent wind or rain storms, on the four li days (the day before the spring and autumn equinoxes and the summer and winter solstices), and on the four jue days (the day before the first days of spring, summer, autumn, and winter).

For the duration of the pregnancy, the woman must hold herself straight when walking, doing anything, sitting, or lying down. Her mouth may not utter foul words, her eyes may not fall on foul sights, her ears may not hear foul sounds, and her heart may not harbor foul thoughts. If she carries out these principles of protecting the fetus, the child born from the pregnancy will be good-looking in appearance and of outstanding intelligence and talent!

Heavenly Nature Affirmations *"Jiao xing* 叫性*"*

Confucius was a sage—one of those extraordinary beings who walked the earth in 500 BCE, and who now symbolizes the human evolution of consciousness. He has become China's prototypical teacher—transmitter of the Way, the Dao, and innovator of the standard of living a virtuous life. His timeless message is: remember who you are and where you come from; honor the Universe, including everything and everybody in it, especially your most immediate family; don't act upon your selfish emotions and strive to be a model for everyone else.

The Confucian virtues, categorized in the 5-Phase-Element mode of his time:
Ren 仁: Compassion, associated with the phase element Wood
Li 禮: Sacred connection or ritual, associated with the phase element Fire
Xin 信: Trust and integrity, associated with the phase element Earth
Yi 義: Justice and righteousness, associated with the phase element Metal
Zhi 智: Wisdom, associated with the phase element Water

The Confucian method of putting the heart of others before one's own has deeply influenced Chinese culture for more than 2000 years. Even today, an age where individualism and selfishness dominate, people are returning to the master's teachings.

Wang Fengyi (1864-1937) was a peasant saint from Northern China who created a complete system of social and emotional healing in the memory of Confucius. During the three years of the filial death watch at his father's grave, he became awakened to the timeless medical truth of the importance of the mind, the spirit, and the emotions in the formation of all disease. Henceforth he made it his mission in life to restore the five inherent basic positive qualities of humanity—the Confucian virtues—by cleansing the five negative emotions of anger, hatred, blame, criticism, and disdain.

At first sight this model appears to differ from the standard Chinese medicine system of pathogenic emotions (anger, excitement, worry, grief, and fear). Wang Fengyi, however, made a deliberate effort to integrate and perhaps deepen standard Chinese medicine theory by blending his intuitive insights with the legacy of all three spiritual traditions of China, namely Daoism, Confucianism, and Buddhism. He focused much on the emotional well-being of the center of the traditional Chinese family, the daughter-in-law, by founding 800 schools for illiterate women in Manchuria. During a life of foot travel in the provinces of Heilongjiang, Liaoning, and Jilin, he spoke to large rural crowds about the healing effect of regulating emotional stagnation and transforming selfish attachments, especially the habit of blaming others rather than seeking to change oneself. Historic observers report that listeners often responded to his transmissions with spontaneous bouts of vomiting, sweating, laughing, or wailing.

Today, there are many practitioners in China's Northern provinces who still practice this method of healing. The following chants were originally created by Wang Fengyi, and are used by this lineage of Confucian five element healers as a daily practice for affirming positive virtues.

The format for the chant is to first ask a question for each element, for instance: "Does the Universe see in me the quality of Direction (Wood)?" Followed by the Answer: "Yes, I do have Direction!" The chant proceeds through the 5-Phase-Element cycle once, and then returns to wood.

The quality of Wood cleanses anger and affirms "*Zhuyi* 主意," direction and motivation of the life force: Shanren Kan Wo You Zhuyi? Wo You Zhuyi!

The quality of Fire cleanses hatred and affirms "*Mingli* 明理," sacred connection: Shanren Kan Wo Mingli? Wo Mingli!

The quality of Earth cleanses doubt and blame and affirms "*Xinshi* 信實," deep trust and integrity: Shanren Kan Wo Xinshi? Wo Xinshi!

The quality of Metal cleanses the tendency to be critical and judgmental and affirms "*Xiangliang* 響亮," the radiance of sound and light: Shanren Kan Wo Xiangliang? Wo Xiangliang!

The quality of water cleanses restlessness and disdain and affirms "*Rouhe* 柔和," softness and harmony: Shanren Kan Wo Rouhe? Wo Rouhe!

In recognition that the cycle is never ending, one returns several times to Wood to conclude the chant.